Publisher

The Bradford Exchange, Ltd.

London

UK Edition

THE BRADFORD BOOK OF

COLLECTORS PLATES

The official guide to all editions

traded on the world's largest Exchange

The Bradford Exchange, Ltd.

Chicago (Niles) · Frankfurt · Copenhagen · London · London (Canada) · Stockholm · Sydney · Vienna · Zürich (Zug)

The editors acknowledge with gratitude the invaluable supplementary information supplied
by all persons and companies involved.

Foreword

It is fascinating to watch the patterns of growth within a market. The popularity of plate collecting is growing not just in the United States and Canada, but in many European countries, Asia and even in Australia.

Most collector's plates are crafted of porcelain and ceramics, but increasingly crystal, pewter, silver, and wood are being used. And more and more fine artists are creating work especially for the medium of collector's plates while we see some of the finest, most prestigious porcelain manufacturers entering the market.

Every aspect of the plate market is presented here in this *Bradford Book of Collector's Plates*. It is the most authoritative international reference work on collector's plates and was written to meet the collector's need to be completely informed on every facet of collector's plates and the collector's plate market.

The introduction provides a brief history of collector's plates and the individual national markets. The main section, the "Gallery of Collector's Plates" presents more than 2000 colour photographs of plates giving a description of the manufacturers who produce them.

That there are over 76 manufacturers from 15 different countries demonstrates the international scope of the manufacturing and trading of collector's plates. And despite the vast numbers of plates illustrated in this book, the international market is so varied and far-flung that we lay no claim to absolute completeness. Rather we have tried here to show *typical* examples of plates in our attempt to demonstrate the different art

trends and tastes throughout the world. For this purpose, series which have found success in different countries are shown to provide the reader with an insight into the structure and development of the market in widely divergent segments of the world's population.

This work is rounded off with artist biographies, a glossary of commonly used terms, and a chapter on Over-the Counter issues, most of which can be obtained through the exchange but are not listed on the Bradex, the price guide for international collector's plates.

The collector's plate market in the USA and Canada is the largest in the world, however the number of collectors in Europe has increased at a surprisingly rapid rate in recent years. This growing interest in collector's plates has resulted in more and more series with European themes by European artists. American plate collectors are taking notice of these new European issues as well.

The Bradford Exchange, with its many years of experience all over the world is always on the lookout for new limited edition plates with a potential for appreciation. *The Bradford Exchange Book of Collector's Plates* is designed to serve the experienced plate collector as well as the novice who may be about to get into the market for the first time, and those who are simply interested in beautiful things. But this book also performs another very important objective: to make the market in different countries more understandable and better organized.

People around the world are becoming interested in collector's plates and the demand for back issues is stimulating the growth of the market. This book explores the many aspects of plate collecting to help you succeed in the market and increase your enjoyment of your collection

John R. MacArthur
Chairman of the Board of Governors
The Bradford Exchange,

Chicago, Illinois USA
March 1988

CONTENTS

THE COLLECTOR'S PLATE MARKET

Introduction

Of all objects prized for their beauty and market value, collector's plates hold a unique position in the art world. They are the only limited-edition issues to be traded in a uniform market, which tracks collector demand around the world.

The porcelain plate that was born in the kilns of China will find its way to the living room wall of a collector in Miami, Florida. And the fine china object that brings so much pleasure to a collector in California may have the same appeal to a collector in Copenhagen or Cologne.

In fact, someday one of those two collectors, thousands of miles apart, may actually buy a plate from the other. This is possible because, while a collector's plate is an object created for its artistic value, it has another important aspect. Each limited-edition plate has the potential to be actively traded among collectors in the fast-paced secondary market.

This potential arises from the basic concept of all limited editions: once the edition limit is fulfilled, *production ends*. The edition is then *closed*, and the subsequent market value of plates from that edition is determined by the laws of supply and demand.

Edition sizes can be large or small. Announced edition sizes in this book range from 500 plates for the 1971 Veneto Flair *Bellini Madonna* to 30,000 for the Haviland *Christmas*. But the undisclosed edition sizes are by far the most frequent, ranging from less than 1,000 for the earliest plates into the tens of thousands for later ones. Regardless of the edition size, a market winner is made when demand outstrips supply. A very small edition does not automatically guarantee demand; in fact, it often discourages it through the restriction of active trading.

Recognition as the World's Most Traded Art

Today, no other art form—regardless of style, medium or popularity—is traded in a reasonably uniform market with the same frequency and volume as collector's plates. In fact, there are more than 14,000 primary and secondary market transactions every business day in the worldwide market. This activity has led to the

Countries in which collector's plates are produced: 1) Australia; 2) Austria; 3) Canada; 4) Denmark; 5) Finland; 6) France; 7) Germany, West (Federal Republic of Germany); 8) Germany, East (German Democratic Republic); 9) Italy; 10) Japan; 11) Norway; 12) People's Republic of China; 13) Republic of China (Taiwan); 14) Spain; 15) Sweden; 16) Switzerland; 17) United Kingdom; 18) United States.

recognition of collector's plates in recent years as "the world's most-traded art."

From Humble Beginnings, the Modern Market Grows

Because the market as we know it today is but 15 years old, sometimes it is surprising to see how far today's plate collectors have come in so short a time. In the early 1970s, collector's plates were just coming into their own as a recognized art form, and information was not easy to come by. Even though the concept of the limited-edition plate had actually developed at the end of the 19th century in Scandinavia and Europe, it took 50 years for the appeal—and the trading potential—of this idea to be recognized in the United States, and shortly thereafter, worldwide.

It also took several forward-thinking American antique and collectibles dealers to create the "spark" that would ignite the idea of back-issue trading.

First this spark set fire to the prices of the blue and white porcelain plates from Europe that were the first true limited editions available here. Later, it ignited the market for plates with increasingly diverse themes and artists. Eventually the steadily burning flame of collector enthusiasm took over what a few insightful dealers had begun . . . and the modern market was born.

The Bradford Exchange Responds to the Need for Market Organization

As active trading in back-issue collector's plates became widespread, the need for an organized market became apparent. This led to the creation of The Bradford Exchange, the world's first organized marketplace for the trading of limited editions. It also contributed directly to the evolution of the plate market as we know it today.

What follows is a concise history of that growth and a look at the current market in all parts of the world in which plates are created, bought and sold.

A Brief History of Collector's Plates

On a cold December morning in 1895, we are told, Mr. Harald Bing, director of the Danish porcelain house of Bing & Grøndahl, ordered his astonished workers to destroy the mould for the small blue-and-white plate produced to commemorate the Christmas holiday.

The plate was entitled "Behind the Frozen Window." With Bing's unprecedented command, it became the first known limited-edition collector's plate, and the cornerstone of what is now a worldwide market. By thus limiting the plate's supply, Mr. Bing established the essential condition where demand for a plate, if it exceeds the edition size, can create an appreciation in price.

Although the idea that the laws of supply and demand can directly affect the prices of sold-out limited editions is a relatively new one, it actually harkens back to the extreme value placed on porcelain objects when the mystery of porcelain manufacture was first revealed.

Birthplace of Porcelain in Ancient China

Although there is still some contention among experts, the birth of porcelain—or technically speaking, the "hard paste" variety of porcelain that requires special ingredients, kiln techniques and glazing processes to produce its enviable whiteness and translucency—occurred in ancient China, in approximately 600 A.D.

Here, near the town of Ching-te Chen, a deposit of remarkably pure kaolin clay—still the one essential ingredient for the production of fine porcelain—was first discovered. For nearly 700 years thereafter, Chinese artisans perfected their techniques of porcelain production, creating objects of breathtaking beauty that were entirely unknown to the Western world.

Trade Routes to Europe Spark Demand

But in the 14th century, as the Orient was opened to European tradesmen for the first time, these magnificent Chinese wares found increasingly greater markets among well-to-do Europeans, who were awed and charmed by the delicacy of their manufacture.

The first limited-edition collector's plate: "Behind the Frozen Window," 1895 issue in the Bing & Grøndahl Christmas series. The series has continued uninterrupted to this day.

So popular was this so-called "Chinese export" porcelain that kings and emperors offered great rewards to any local potter who could learn to duplicate the Chinese process. Yet, for over three centuries, the only form of porcelain the Europeans could master was the "soft paste" variety, inferior in colour, translucency and strength to the "hard paste" products of the East. And the more impossible it seemed that Europeans could create their own porcelain, the more obsessive their collecting of the Chinese porcelain became.

German Unlocks the Ancient Secret

Then in 1708, an enterprising German potter named Johann Friedrich Bottger—in an attempt to placate royalty after his attempts at alchemy (turning lead to gold) had understandably failed—took on the task of duplicating the Chinese process in earnest. The key to the process became not only the discovery of kaolin clay in Saxony, near the town of Meissen, but also a way to fire the kiln to the extreme high temperatures necessary to achieve hard-paste quality. Through an ingenious use of solar energy, Bottger's kiln was finally pushed to the required 1350 degrees Celsius, and the first true European hard-paste porcelain was created.

The factory to produce this revolutionary ware was opened in 1710, under the name of the Royal Saxon Porcelain Manufactory in Meissen, and remains active to this day. Within a decade this factory was creating porcelain ware of equal or greater beauty than that of China. Soon, master potters trained at Meissen left to establish other factories throughout Europe, most often in areas with extensive kaolin deposits nearby.

Commemorative Plates Become Popular

By the mid-18th century, the Konigliche Porzellan-Manufaktur Berlin (KPM) and the French Royal Factory at Sèvres were also producing fine porcelain. At roughly this period in the modern history of collecting, the idea of creating a fine porcelain plate as a decorative object, rather than just for food service, first arose.

Meissen, KPM, Sèvres and other potteries issued earthenware, china and porcelain plates honouring coronations, great battles and notable personalities of the age. The idea that fine porcelain objects are worthy of collection—which had taken hold among the wealthy years earlier—was now catching on throughout the populace.

Firsts in Plate Collecting*

(Adapted from *Plate World* magazine)

First Limited-Edition Collector's Plate:
1895 Bing & Grøndahl *Christmas*
"Behind the Frozen Window"

First Crystal Plate:
1965 Lalique *Annual* "Deux Oiseaux (Two Birds)"

First Square Plate:
1969 Rörstrand *Christmas*
"Bringing Home the Tree"

First Bas-Relief Plate:
1969 Wedgwood *Christmas* "Windsor Castle"

First Plate in Full Colour:
1970 Pickard *Lockhart Wildlife*
"Woodcock/Ruffled Grouse" (pair)

First Christmas Plate in Colour
(other than blue-and-white):
1970 Spode *Christmas* "Partridge in a Pear Tree"

First Christmas Plates in Silver:
1970 Franklin Mint *Christmas*
"Bringing Home the Tree"
1970 Reed and Barton *Christmas*
"A Partridge in a Pear Tree"

First Norman Rockwell Series:
Franklin Mint *Christmas*

First Norman Rockwell Series in Full Colour:
1971 Gorham *Rockwell*
Four Seasons: "A Boy and His Dog" (4-plate set)

First Plates Showing Children:
1971 Gorham *Rockwell*
Four Seasons: "A Boy and His Dog" (4-plate set)
1971 Goebel *Hummel Annual*
1971 Schmid *Hummel Christmas*

First Plate in Wood:
1971 Anri *Christmas* "St. Jakob in Groden"

First Plate in Ivory Alabaster:
1976 Studio Dante di Volteradici *Grand Opera*
"Rigoletto"

First Movie Plate:
1977 Knowles *The Wizard of Oz* "Over the Rainbow"

**First Plate Sponsored by
The Rockwell Society of America:**
1974 *Christmas* "Scotty Gets His Tree"

First Plate in Cameo Stone:
1977 Incolay *Romantic Poets*
"She Walks in Beauty"

**First Plate Endorsed by
the Family of Norman Rockwell:**
1985 Rockwell Society *Rockwell's American Dream*
"Young Girl's Dream"

**First Plate from the Birthplace of Porcelain,
The People's Republic of China:**
1986 Imperial Ching-te Chen
Beauties of the Red Mansion "Pao-chai"

* Among plates listed on The Bradford Exchange worldwide.

Rise of the Great Ceramic Houses of Europe

In the early part of the 18th century, monarchs and princes lined entire salons from floor to ceiling with exquisite porcelain wares. By the middle of that century, there were enough production facilities in Europe to make porcelain affordable for many levels of society other than royalty. In fact, many of the manufacturers of porcelain or bone china who are still active in today's collector's plate market established their factories in this "golden age" of European porcelain.

The oldest among Bradex-listed producers is Rörstrand, founded in Sweden in 1726, followed by Wedgwood of Great Britain in 1759, Royal Copenhagen of Denmark, founded in 1775 and Spode, founded in 1776 in England. Royal Tettau, established in Bavaria in 1794, is the parent company of another Bradex-listed plate maker features in this book, Royal Bayreuth.

Today's Producers Have 19th Century Origins

Because production techniques improved greatly in the 19th century, porcelain had soon evolved from the "collectible of kings" to something the common man could afford and was proud to display. Between the years 1815 and 1898, no less than 17 producers of porcelain or fine china—whose plate issues are Bradex-listed today—opened their doors, both in Europe and the United States. Among them were: Arabia, Bing & Grøndahl, Haviland, Bareuther, Berlin Design, Goebel, Heinrich, Hutschenreuther, Kaiser, Rosenthal, Belleek, Royal Doulton, Fukagawa, Orrefors, Gorham, Edwin M. Knowles and Lenox.

Collecting Plates Stems from Danish Holiday Tradition

Among wealthy Danish landowners, it had long been the custom to distribute Christmas gifts of food to the families living on and working their lands. Eventually these gifts developed even greater value because they arrived on a decorative painted plate, most often of wood, that could be kept and displayed in the home long after Christmas. Families kept these plates for generations, and they were displayed not unlike the way modern collector's plates, issued in series, are today.

It was not surprising, then, that Danish porcelain houses would create decorative plates meant to be offered at Christmas, topped with the traditional gift of food. These, too, were kept and displayed in Scandinavian homes, but none were ever issued in limited editions of any kind.

That is, until Mr. Harald Bing broke tradition by breaking the mould of his 1895 Christmas plate—and started a collecting phenomenon that swept around the world.

How to Judge the Merits of a Plate Issue:
The Bradford Exchange Eight-Point Checklist

In 1974, The Bradford Exchange created this eight-point checklist to establish standards for collector's plates that can be used by both new and experienced collectors. But in using it, it's wise to keep in mind that not *all* points apply to all plate issues. A general "rule of thumb" in choosing issues is: if the plate matches on *five points or more*, it is a *good acquisition*; if it matches on *less than five points, reconsider.*

1. MAKER:
Is the plate maker known for its insistence on fine workmanship? Is the continuity of its past and present series reliable in regard to adherence to edition limit, delivery schedules and price?

2. ARTISTRY:
Is the plate artwork original, created especially for this plate by a noteworthy artist? Or is the artwork a quality adaptation of a work by a famous artistic personality? Is the subject matter one of broad, but not trite, appeal?

3. EDITION LIMIT:
Is the edition clearly limited, but not too limited to create a true market? If the edition is sold out, is there sufficient evidence to suggest present or future secondary market activity?

4. COLLECTIBILITY:
Is the plate one of a collectible periodic series, or merely a single issue? Does the theme of the series have widespread appeal?

5. TIME OF ACQUISITION:
Is the plate available at issue price (always preferable with new issues), or at a time when the price is still likely to rise on the secondary market?

6. SPONSORSHIP:
Is the plate, or the series, issued in association with a prestigious institution—preferably one which is not, in and of itself, a producer of plates?

7. COMMEMORATIVE IMPORTANCE:
Does the plate or the series commemorate a seasonal or historic event? If so, does it offer new insight into the event?

8. MATERIALS:
If ceramic, is the plate true hard-paste porcelain, bone china or fine china? If of other materials such as metal or crystal, are they of appropriate quality? Is the plate unique in its workmanship? Does it have a special feature that sets it apart from other issues?

GROWTH OF PLATE COLLECTING

1895:
First true limited-edition series, Bing & Grøndahl Christmas, introduced.

1895

1900

1905

1908:
Royal Copenhagen Christmas Series

1910:
Rosenthal Christmas Series

1908

1910

1910-1935:
Hutschenreuther Christmas Series

1914   1914-mid-1920's: KPM Christmas Series
1915
1920

1925

1920's-1940's:
Danish and German Christmas plates continue to be held by European families, and by families of Scandinavian or German descent in the U.S.—but are not actively traded.

1930

1935

1940

1945

1947:
William G. Freudenberg becomes first U.S. dealer to import and sell limited-edition collector's plates from Europe.

1947

1949:
Pat Owen (Viking Imports) becomes first wholesaler of collector's plates, offering them to gift shops and department stores.

1949

1950
1951

1951:
Svend Jensen, a dealer, produces first back-issue price list for plates, establishing higher value for older, sold-out blue-and-white issues.

Mid-1950's:
American collectors scramble to fill in their collections, bidding up back-issues to new highs. Examples: 1945 Royal Copenhagen Christmas, Issue price: $3.00; 1951 Royal Copenhagen Christmas, Issue price: $4.00; 1959 price (both): $300.

1955

IN THE UNITED STATES AND EUROPE

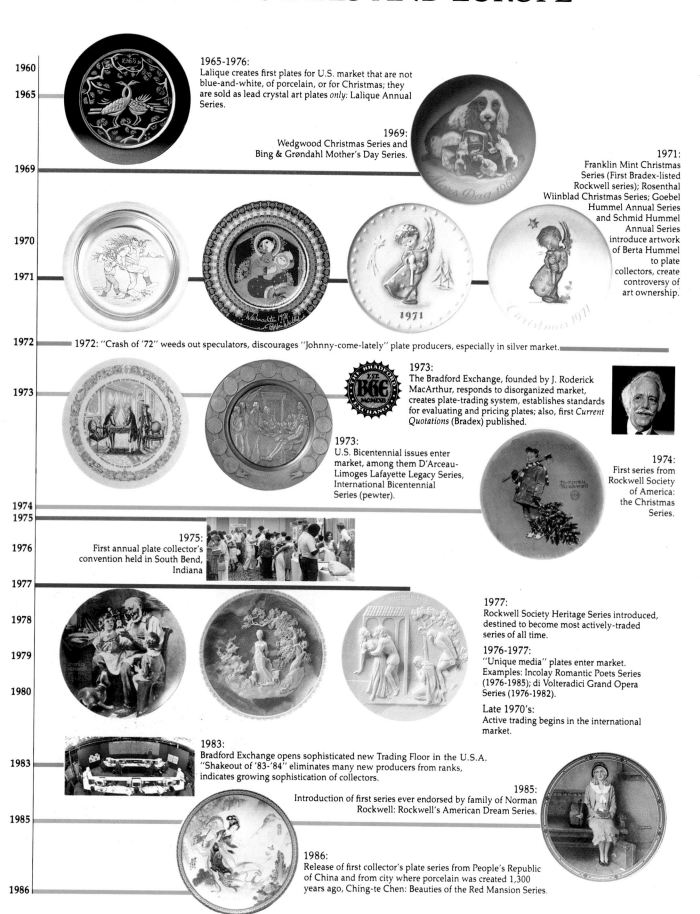

1960
1965

1965-1976:
Lalique creates first plates for U.S. market that are not blue-and-white, of porcelain, or for Christmas; they are sold as lead crystal art plates *only:* Lalique Annual Series.

1969:
Wedgwood Christmas Series and Bing & Grøndahl Mother's Day Series.

1969

1971:
Franklin Mint Christmas Series (First Bradex-listed Rockwell series); Rosenthal Wiinblad Christmas Series; Goebel Hummel Annual Series and Schmid Hummel Annual Series introduce artwork of Berta Hummel to plate collectors, create controversy of art ownership.

1970
1971

1972

1972: "Crash of '72" weeds out speculators, discourages "Johnny-come-lately" plate producers, especially in silver market.

1973

1973:
The Bradford Exchange, founded by J. Roderick MacArthur, responds to disorganized market, creates plate-trading system, establishes standards for evaluating and pricing plates; also, first *Current Quotations* (Bradex) published.

1973:
U.S. Bicentennial issues enter market, among them D'Arceau-Limoges Lafayette Legacy Series, International Bicentennial Series (pewter).

1974:
First series from Rockwell Society of America: the Christmas Series.

1974
1975

1975:
First annual plate collector's convention held in South Bend, Indiana

1976

1977

1977:
Rockwell Society Heritage Series introduced, destined to become most actively-traded series of all time.

1978

1976-1977:
"Unique media" plates enter market. Examples: Incolay Romantic Poets Series (1976-1985); di Volteradici Grand Opera Series (1976-1982).

1979

Late 1970's:
Active trading begins in the international market.

1980

1983:
Bradford Exchange opens sophisticated new Trading Floor in the U.S.A. "Shakeout of '83-'84" eliminates many new producers from ranks, indicates growing sophistication of collectors.

1983

1985:
Introduction of first series ever endorsed by family of Norman Rockwell: Rockwell's American Dream Series.

1985

1986:
Release of first collector's plate series from People's Republic of China and from city where porcelain was created 1,300 years ago, Ching-te Chen: Beauties of the Red Mansion Series.

1986

"Flight into Egypt" by Edna Hibel
Christmas plate 1987, Edwin M. Knowles

The collector's plate market in the United States remains the largest and most active in the world, with an estimated seven million collectors. However, up until the late 1940's very few Americans had even seen a collector's plate, despite the fact that Danish immigrants to the U.S. had, following the traditions of their homeland, brought their cherished collections of plates with them.

It was the American soldiers returning home from Europe after World War II who had introduced the idea of collecting plates to their homeland. And the idea caught on very quickly.

By 1949, department stores and gift shops were offering collector's plates by such well-known makers as Bing & Grøndahl and Royal Copenhagen. The collector's plate market had taken off in the U.S. with a bang.

In 1951, Svend Jensen, a Danish immigrant who had settled in New York, took the first step toward creating the modern plate market when he published a price list of back issue collector's plates and circulated it among antique dealers and their customers. To some extent the evaluations were arbitrary, based simply on the prices of current plate series and the numbers Jensen knew the dealers possessed. Nevertheless it established price guidelines for the very first time, and before long antique dealers across the country were quoting Jensen's prices. For the first time, collectors became aware of the value of their collections and the importance of series continuity; many began to seek out back issues to complete their collections. Due to this new demand, prices skyrocketed and activity

among collectors greatly increased. By 1960, as the stock of old plates was becoming increasingly scarce, collectors shifted their attention to current issues of Danish and German manufacturers.

In 1973, The Bradford Exchange, founded by J. Roderick MacArthur responded to the need for an organized marketplace for collector's plates. MacArthur developed a uniform trading system, objective criteria for evaluation of collector's plates, and published the first *Bradex* price index for international collector's plates. The result was a clearly defined market which greatly enhanced the public's interest in collecting. New collectors were quick to join the ranks. Porcelain manufacturers – including a number of American makers who also wanted a piece of the rapidly growing market – responded to this growing interest by creating new plate collections.

Trends and Preferences

In contrast to the European collector whose loyalty lies with one or two particular makers, American collectors make their decision to acquire series based on their individual enthusiasm for the theme or a preference for the work of a particular artist.

One such favourite artist is Norman Rockwell whose work is considered to be uniquely and quintessentially American. He is deemed one of the great genre painters (an artist who portrays everyday life with humour and warmth) and his direct approach to his subjects involves the use of bold, clear colours and sharp contours. His milieu is the world of close family relationships, the bond between the very young

First issue in "Rockwell's Golden Moments,
Rockwell Society 1987, "Grandpa's Gift"

and very old, and "puppy love." Another artist who has achieved legend status in her own lifetime is Edna Hibel, affectionately known as "the first lady of American plate art."

Due to the Americans' highly developed sense of family and their somewhat effusive emphasis on emotional subjects, many of the best-selling plates in the U.S.A. are based on children's or family themes.

Norman Rockwell and Edna Hibel may be the masters of the genre but artists such as Donald Zolan and John McClelland are also highly successful in this sphere. And of course there are the Hummel series which have been enthusiastically collected by Americans for a good many years.

Increasingly, European artists have been gaining popularity in the United States and chances for success of a number of recent creations from Europe are good. These include the English Christmas plates from Wedgwood, the *European Songbirds* series by artist Ursula Band, Furstenberg's *Romantic Winter Impressions* series by Ludwig Muninger, and *Braithwaite's Game Birds* collection by Royal Grafton China.

The successes of new themes and art trends in the American market confirm the theory that even where taste appears to be very traditional and hidebound, good design and high quality will find its way to the collector. The American collector is open to new ideas and is always ready to take advantage of exciting speculative opportunities.

An Organized, Active Market

For a look at the future of the European market, take a look at the American market today. A network of more than 1000 dealers cover the country, many of them holding regular meetings to distribute information about trends in the market. In addition there are well over 100 active plate collecting clubs.

High points of the year are the annual plate shows held in South Bend, Indiana, and Pasadena, California. Together these shows attract over 30,000 visitors from all over the country to see the latest offerings from the finest European, North American, and Asian manufacturers.

How much an issue may increase in value on the secondary market is an important consideration to the American collector. Plates are regularly bought and sold through the network of authorized dealers as well as at "Swap 'n Sell" events that take place during the big plate shows. In response to the laws of supply and demand the market price of certain issues can fluctuate from one hour to the next. Guiding this frenzied activity is the *Bradex* list of current price quotations, for years the acknowledged reference source for determining current value of international collectors plates. In addition, the U.S. Exchange is outfitted with a computerized trading system. Collectors and dealers with access to this system can get instant information on current prices and sales transactions.

Collectors also follow the up-to-the-minute goings-ons of the plate market through a number of special periodicals; "Antique Trader", "Collector's Market," and "Plate World" appear at regular intervals with the latest on new editions, artists, collector's gatherings, and coverage of all aspects of the collector's plate market.

"Judgement of Paris", first issue in
"The Fall of Troy", by sculptor Alan Brunettin,
Incolay, California

Since the Bradford Exchange opened its United Kingdom office in a London suburb seven years ago the popularity of plate collecting in the U.K. has grown dramatically. As of Autumn 1987 the British Current Quotations showed that over 1000 collector's plates by 53 makers in 11 different countries are traded on the U.K. market alone.

This growth in Britain is due to an increasing awareness of the investment potential of collector's plates allied to the pure pleasure and enjoyment that plate collecting brings. There seems to be a greater understanding of this exciting, often complex, world.

In terms of growth and potential the British market became the one to watch in recent years. Market analysts estimate that, as of 1987, the size of the U.K. market swelled to 750,000 collectors among 56 million inhabitants, making it the largest outside North America.

Although this growth initially evolved around largely American plate series, the trend has changed in the last three years. The emergence of bestseller British and other European plate series such as Wedgwood's *Street Sellers of London* series and Tirschenreuth's *Songbirds of Europe* has seen a tremendous upturn in the U.K. market and heralded a significant swing plate collecting tastes. More recently, other winning series show the international diversity of British preferences:

Seltmann's *Lueckel's Idyllic Village Life* series, Wedgwood's *Country Panorama* collection and the Rockwell Society's *Rockwell's American Dream* series.

A further development has been the enthusiasm of British collectors for plates from the Orient. Taiwan's *Chinese Children's Games* and the *Beauties of the Red Mansion* from the People's Republic of China have both been very well received by British plate collectors.

A Taste for the Original

The developing tastes of the British public are not just confined to the countries of origin — there is a growing appreciation of different art styles, of different materials as well as different themes. Indeed, plates which are unique in some way, which are 'firsts' for a particular reason, are consistently in great demand. For example, the *Voyage of Ulysses* by Alan Brunettin was the first plate series to be produced in lapis-blue Incolay stone and it generated huge interest among British collectors. Similarly, the market reaction to ivory alabaster series, such as the *Ghiberti Doors* collection by Alberto Santangela, has been very favourable.

Over the past few years many different art styles have been successful — from Ursula Band's exacting Realism to Michel Julien's subtle blend of Impressionism and Realism to Bjorn Wiinblad's Primative art style.

"Meadows and Wheatfields" first issue in Colin Newman's "Country Panorama", Wedgwood

"The Pheasant" by Derek Braithwaite, first issue in the "Gamebirds" series from Royal Grafton

The United Kingdom

Patterns of Collecting Identified

In a recent survey of plate collectors in the U.K. the typical collector of modern limited-edition plates in the United Kingdom considers children as popular subjects for plate series, although animals and bird scenes offered stiff competition. Also high on the list of favourites were country scenes and landscapes, scenes with great human interest and movie-theme series.

Among the most favoured primary market plates were "Jack and Jill", the final issue in McCelland's *Mother Goose* series, and "Blue Titmice" premier issue in Ursula Band's *Songbirds of Europe* collection.

The survey also found that most collectors continue to acquire their plates for the pleasure they bring into the home, although a third of the market collects for both pleasure *and* investment. While there is obviously loyalty to favourite artists the majority of collectors surveyed said that it is the theme and the artwork itself that determines whether they'll buy a plate — not just who painted it.

Respect continues for Time-Honoured Makers

In the North American market, some newer plate producing companies have built their reputations exclusively in limited editions. By contrast, in the United Kingdom, the most popular limited editions are from older, established companies whose reputations were built on quality dinnerware, giftware and figar, and fragmeries. However, limited-edition plates as a collectible on their own have been steadily growing in importance.

For example, Wedgwood is a time honoured firm which in 1969 introduced a classic style Jasperware Christmas plate, "Windsor Castle". This notable first issue is one of the most sought-after on the U.K. secondary market.

John Finnie's "Baked Potato Man", issued in 1986 by Wedgwood in the "Streetsellers of London" collection

A Developing Secondary Market

As well as boasting a booming primary market the U.K. can claim a rapidly developing secondary market. As more collectors recognise the secondary market potential of their plates, more plates are being actively bought and sold.

High market prices in mid 1986 saw many collectors rush to sell their plates. There followed a noticeable market decline until the trend reversed in Spring 1987. In the past six months, however, the market has gone from strength to strength. The current Market Bradex* stands at 279, almost back to the high of 280 in the middle of 1986.

Among the plates that are most actively traded on the U.K. secondary market are: "Lavender Fairy", first issue in Heinrich/Villeroy & Boch's Flower Fairies series; "Touching the Sky", first issue in Zolan's Wonder of Childhood series; "The Baked Potato Man", first issue in John Finnie's Street Sellers of London series from Wedgwood; "Blue Titmice", first issue in Ursula Band's Songbirds of Europe collection and "A Puzzlement" first plate in Knowles' The King and I series.

A New Acceptance of Diversity and Style

In the United Kingdom plate issues that present traditionally British themes of local history, landscapes and decorative arts have always won approval. Even so, British collectors are now enjoying art from many sources and cultures. Their fondness for American, European, Chinese and Canadian issues shows that the British market is growing not only in numbers but also in diversity and sophistication.

"Arthur draws the Sword", first plate in Richard Hook's "King Arthur" series, Wedgwood

* The Market Bradex is the Bradford Index of overall market performance determined by the current quote-price/issue-price of 10 significant plate series.

"Meuschenmühle", first plate in the "Historic Watermills" collection by Karl Bedal, 1987 Königszelt Bayern

After Great Britain, the Federal Republic of Germany is probably the most productive and active plate market in Europe. There are approximately 500,000 plate collectors in the German market today. And the German porcelain houses have experienced enormous international success with a number of recent series.

The market in Germany is characterized by a number of porcelain dealers who sell the better known names in fine porcelain such as Rosenthal, Hutschenreuther and Heinrich/Villeroy & Boch. Although these dealers usually carry a rather broad selection of collector's plates, current market volume makes it very difficult for them to focus exclusively on the marketing of collector's plates, as this requires additional expertise which is difficult and time consuming to develop.

Also, many such dealers find that to effectively meet customer demand they must be able to predict the market winners...to stock the right plate at the right time. Since 1979, the Bradford Exchange has been actively supporting the collector's plate market in Germany with the publication of the German *Bradex*. This index of current prices has given dealers a solid marketing base and allows them to handle trades of international plates without assuming any extraordinary risk.

A long Tradition

In 1895, Bing & Grøndahl issued their first blue and white Christmas plate collection and the market for collector's plates in Germany was born. As early as 1905, the German manufacturer, Rosenthal, produced

Christian Lückel's "The Blacksmith", 1986 Seltmann Weiden

a Christmas plate series for the Danish market. And as interest in such objets d'art began to flourish in Germany, Rosenthal began to pay more attention to the promotion of collector's plates within Germany. In 1910, the company issued the plate "Winterfrieden", the first issue of their traditional Christmas series which was continued for 65 years, until 1974.

At around the same time two other German manufacturers were introducing their own collector's plates. Hutschenreuther's Christmas series was launched in 1910 and continued until 1935. Konigliche Porzellanmanufaktur Berlin (KPM) started their Christmas series in 1914 but ceased production in the late nineteen twenties. The world economic situation was largely to blame for the waning plate market in the 1930's. The people had neither the money to spend on such "nonessentials" nor the interest in acquiring "mere curiosities", while the manufacturers were hesitant to launch new series until the economic situation had improved.

The Collector's Plate Market in Germany

Although the early German plates were indeed genuine collector's plates, when they were issued they were not marketed as such. These plates were bought by Danish and German families who acquired them for their decorative or gift value. They had no notion then that in years to come, one issue might be worth more than another. Consequently little effort was made to complete collections or seek out back issues that were missing from a series. However, those original Christmas plates issued in such small editions have subsequently increased greatly in value.

Outside Stimulation

In the 1970's the German porcelain houses followed the lead of the American plate market and issued their first limited edition plates in full colour, and national interest in collecting was stimulated once again. But the late 1970's was a turbulent time in the plate market – the market was glutted with new issues which resulted in a downward market trend.

Although there are still some plates listed on the exchange at below their issue price, a strong market recovery and exciting new series from a variety of makers has revitalised the market and helped it to consolidate. Such series as Heinrich/Villeroy & Boch's "Russian Fairy Tales" and Rosenthal's Wiinblad "Christmas" appeal to many and have helped to popularise plate collecting.

Romantic Impressions and Nature

Landscapes and scenes from field and forest are the great favourites of German collectors. This is apparent from the success of the series *German Half-Timbered Houses* from Konigszelt Bayern. The series *European Songbirds* from Tirschenreuth and *Bouquets of the Season* from Hutschenreuther, both by artist Ursula Band, have evoked a hearty welcome from collectors. But interest is hardly confined to German artists. The artwork of Norman Rockwell, Bjørn Wiinblad and Eve Licea have also known great success in Germany. And we should note the recent success of Christian Lueckel, whose series *Idyllic Village Life* really touches the collector's yearning for scenes that are nostalgic, romantic and serene.

Other recent favourites have been Ludwig Muninger's *Romantic Winter Impressions* which shows man at one with nature, and the Christmas and Mother's Day series from Rhenish painter Sulamith Wulfing. It is upon the talent and skills of these fine artists that the foundation of the flourishing German plate market is based.

"Iceskaters in the Evening Sun", first issue in Muninger's "Romantic Winter Impressions", 1987 Fuerstenberg

Tradition is Paramount among the Swiss: The Collector's Plate Market in Switzerland

Switzerland is a country that is very conscious of its traditions. Year after year the same events and celebrations are held in the individual cantons testifying to the variety of lively customs and fierce regional pride. This same spirit is also apparent in the relatively young plate market. The collection "Appenzell Traditions" from the Swiss porcelain maker Langenthal, portrays scenes of farm life in this canton painted in the charming folk-art style for which this region is well-known. These plates appeal especially to collectors who have maintained strong emotional ties to their home districts in Switzerland. The fact that the Swiss porcelain manufacturer Langenthal is now producing

The first plate in "Anker's Heritage",
1986 Langenthal, "Grandpa's Story"

collector's plates in addition to the fine tableware for which they are noted, emphasises the growth in popularity that collector's plates are beginning to have in this country.

The Swiss were slow to accept the concept of collector's plates. At first of course there were those who acquired the early plates from Denmark, however the idea of collecting did not really spread until other countries' manufacturers – particularly Germany's – started offering their plate series. Until a few years ago, plates series from Scandanavia, Germany, France, and Italy ranked as collectors' favourites. Such series as *European Songbirds* from Tirschenreuth, *Napoléon and Joséphine* from D'Arceau Limoges, *Sulamith's Love Songs* from Konigszelt Bayern and *Renaissance Madonnas* from Studio Dante di Volteradici are typical success stories on the Swiss market.

With the first issue of a limited edition plate by a Swiss manufacturer, a new age began for the plate market in Switzerland. The plate was "Grandfather Tells a Story" first in the *Anker Heritage* series honouring the beloved Swiss genre painter Albert Anker (1831 – 1910). With the release of this issue, the plate market in Switzerland took a giant upswing in popularity.

Right now it is estimated that there are approximately 50,000 collectors combined in both the French- and German-speaking parts of Switzerland. Market experts believe that this number could easily double within the next few years.

Already the numbers of collectors are such that international manufacturers are reserving larger allotments of plates for this market and Langenthal, the premier porcelain Swiss porcelain manufacturer of collector's plates has announced plans for future series.

Collectors are looking forward with great interest to the release of the new series, *Alpine Wildlife,* an idyllic, but precise and accurate presentation of alplands animals in their natural habitats.

It will be very interesting to follow this young Swiss market from an international point of view. Already clear preferences for certain themes are developing. Apart from traditional and historical subjects, there is a growing demand for nature and wildlife theme plates, which are sure to have an impact on the collector's plate market.

"Summer Trip to the Alp"
in the "Appenzell Traditions"
series from Dolf Mettler, 1987 Langenthal

Fascinated by Nature:
The Collector's plate market in Austria

There are many parallels between the development of the collector's plate market in Austria and with those of Germany and Switzerland. The Austrians love for nature is clear in their preference for its reproduction on fine collector's plates.

Currently there are an estimated 15,000 plate collectors in Austria. From the very beginning, the issue of the great German manufacturers such as Rosenthal and Hutschenreuther were in demand by an elite group of collectors.

In recent years the tastes of this market have become more narrowly defined and it is nature and wildlife themes that are in most demand. Among the best selling series on the Austrian market are *European Songbirds* from Tirschenreuth, *Lueckel's Idyllic Village Life* from Christian Seltmann, *Band's Bouquets of the Seasons* from Hutschenreuther and *Romantic Winter Impressions* from Furstenberg.

The collector's plate market in Austria is still developing and further trends have yet to be identified. However, plans for the first Austrian plate series on the collector's plate market are currently in the works and it is thought that this introduction will go far to stimulate interest in plate collecting.

This series which will be produced by Lilien Porzellan, is entitled *Masterpieces of Defregger* and will honour the work of one of Austria's most distinguished painters Franz von Defregger. Defregger was born in Tirol in 1835 and was one of the leading representatives of the Munich School. His works were exhibited at the 1873 Vienna World Exposition and the overwhelming success of this showing made him the best known Munich painter of the 1880's and 1890's. From 1878 to 1910 he served as a professor at the Munich Academy. His landscapes and portraits continue to fascinate and influence many today.

"Saying Grace", first plate from
"Defregger's Masterpieces", Lilien Porzellan

This series is seen as a pioneering effort for the Austrian collector's plate market and experts agree that the popularity of the themes along with the fine reputation of the manufacturer are bound to spark expansion of the market.

"Blue Titmice", first issue in
Alt Tirschenreuth's collection "Songbirds of Europe"
by Ursula Band.

*"The Landing", first in the
"Wings upon the Wind"
series by Donald Pentz, Dominion China*

Like the U.S. market, the Canadian market for collector's plates developed chiefly after World War II, and has been growing fairly steadily ever since.

Canada now boasts a number of manufacturers producing collector's plates which are in demand all over the world, and popular artists such as Donald Pentz, Gerda Neubacher and Stewart Sherwood. Their subjects... Canadian family life, exquisite landscapes, and the animal world. The wildlife-themed *"Wings upon the Wind"*, first issue from Dominion China Ltd. has found brisk demand in Canada, the U.S. and the European markets.

This market is constantly growing. It is estimated that there are now approximately 840,000 collectors primarily in the English-speaking areas of Canada, but of late there is a growing market interest in the French-speaking areas as well.

There is a great deal of regional collector activity — scattered across the vast geographical expanse of country are 22 collectors' clubs with approximately 1,800 members. These clubs keep Canadian plate enthusiasts informed about new issues and trading trends. Most such activity, however, is concentrated in southern Ontario and in British Columbia.

The Collectors Platemakers Association of Canada disbanded following the collector exposition in Toronto in 1986. However the gap which was left by the dissolution of this organisation has been filled by a number of other local events. Among these are the buy-and-sell events conducted by The Bradford Ex-

change in such cities as Calgary, Alberta and London, Ontario.

Collectors in Canada have also been introduced to the concept of active trading at home and garden shows where the The Bradford Exchange maintained a booth. These shows have been held in Vancouver, British Columbia, Winnipeg, Manitoba, Halifax, Nova Scotia, Toronto, Ontario and London, Ontario.

Dealer-sponsored shows are also popping up everywhere, which helps to establish Canadian dealers as local authorities in their areas.

The Bradford Exchange continues to expand its trading centre; by 1987 it offered collectors increased opportunities for buying and selling on the collector's plate market.

*"Timber Country", 1984
Christian Bell, by Theodor Xaras*

Representatives of a Proud Heritage:
The Collector's Plate Market in Denmark

Without question, the Danes are the pioneers in plate collecting. The small blue and white Christmas plates from Bing & Grøndahl which started it all have set a record for longevity with an uninterupted series of 93 plates since 1895. And it was from Denmark that enthusiasm for collecting limited edition plates originated, and spread to the rest of the world.

Since those early days when "Behind the Frozen Window" was first issued, the Danish plate market has undergone a natural evolution. While plate collectors in Denmark are still much aware of the artistic heritage of the blue and white Bing & Grøndahl plates, their aesthetic awareness and appreciation today extends much further.

Bing & Grøndahl's *Summer at Skagen* series honouring the work of the great Danish impressionist Peter Severin Krøyer was received in 1986 with much interest. *Moments of Truth* by Kurt Ard has been another resounding success.

There are approximately 150,000 collectors in Denmark, and to most of these, maker name is very important. Old, established manufacturers such as Bing & Grøndahl and Royal Copenhagen have a firm grip on the Danish market which is supported by more than 100 shops or dealers specialising in meeting the needs of collectors. In addition The Bradford Exchange's Copenhagen branch was opened in 1983 to further meet the needs of traders.

Hand in hand with the coloured plates which are currently in so much demand, is a developing generation of Danish collectors who appear ready to encourage and support innovation and change in the plate market...perhaps on the spectacular scale of Harald Bing who started it all with his order to break a Christmas plate mold thereby creating the first limited edition plate.

"Summer Evening in Skagen"
by Peter S. Krøyer, 1986 Bing & Grøndahl,
first plate in the "Skagen" series

Success with New German Issues:
The Collector's Plate Market in Sweden

In Sweden, as in Denmark, the collecting of Christmas plates has a long tradition.

Today there are approximately 110,000 plate collector's in Sweden, and their interest is not confined to only Swedish issues.

Apart from their enthusiasm for collections from Sweden's own Rorstrand and Danish manufacturers Bing & Grøndahl and Royal Copenhagen, the Swedish market has demonstrated a great degree of interest in German series. *European Songbirds* from Tirschenreuth and *Lueckel's Idyllic Village Life* have met with solid success in Sweden.

Meanwhile Rorstrand, one of the oldest porcelain houses in Europe has released new, full-coloured series for the Swedish market and market analysts believe that before long, these new series will be met with international acclaim by the public.

Esprit and Charme:
The Collector's Plate Market in France

French porcelain from Limoges and Sevres were famed and coveted as far back as the 18th century. From these remarkable artifacts developed a rich culture of collectors's items that are even more eagerly sought today as highly prized antiques.

Today, the hallmarks of manufacturers such as Lalique, Haviland , D'Arceau-Limoges and Limoges Turgot represent new standards of excellence in collector's plates. Such plates are particularly popular among collectors in Germany and Switzerland, as they capture the charm, the esprit, the essence of French culture and taste. Examples of such plates are the series *Les Femmes de Siecle* and *La Belle Epoque,* both by D'Arceau Limoges.

In addition, the French have established new trends in the international collector's plate market with such acclaimed series as Lalique's etched crystal plates.

Although collector's plates are accepted in France as decorative objets d'art, the organized plate market there is in its infancy and is still developing.

"Scarlet en Crinoline"
first issue of the "Ganeau's Women" series,
D'Arceau Limoges

A Classical Heritage:
The Collector's Plate Market in Italy

Like its French counterpart the plate market in Italy is still developing. Nevertheless collector's plates from Italy have gained great importance on the international market.

The collections from Studio Dante di Volteradici in particular have been met with great success. Cameo crafted from ivory alabaster, these Italian works recall classical themes, making reference to the artistic style of the Renaissance, the golden age of Italian sculpture. Their acclaimed *Ghiberti Doors* and *Renaissance Madonnas* series refer to religious themes, while their *Grand Opera* collection, another celebration of traditional Italian culture was the first series to have attained international success.

A very special place among collector's plates is held by the wooden plates made by Anri which present motifs from the rural tradition in the Alps.

"Adoration of the Magi"
from the "Ghiberti Doors" collection,
Studio Dante di Volteradici

The Fifth Continent Discovers Art on Porcelain: The Collector's Plate Market in Australia

Australia is nearly as large as the United States geographically but has only 16 million inhabitants. Yet the number of collectors there is estimated at 110,000 and appears to be growing. Collecting habits and tastes there are formed somewhat by British traditions, but also by the national influences of European immigrants. Collector's preferences therefore seem to run to issues by the manufacturers Wedgwood, Royal Doulton, Royal Copenhagen, and Bing & Grøndahl. Yet Australian "native sons" are starting to produce their own collections such as *Ships that Made Australia* from Benz Ceramics and *Australian Songbirds* from Westminster.

Prominent German manufacturers such as Tirschenreuth, Christian Seltmann and Villeroy & Boch are also selling well "down under."

Collector's plates are sold through dealers as well as the representatives of European and American manufacturers. Almost all American consignors specializing in collector's items have representatives in Australia.

A particularly curious fact about the country which has a measureable impact upon the plate market is that due to its location in the southern hemisphere Christmas in Australia is celebrated in the middle of summer. There are areas of the country, however, that celebrate Christmas twice – once by date (December) and once by season (end of July).

The Birthplace of Porcelain: The Collector's Plate Market in Asia

Although the origins of porcelain are intimately associated with this continent, very little is known about Asian collectors' numbers, activities, and preferences. However, market experts agree that the orient is becoming an increasingly important source for internationally significant limited editions.

Japan, for example has no organzied plate market to speak of, yet Japanese manufacturers Fukagawa and Noritake do produce limited edition collector's plates.

The *Chinese Children's Games* series by artist Kee Fung Ng originated in the Republic of China (Taiwan) in 1986 and has sold quite well in the USA and in Europe.

From The People's Republic of China comes the current international sensation, "Pao-chai," first plate in the *Beauties of the Red Mansion* series from Imperial Ching-te-Chen Porcelain, the first porcelain collector's plate ever from the actual birthplace of porcelain, the city of Ching-te-Chen. It was apparent from the moment it was introduced that this series would represent a milestone in the history of the collector's plate market. The enthusiastic reception given this series has been so great that officals from Ching-te-Chen have visited the USA to witness the excitement for themselves. It is believed that a second series from Imperial Ching-te-Chen is forthcoming.

"Pao-chai", first issue in the series
"Beauties of the Red Mansion"
Imperial Ching-te Chen Porcelain

International Trademarks...

...Signs of Quality
of selected Collector's Plates

How a Plate is Made:
The Bing & Grøndahl Christmas Plate

Bing & Grøndahl, the very first maker of limited-edition collector's plates, produces its annual *Christmas* issue as shown below. All underglaze blue-and-white plates are produced in this way. Four-color plates differ in that they may be hand painted, or in that an art transfer may be applied to the plate before the final firing. Either of those steps would replace Steps 6 and 7 below.

1. From the artwork, a modeller sculpts the master mold from which working molds will be made.

2. Pouring liquid plaster into the mold, a mold-maker casts a working mold.

3. Quartz, feldspar and kaolin are the raw materials from which porcelain is made.

4. After these materials are mixed, the resulting clay is pressed over a plaster mold and fired.

5. These bisquit-fired plates are being carried to the decorating area.

6. A painter applies a spray of cobalt blue to the bisque porcelain.

7. A decorator selectively removes the blue to highlight the design.

8. The plate's backstamp, its "birth certificate," is applied.

9. The plate is sprayed with a glaze which will become clear in firing.

10. Plates are fired in the kiln 48 hours to become hard-paste porcelain.

11. The fired plates are removed, sorted and inspected for imperfections.

12. Imperfect plates are destroyed; perfect ones are issued worldwide.

The Backstamp: Important Information

Through the Backstamp manufacturers guarantee the origin of a plate. Traditionally the "mark" is the first sign, also serving as an assurance of quality. Most often collector's plates will also show the plate title, the number in the series, the artist's name and the limitation. With a view to secondary market trading, manufacturers often request a BRADEX number. This unique identification avoids potential confusion with other plates.

Trading on the Secondary Market

When items which appreciate in value are collected, the possibility of profit-taking exists. In order for a collector to sell a particular edition, there must be someone interested in buying. Naturally the seller can find a buyer in a number of ways, for example he can purchase a small advertisement in a newspaper. But here, costs are incurred, success is uncertain and the risk in carrying out such a transaction with a stranger is enormous. If the plate is a relatively old edition, the seller might be able to dispose of it at an art and antique auction. But here, the price realized depends on the audience and the skill of the auctioneer.

Furthermore, the auctioneer may receive up to 40% of the selling price. When a plate is offered through the secondary market of the Bradford Exchange, the brokerage fee of 20% is incurred only if the an actual sale is made...any collector can place a sell order free of charge. If the sale is made, the seller is financially safeguarded as the transaction is handled through the Bradford Exchange. And the buyer can be assured that the plate he is getting is in perfect, mint condition. Only limited edition collector's plates which comply with one of the following conditions limiting the edition are traded through the Bradford Exchange.

Limitations

Secondary Market collector's plates must be limited in one of the following four ways:

| 1.) Limited to a specified unit quantity, with each plate being individually numbered (e.g. 19,900 plates). | 2.) Limited to a specified unit quantity, with the plates not being individually numbered. | 3.) Limited by announced production period, such as number of firing days (plates may/may not be numbered). | 4.) Limited to a specified time after which time no more plates will be made (e.g. 31.12.87). |

The Bradford Exchange Current Quotations

The Standard Comprehensive Market as Determined by the World's Largest Exchange in All Major Collector's Plates Currently Traded

All prices in U.K. pounds (inc. VAT); prices in other currencies (inc. Eire) at the pound buying rate in London on the day of transaction. Every effort made to maintain uniform international open market with most precise quotations of actual available prices which are subject to market demand but may be generally relied upon to date shown.

All Prices other than Issue Prices Subject to Daily Marketing Fluctuations.

BRADEX No.	PLATE	ISSUE PRICE	HIGH	LOW	QUOTE	CHANGE
CANADA						
Dominion China Wings upon the Wind (08-D52-1)						
08-D52-1.1	86 The Landing*	17.75	17.75	17.75	17.75	0.00
08-D52-1.2	86 The Nesting*	17.75	17.75	17.75	17.75	0.00
08-D52-1.3	86 The Courtship*	17.75	17.75	17.75	17.75	0.00
08-D52-1.4	87 The Family*	18.85	18.85	18.85	18.85	0.00
08-D52-1.5	87 Southward Bound*	18.85	18.85	18.85	18.85	0.00
08-D52-1.6	87 Winter Home*	18.85	18.85	18.85	18.85	0.00
	Collection	109.80	109.80	109.80	109.80	0.00
Dominion China Reflections of Canadian Childhood (08-D52-2)						
08-D52-2.1	87 Dreams of Glory*	21.95	21.95	21.95	21.95	0.00
08-D52-2.2	87 A Quiet Moment*	21.95	21.95	21.95	21.95	0.00
CHINA						
Ching-te Chen Beauties of the Red Mansion (10-I50-1)						
10-I50-1.1	86 Pao-Chai*	19.95	19.95	19.95	19.95	0.00
Pavilion of Tsang Ying Chinese Children's Games (10-P8-1)						
10-P8-1.1	86 Chinese Chess	15.75	25.00	15.75	25.00	0.00
10-P8-1.2	87 Kite Flying*	15.75	15.75	15.75	15.75	0.00
10-P8-1.3	87 Spinning Tops*	19.95	19.95	19.95	19.95	0.00
10-P8-1.4	87 Rolling Hoops*	19.95	19.95	19.95	19.95	0.00
DENMARK						
Bing & Grondahl Christmas (14-B36-1)						
14-B36-1.1	95 Frozen Window	.25	3070.00	1852.00	2652.00	0.00
14-B36-1.2	96 New Moon	.25	1491.00	593.00	1008.00	0.00
14-B36-1.3	97 Sparrows	.40	745.00	407.00	604.00	0.00
14-B36-1.4	98 Roses & Star	.40	438.00	207.00	389.00	0.00
14-B36-1.5	99 Crows	.40	964.00	506.00	708.00	0.00
14-B36-1.6	00 Church Bells	.40	701.00	296.00	582.00	0.00
14-B36-1.7	01 Three Wise Men	.50	245.00	74.00	200.00	0.00
14-B36-1.8	02 Gothic Church Interior	.50	236.00	104.00	191.00	0.00
14-B36-1.9	03 Expectant Children	.50	175.00	89.00	133.00	0.00
14-B36-1.10	04 Fredericksberg Hill	.50	96.00	41.00	78.00	0.00
14-B36-1.11	05 Christmas Night	.50	105.00	67.00	100.00	0.00
14-B36-1.12	06 Sleighing to Church	.50	61.00	37.00	61.00	0.00
14-B36-1.13	07 Little Match Girl	.50	70.00	33.00	73.00	+3.00
14-B36-1.14	08 St. Petri Church	.50	43.00	22.00	41.00	+5.00
14-B36-1.15	09 Yule Tree	.75	43.00	30.00	42.00	0.00
14-B36-1.16	10 The Old Organist	.75	43.00	28.00	46.00	+1.00
14-B36-1.17	11 Angels and Shepherds	.75	38.00	15.00	37.00	+1.00
14-B36-1.18	12 Going to Church	.75	43.00	31.00	41.00	0.00
14-B36-1.19	13 Bringing Home the Tree	.75	43.00	31.00	41.00	0.00
14-B36-1.20	14 Amalienborg Castle	.75	39.00	23.00	37.00	0.00
14-B36-1.21	15 Dog Outside Window	.75	79.00	33.00	70.00	0.00
14-B36-1.22	16 Sparrows at Christmas	.75	57.00	22.00	46.00	+1.00
14-B36-1.23	17 Christmas Boat	.75	39.00	22.00	41.00	+3.00
14-B36-1.24	18 Fishing Boat	.75	49.00	30.00	42.00	0.00
14-B36-1.25	19 Outside the Window	1.00	43.00	22.00	41.00	0.00
14-B36-1.26	20 Hare in the Snow	1.00	47.00	25.00	42.00	0.00
14-B36-1.27	21 Pigeons	1.00	33.00	21.00	30.00	0.00
14-B36-1.28	22 Star of Bethlehem	1.00	35.00	22.00	30.00	+2.00
14-B36-1.29	23 The Ermitage	1.00	35.00	22.00	39.00	+1.00
14-B36-1.30	24 The Lighthouse	1.25	35.00	22.00	38.00	+1.00
14-B36-1.31	25 Child's Christmas	1.25	35.00	22.00	39.00	+1.00
14-B36-1.32	26 Churchgoers	1.25	52.00	19.00	41.00	+5.00
14-B36-1.33	27 Skating Couple	1.25	75.00	37.00	61.00	0.00
14-B36-1.34	28 Eskimos	1.25	37.00	24.00	31.00	0.00
14-B36-1.35	29 Fox Outside Farm	1.25	43.00	30.00	46.00	0.00
14-B36-1.36	30 Town Hall Square	1.25	43.00	22.00	53.00	+3.00
14-B36-1.37	31 Christmas Train	1.25	48.00	22.00	45.00	0.00
14-B36-1.38	32 Lifeboat	1.25	43.00	22.00	43.00	0.00

BRADEX No.	PLATE	ISSUE PRICE	HIGH	LOW	QUOTE	CHANGE
14-B36-1.51	45 The Old Water Mill	2.50	70.00	52.00	73.00	+4.00
14-B36-1.52	46 Commemoration Cross	2.50	57.00	26.00	41.00	+3.00
14-B36-1.53	47 Dybbol Mill	2.50	48.00	30.00	42.00	+3.00
14-B36-1.54	48 Watchman	2.75	37.00	19.00	36.00	+2.00
14-B36-1.55	49 Landsoldaten	2.75	39.00	22.00	38.00	0.00
14-B36-1.56	50 Kronborg Castle	2.75	74.00	44.00	70.00	0.00
14-B36-1.57	51 Jens Bang	3.00	74.00	33.00	54.00	0.00
14-B36-1.58	52 Thorvaldsen Museum	3.00	39.00	22.00	39.00	+1.00
14-B36-1.59	53 Royal Boat	3.25	39.00	20.00	40.00	0.00
14-B36-1.60	54 Snowman	3.25	57.00	41.00	52.00	0.00
14-B36-1.61	55 Kalundborg Church	3.25	89.00	41.00	59.00	0.00
14-B36-1.62	56 Christmas in Copenhagen	3.25	65.00	44.00	65.00	0.00
14-B36-1.63	57 Christmas Candles	3.50	67.00	44.00	74.00	0.00
14-B36-1.64	58 Santa Claus	3.50	57.00	30.00	56.00	0.00
14-B36-1.65	59 Christmas Eve	3.50	70.00	44.00	54.00	0.00
14-B36-1.66	60 Village Church	3.50	105.00	59.00	94.00	-8.00
14-B36-1.67	61 Winter Harmony	3.50	61.00	30.00	56.00	0.00
14-B36-1.68	62 Winter Night	3.75	52.00	19.00	37.00	0.00
14-B36-1.69	63 The Christmas Elf	3.75	70.00	37.00	61.00	0.00
14-B36-1.70	64 The Fir Tree and Hare	3.75	37.00	22.00	34.00	0.00
14-B36-1.71	65 Bringing Home the Tree	3.75	33.00	16.00	31.00	0.00
14-B36-1.72	66 Home for Christmas	3.75	30.00	15.00	29.00	0.00
14-B36-1.73	67 Sharing the Joy	3.75	28.00	15.00	26.00	0.00
14-B36-1.74	68 Christmas in Church	3.95	27.00	11.00	21.00	0.00
14-B36-1.75	69 Arrival of Guests	3.95	22.00	11.00	15.00	-1.00
14-B36-1.76	70 Pheasants in Snow	4.50	17.00	10.00	14.00	0.00
14-B36-1.77	71 Christmas at Home	4.95	17.00	7.00	15.00	-1.00
14-B36-1.78	72 Christmas in Greenland	5.95	15.00	9.00	13.00	0.00
14-B36-1.79	73 Family Reunion	5.95	26.00	11.00	17.00	0.00
14-B36-1.80	74 Christmas in the Village	6.95	14.00	7.00	14.00	0.00
14-B36-1.81	75 Old Water Mill	8.50	14.00	7.00	14.00	0.00
14-B36-1.82	76 Christmas Welcome	9.95	17.00	9.00	13.00	0.00
14-B36-1.83	77 Copenhagen Christmas	11.00	16.00	5.00	17.00	0.00
14-B36-1.84	78 Christmas Tale	12.80	16.00	9.00	18.00	0.00
14-B36-1.85	79 Winter Christmas	14.00	14.00	9.00	17.00	0.00
14-B36-1.86	80 Christmas in Woods	18.65	22.00	9.00	18.00	0.00
14-B36-1.87	81 Christmas Peace	19.95	21.00	10.00	20.00	0.00
14-B36-1.88	82 Christmas Tree	21.00	23.00	14.00	21.00	0.00
14-B36-1.89	83 Christmas in Old Town	21.00	26.00	15.00	24.00	0.00
14-B36-1.90	84 Christmas Letter	21.00	21.00	19.00	25.00	0.00
14-B36-1.91	85 Christmas Eve on Farm	21.50	22.00	21.50	32.00	0.00
14-B36-1.92	86 Silent Night	23.00	23.00	23.00	26.00	0.00
14-B36-1.93	87 Snowman's Christmas Eve	27.50	27.50	27.50	27.50	0.00
	Collection to Date	325.05	12262.50	5862.00	10233.50	+18.00
Bing & Grondahl Mother's Day (14-B36-3)						
14-B36-3.1	69 Dog and Puppies	2.50	341.00	144.00	269.00	0.00
14-B36-3.2	70 Bird and Chicks	2.50	22.00	7.00	20.00	0.00
14-B36-3.3	71 Cat and Kitten	3.95	11.00	4.00	10.00	0.00
14-B36-3.4	72 Mare and Foal	3.95	11.00	5.00	14.00	0.00
14-B36-3.5	73 Duck and Ducklings	5.50	11.00	5.00	11.00	0.00
14-B36-3.6	74 Bear and Cubs	6.50	25.00	9.00	22.00	-3.00
14-B36-3.7	75 Doe and Fawns	7.50	9.00	8.00	11.00	0.00
14-B36-3.8	76 Swan Family	8.00	20.00	8.00	11.00	0.00
14-B36-3.9	77 Squirrel and Young	8.44	19.00	9.00	11.00	0.00
14-B36-3.10	78 Heron	9.50	14.00	7.00	11.00	0.00
14-B36-3.11	79 Fox and Cubs	10.90	20.00	11.00	12.00	0.00
14-B36-3.12	80 Woodpecker and Young	13.35	19.00	14.00	18.00	0.00
14-B36-3.13	81 Hare and Young	16.10	17.00	14.00	16.00	0.00
14-B36-3.14	82 Lioness and Cubs	16.10	32.00	16.00	21.00	0.00
14-B36-3.15	83 Racoon and Young	16.10	23.00	16.00	17.00	0.00
14-B36-3.16	84 Stork and Young	16.90	17.00	17.70	17.00	0.00
14-B36-3.17	85 Bear and Cubs	16.90	18.00	16.90	16.00	0.00
14-B36-3.18	86 Elephant and Young	16.90	20.25	16.90	19.00	+1.00
14-B36-3.19	87 Ewe and Lambs	16.90	16.90	16.90	18.00	+1.10

Plates limited by announced production periods such as the number of firing days are by far the most frequent, ranging from less than one thousand to the tens of thousands. Regardless of the edition size, a market winner is made when demand outstrips supply. A very small edition does not automatically guarantee demand; in fact it often discourages it through the restriction of active trading. The success of a collector's plate in terms of sales is determined by supply and demand, which can only develop freely on an organized market. To this end, interest must be stimulated and collectors furnished with enough information on which to base a buy or sell decision. The *Bradex* price index of international collector's plates lists the market prices and indicates trends and developments in the marketplace.

Issue Price:
The original or first price of the plate established by the maker at the time the plate is released for sale. Any quotations refer to this price.

High price:
Highest known historical asked/offering price.

Low price:
Lowest known historical asked/offering price.

Quote price:
The exchange's best estimate of a plate's selling price in the current trading period (subject to fluctuation).

Change:
increase or decrease in Quote price since the previous bi-monthly trading period.

Collecting By Theme

Many collectors get great pleasure by collecting series or single issues with artwork that has the same subject, or *theme*. To help you discover subjects in this book that interest you, here are 21 major themes in which collector's plate art can be grouped.

Under each theme category are the names of all series in this book with that theme. The series are listed in the order in which they appear in this book; to locate each series, see the *Table of Contents*.

ANIMALS (Domestic and Pets):
Bing & Grøndahl *Mother's Day*; Royal Copenhagen *Motherhood*; Lalique *Annual*; Anna-Perenna *Uncle Tad's Cats, Uncle Tad's Golden Oldies*; Kaiser *Mother's Day*; Edwin M. Knowles *Friends in the Forest, Amy Brackenbury's Cat Tales* (See also: WILDLIFE)

ARCHITECTURE:
D'Arceau-Limoges *Twelve Parisian Places of Louis Dali*; Bareuther *Father's Day*; Königszelt-Bayern *German Half-Timbered Houses*; Wedgwood *Christmas*; Orrefors *Annual Cathedrals*

ARTISTS:

Chambers, William:	Edwin M. Knowles *Annie, The King and I, Portraits of Motherhood, Tom Sawyer*
DeGrazia, Ted:	Artists of the World *Children of the Sun*; Fairmont *DeGrazia Holiday, Children, Children at Play, Western*; Gorham *DeGrazia Children*
Hibel, Edna:	Hibel Studio *David*, Rosenthal *Nobility of Children, Oriental Gold*; Royal Doulton *Mother and Child*; Edwin M. Knowles *Hibel Christmas; Hibel Mother's Day*
Hook, Frances:	Edwin M. Knowles *Frances Hook Legacy*; Roman *A Child's Play*
Hummel, Berta (or Sister M. I.):	Goebel Hummel *Annual, Anniversary*; Schmid *Christmas, Mother's Day*
Kuck, Sandra:	Reco *Days Gone By*
McClelland, John:	Reco *World of Children, Mother Goose, Children's Circus, Becky's Day*
Perillo, Gregory:	Vague Shadows *Chieftains I*
Rockwell, Norman:	Franklin Mint *Christmas*; Gorham *Four Seasons, Rockwell Christmas*; Rockwell Society of America *Christmas, Mother's Day, Heritage, Rediscovered Women, Rockwell on Tour, Light Campaign, American Dream, Colonials: The Rarest Rockwells, A Mind of Her Own, Golden Moments, Royal Devon Christmas*
Skelton, Red:	Crown Parian *Freddie the Freeloader, Freddie's Adventures*; Fairmont *Famous Clowns*
Spencer, Irene:	Pickard *Mother's Love, Symphony of Roses*
Zolan, Donald:	Pemberton & Oakes *Wonder of Childhood, Children at Christmas, Children and Pets*; Viletta *Zolan's Children*

BEAUTIFUL WOMEN:
Imperial Ching-te Chen *Beauties of the Red Mansion*; D'Arceau-Limoges *Women of the Century, Girls of the Seasons, Women of the Belle Epoque*; Haviland Parlon *The Lady and the Unicorn*; Heinrich/Villeroy & Boch *Dreams of Katharina*; Le Porcellane Fontana Dei Medici *Women of Puccini*; Studio Dante di Volteradici *Benvenuti's Muses*; Fairmont *Classical American Beauties*; Edwin M. Knowles *Four Ancient Elements*; Morgantown Crystal *Michael Yates' Country Ladies*; Pickard *Oleg Cassini's Most Beautiful Women of All Time, Symphony of Roses*; Rockwell Society of America *Rediscovered Women*

BIRDS:
Dominion China *Wings Upon the Wind*; Grande Copenhagen *Ugly Duckling*; Tirschenreuth *Songbirds of Europe*; Royal Grafton *Braithwaite Game Birds Collection*; Lenox *Boehm Bird*; Edwin M. Knowles *Birds of Your Garden, Upland Birds of North America, Living with Nature: Jerner's Ducks*

CARTOON CHARACTERS:
Schmid *Peanuts Christmas, Disney Christmas, Disney Mother's Day*

CHILDREN (contemporary):
Dominion China *Reflections of Canadian Childhood*; Pavilion of T'sang Ying Hsuan *Chinese Children's Games*; Bing & Grøndahl *Moments of Truth, Children's Day, Family Portraits*; D'Arceau-Limoges *Christmas in France*; Limoges-Turgot *Durand's Children*; Wedgwood *Blossoming of Suzanne, My Memories*; Artists of the World *Children of Aberdeen, DeGrazia's Children of the Sun*; Ernst *Seems Like Yesterday*; Fairmont *DeGrazia Children, Playful Memories, DeGrazia's Children at Play*; Gorham *Sugar & Spice*; Kern *Leaders of Tomorrow*; Edwin M. Knowles *Jeanne Down's Friends I Remember, Frances Hook Legacy, A Swan Is Born*; Pemberton & Oakes *Wonder of Childhood, Children at Christmas, Children and Pets*; Roman *A Child's Play*; Viletta *Zolan's Children*

CHILDREN (nostalgic):
Limoges-Turgot *Children of the Turn of the Century*; Goebel Hummel *Annual, Hummel Anniversary*; Kaiser *Classic Lullabies of the World*; Rosenthal *Nobility of Children*; Schmid *Christmas, Mother's Day*; Davenport Pottery *Treasury of Classic Children's Verse*; Royal Doulton *Portraits of Innocence*; Fukagawa *Haiku About Children*; Langenthal *Anker's Heritage*; Edwin M. Knowles *Americana Holidays, American Innocents, J. W. Smith's Childhood Holiday Memories*; Newell Pottery *S. S. Weber Calendar*; Pickard *Children of Renoir*; Rockwell Society of America *A Mind of Her Own*

CHRISTMAS:
Bing & Grøndahl, Grande Copenhagen, Royal Copenhagen, D'Arceau-Limoges *Stained Glass Christmas, Christmas in France*; Haviland *Twelve Days of Christmas*; Haviland & Parlon, Bareuther, Berlin Design, Kaiser, Königszelt-Bayern *Heidi Keller Christmas*; Rosenthal *Traditional Classic Rose Christmas, Winblad Christmas*; Schmid *Hummel Christmas*; Belleek *Christmas, Irish Wildlife Christmas*; Royal Doulton *Beswick Christmas*; Spode; Wedgwood; Anri; Schmid *Peanuts Christmas, Disney Christmas*; Porsgrund *Christmas, Traditional Norwegian Christmas*; Rörstrand; Franklin Mint *Rockwell Christmas*; Edwin M. Knowles *Hibel Christmas, Licea Christmas*; Pemberton & Oakes *Children at Christmas*; Pickard; Rockwell Society of America; Reed & Barton; Roman *Fantanini Christmas Story*; Royal Devon; Viletta *Nutcracker Ballet*

FANTASY:
Grande Copenhagen *Christmas*; Haviland-Parlon *Tapestry, The Lady and the Unicorn*; Limoges-Turgot *Quellier's Morals of Perrault*; Anna-Perenna *Uncle Tad's Golden Oldies*; Heinrich/Villeroy & Boch *Russian Fairy Tales, Fairies of the Fields and Flowers, Once Upon a Rhyme*; Königszelt *Grimm's Fairy Tales*; Viletta *Nutcracker Ballet*

FATHERS/FATHER'S DAY/GRANDFATHERS:
Bareuther *Father's Day*; Edwin M. Knowles *Csatari Grandparents, A Father's Love*, Rockwell Society *Heritage, Golden Moments*

FLOWERS:
Heinrich/Villeroy & Boch *Fairies of the Fields and Flowers*; Hutschenreuther *Bouquets of the Seasons*; King's *Flowers of America*; Pickard *Symphony of Roses*

FOLKLORE:
Arabia *Kalevala*; Davenport Pottery *Toby*; Royal Doulton *Commedia Dell-Arte*; Wedgwood *Legend of King Arthur*; Studio Dante di Volteradici *Benvenuti's Muses*; Crown Parian *American Folk Heroes*; Incolay *Voyage of Ulysses, The Fall of Troy*; Edwin M. Knowles *Four Ancient Elements*

HISTORY:
Christian Bell *Age of Steam, Yesterday's Memories*; D'Arceau-Limoges *Lafayette Legacy, Women of the Century, Very Rich Hours, Josephine and Napoleon, Women of the Belle Epoque*; Hibel Studio *David*; Royal Doulton *The Log of the "Dashing Wave;"* Wedgwood *Street Sellers of London*; Incolay *Great Romances of History*; Edwin M. Knowles *Lincoln—Man of America*; Rhodes Studios *Treasures of the Doré Bible*; RiverShore *Famous Americans*; Rockwell Society *Rockwell's Colonials—The Rarest Rockwells*; Vague Shadows *The Chieftains I*

LITERATURE:
Imperial Ching-te Chen *Beauties of the Red Mansion*; Grande Copenhagen *Ugly Duckling*; Arabia *Kalevala*; Haviland *1001 Arabian Nights*; Porcelain Georges Boyer *Alice in Wonderland*; Heinrich/Villeroy & Boch *Russian Fairy Tales*; Davenport Pottery *Treasury of Classic Children's Verse*; Longton Crown *Canterbury Tales*; Studio Dante di Volteradici *Grand Opera*; Fukagawa *Haiku About Children*; Incolay *Romantic Poets, Voyage of Ulysses, Love Sonnets of Shakespeare, The Fall of Troy*; Edwin M. Knowles *Tom Sawyer*

LOVERS/VALENTINE'S DAY:
Anna-Perenna *Romantic Loves*; Hutschenreuther *Love for All Seasons*; Königszelt-Bayern *Sulamith's Love Song, A Woman's Love and Life*; Royal Doulton *Valentine's Day*; Incolay *Romantic Poets, Great Romances of History*

MOTHERS AND CHILDREN/MOTHER'S DAY/ GRANDMOTHERS:
Bing & Grøndahl *Mother's Day*, Royal Copenhagen *Motherhood*; D'Arceau-Limoges Cambier *Mother's Day*; Kaiser *Mother's Day*; Königszelt-Bayern *Wulfing Mother's Day*; Royal Bayreuth *Mother's Day*; Schmid *Mother's Day*; Royal Doulton *Mother and Child*; Wedgwood *Mother's Day*; Studio Dante di Volteradici *Living Madonnas, Renaissance Madonnas: Gifts of Maternal Love*; Schmid *Disney Mother's Day*; Porsgrund *Mother's Day*; Lladró *Mother's Day*; Edwin M. Knowles *Csatari Grandparents, Biblical Mothers, Hibel Mother's Day, Portraits of Motherhood*; Pickard *Christmas, Mother's Love*; RiverShore *Signs of Love*; Rockwell Society of America *Mother's Day*

MOVIES:
D'Arceau-Limoges *Gigi*; W. S. George Pottery *Gone With the Wind: Golden Anniversary*; Edwin M. Knowles *The Wizard of Oz, Gone With the Wind, Annie, The King and I, Oklahoma, The Sound of Music, South Pacific*

RELIGIOUS (Madonnas, Biblical Figures, Churches):
Haviland-Parlon *Christmas*; Anna-Perenna *Triptych*, Hibel Studio *David*; Veneto Flair *Bellini Madonna, The Last Supper, St. Mark's of Venice*; Studio Dante di Volteradici *Living Madonnas, Ghiberti Doors, Renaissance Madonnas: Gifts of Maternal Love, The Christmas Creche*; Orrefors *Annual Cathedrals*; Edwin M. Knowles *Biblical Mothers*; Pickard *Christmas*; Rhodes Studio *Treasures of the Doré Bible*; Roman *Fontanini Christmas Story*

SCENIC:
Bing & Grøndahl *Summer at Skagen*; D'Arceau-Limoges *Twelve Parisian Places of Louis Dali, French Country Landscapes*; Berlin Design *Holiday Week of the Family Kappelmann*; Christian Seltmann *Lückel's Idyllic Village Life*; Fürstenberg *Romantic Winter Impressions*; Royal Worcester *Happy England*; Wedgwood *Colin Newman's Country Panorama*; Edwin M. Knowles *Living with Nature: Jerner's Ducks*

WESTERN:
Fairmont *DeGrazia Western*; Edwin M. Knowles *Oklahoma!*; Vague Shadows *The Chieftains I*

WILDLIFE:
Dominion China *Wings Upon the Wind*; Belleek *Irish Wildlife Christmas*; Royal Grafton *Braithwaite Game Birds Collection*; Edwin M. Knowles *Birds of Your Garden, Upland Birds of North America, Living With Nature: Jerner's Ducks, Friends in the Forest*; Lenox *Boehm Bird*; Pickard *Lockhart Wildlife*; RiverShore *Signs of Love*

Decorating With Collector's Plates:
A Guide to the Display of the Most Common Series Lengths

Artwork you love deserves to be displayed to its best advantage. Why hang your plates in even, horizontal rows—even though it saves a bit of space—when there's so much *more* you can do to make them look their very best in each room?

This pictorial guide shows eight different plate display ideas, two each for the four most common series lengths: *four, six, eight* and *twelve* plates. You can also adapt these ideas for plates series of other lengths (three, five, seven, nine, etc.).

Four Plates: *Setting A* displays the *Uncle Tad's Cats* series in an arched arrangement. This idea also works well over a sofa or a wide doorway. *Setting B* offers a variation, a four-point "diamond" pattern.

Six Plates: *Setting C* staggers three vertical rows and repeats the shape of the wrought iron bed. *Setting D* nestles six plates in the *McClelland's Mother Goose* series into a narrow space between headboard and window. This puts them in a well-lit area right at eye level for best viewing.

Eight Plates: Why restrict a favorite series to just one room? The *Days Gone By* series in *Setting E* is positioned to be dramatic in both living and dining room. A variation in *Setting F* leads the eye from one room to the other.

Twelve Plates: Longer series also look extra-special when displayed in more than one room, as in *Setting G*. In *Setting H*, a plate rail allows the *Rockwell's Rediscovered Women* series to be displayed harmoniously in very little space.

Plate frames and rails courtesy of Van Hygan & Smythe.

Setting A

Setting B

Setting C

Setting D

Setting H

34

Setting E

Setting G

Setting F

AN INTRODUCTION TO INFORMATION IN THE GALLERY SECTION

The following Gallery section of *The Bradford Book of Collector's Plates* offers complete information on all major issues *regularly traded in the market.* The plates are arranged in an order exactly corresponding to the Bradford Exchange *Current Quotations:* first, by *country* of the plate's origin, in alphabetical order; second, by *plate maker* within each country, also in alphabetical order; third, by *series* of each maker, in chronological order beginning with the maker's first series and fourth, by *plate position* in each series, also in chronological order beginning with the first plate.

To speed identification, each plate is listed by its Bradex number, a codified form of the information above. *These numbers are in sequence but not necessarily consecutive.* The number on the upper left-hand corner of each page indicates the first plate listed on that page.

HOW TO READ THE BRADEX NUMBER

(The number used as an example here is that of the 1904 Bing & Grøndahl *Christmas* plate)

14-B36-1.10

COUNTRY	MAKER	SERIES	PLATE OR SET OF PLATES
The first identifier indicates *the country of origin;* in this case the number *14* is for Denmark.	The second identifier indicates the *plate maker.* The alpha-numeric combination of *B36* represents Bing & Grøndahl. This number is assigned according to a system similar to that used in libraries for the classification of authors' works.	The third identifier indicates the maker's *series,* listed in the chronological order in which it was produced. Thus the number *1* represents Bing & Grøndahl's first series, the *Christmas* series.	The fourth identifier indicates the individual plate (or set of plates) within each series, listed in chronological order. The number *10* is for the tenth plate in the Bing & Grøndahl *Christmas* series, *View of Copenhagen from Frederiksberg Hill,* the 1904 issue. Plates issued in sets use an additional successive digit to indicate their position within a set (example: 22-A3-3.1-1).

Country Code Register

05 = Austria	34 = Ireland
06 = Belgium	38 = Italy
08 = Canada	42 = Japan
10 = China	50 = Netherlands
12 = Czechoslovakia	54 = Norway
14 = Denmark	72 = Spain
16 = Finland	76 = Sweden
18 = France	78 = Switzerland
22 = Germany	84 = United States
26 = Great Britain	

AUSTRIA
LILIEN PORZELLAN

5-L32-0.0

LILIEN PORZELLAN
Vienna, Wilhelmsburg

Lilien Porzellan has a longstanding tradition. Its beginnings can be traced back to an earthenware factory which was founded in Wilhelmsburg in 1795. It was taken over by the industrialist Heinrich Lichtenstern in 1883. His son Richard developed it into a large pottery concern with further factories in Znaim and Teplitz-Schönau (now Czechoslovakia) and became one of the largest producers of stoneware under the Austro-Hungarian monarchy. After the Second World War the company was completely reorganized. Concentration on just two porcelain product lines resulted in an extremely rapid development. In 1960 the company was renamed ÖSPAG and 1967 the Laufen Group acquired a majority of the shares. With two factories in Wilhelmsburg and Gmunden-Egelhof the company now counts among the most successful porcelain manufacturers in Austria. The Lilien Porzellan trademark enjoys international renown.

Masterpieces of Franz von Defregger

Reproductions from artworks of the artist

Porcelain

Diameter: 19 centimetres (7 ¹/₂ inches)

Porcelain, banded in gold

Edition size undisclosed, limited by announced period of issue

Numbered with certificate

5-L32-1.1
1988 *Saying Grace*
Issue price: not available at press time

5-L32-1.2
1988 *Poachers in the Chalet*
Issue price: not available at press time

CANADA
CHRISTIAN BELL

8-C30-0.0

CHRISTIAN BELL
Mount Forest, Ontario

Founded in 1979, Christian Bell Porcelain Ltd. traces its name to founder Horst S. Muller's great-grandfather, Christian Bell, a prominent figure in the whiteware industry of Siebenbürgen in pre-World War I Austria-Hungary.

The firm's first collector's plate series, *Preserving a Way of Life,* (not U. K. Bradex-listed) began in 1980. Their *Age of Steam* series began in 1981 and celebrates the vital role of the railroads in Canada's national heritage.

Age of Steam Series

Artist: Theodore Xaras. Artist's signature appears on front

Hard-paste porcelain

Diameter: 24.1 centimetres (9 ½ inches)

No hanger

Edition size limited to 15.000

Numbered, without certificate through 1982; with certificate thereafter

8-C30-1.1
1981 *Symphony in Steam*
Issue price: £ 39.40

8-C30-1.2
1982 *Brief Encounter*
Issue price: £ 39.40

8-C30-1.3
1983 *No Contest*
Issue price: £ 39.40

8-C30-1.4
1984 *Timber Country*
Issue price: £ 39.40

8-C30-1.5
1985 *White Pass Gateway to the Yukon*
Issue price: £ 39.40

Yesterday's Memories Series

Artist: Theodore Xaras. Artist's signature appears on front

Hard-paste porcelain banded in 22 k gold

Diameter: 21 centimetres (8 ¼ inches)

No hanger

Edition size undisclosed, limited by announced period of issue

Not numbered, without certificate

8-C30-8.1
1984 *Ice*
Issue price: £ 27.30

CANADA
DOMINION CHINA
8-D52-1.1

ONTARIO
CANADA

DOMINION CHINA
Toronto, Ontario

Dominion China, Ltd. produces fine china using the exact standards and time-honoured techniques of porcelain-making that have been practiced for centuries. Today, it is one of the best-known of the Canadian plate-producing companies to have recently entered the market.

Dominion China, Ltd. initiated its first collector's plate series in 1986 with the *Wings Upon the Wind* series by wildlife artist Donald Pentz, a native Canadian and resident of Nova Scotia. The *Wings Upon the Wind* series depicts scenes of migratory behaviour of the most graceful and majestic of wildfowl, the Canada goose.

In 1987, Dominion China introduced its second series, *Reflections of Canadian Childhood,* by Steward Sherwood. This series features children in well-remembered activities, set amidst a variety of Canadian landscapes.

Wings Upon the Wind Series

Artist: Donald Pentz. Artist's signature appears on front
China

Diameter: 21.6 centimetres (8 ¹/₂ inches)

No hanger

Edition size undisclosed, limited by announced period of issue

Numbered, with certificate

8-D52-1.1
1986 *The Landing*
Issue price: £ 17.75

8-D52-1.2
1986 *Nesting*
Issue price: £ 17.75

8-D52-1.3
1986 *The Courtship*
Issue price: £ 17.75

8-D52-1.4
1987 *The Family*
Issue price: £ 18.85

8-D52-1.5
1987 *Southward Bound*
Issue price: £ 18.85

Reflections of Canadian Childhood Series

Artist: Steward Sherwood.
Artist's signature appears on front

China

Diameter: 21.6 centimetres
(8 ¹/₂ inches)

No hanger

Edition size undisclosed,
limited by announced period of
issue

Numbered, with certificate

8-D52-2.1
1987 *Dreams of Glory*
Issue price: £ 21.95

8-D52-2.2
1987 *A Quiet Moment*
Issue price: £ 21.95

8-D52-2.3
1987 *Pick of the Crop*
Issue price: £ 21.95

CHINA, THE PEOPLE'S REPUBLIC OF
IMPERIAL CHING-TE CHEN

10-I50-0.0

IMPERIAL CHING-TE CHEN

Ching-te Chen, (Jingdezhen),
Kiangxi Province

Imperial Ching-te Chen Porcelain is located in the area where porcelain was first created, in the People's Republic of China. Most scholars agree the the porcelain-making process was most likely invented during the Sui dynasty (sixth century A.D.). Thus, Chinese potters and been working with porcelain for twelve centuries before European porcelain makers began their craft in the 1700s.

In the T'ang dynasty (A. D. 621), the porcelain makers of the city of Ching-te Chen were officially charged with the responsibility of supplying the emperor. During the reign of the Sung Emperor, Chen Tsung (A. D. 1004), the emperor gave the city its modern name. In the Ming dynasty (A.D. 1369), the imperial factory was established just south of the city's Pearl Hill.

Imperial Ching-te Chen Porcelain works under the patronage of China National Arts and Crafts, which is responsible for disseminating Chinese cultural artifacts to other countries. China National Arts and Crafts applies rigorous standards to artistic objects before they are approved for export.

Porcelain from Ching-te Chen is known throughout the world for its translucent delicacy and beauty. The eggshell-thin, luminous quality of the pieces has been a tradition for centuries. Today, the artisans of Ching-te Chen draw upon skills of ceramic manufacture that have been handed down for generations, to create the first "modern" collector's plate series from The People's Republic of China: *Beauties of the Red Mansion*.

The series presents the work of native Chinese artisan Zhao Huimin in a skilful fusion of figurative and landscape painting. The series is based on "A Dream of Red Mansions", a classic romantic novel of the eighteenth century, and one of China's greatest literary masterpieces. Imperial Ching-te Chen Porcelain introduced the *Beauties of the Red Mansion* series in 1986.

IMPERIAL CHING-TE CHEN

10-I50-1.1

Beauties of the Red Mansion Series

Artist: Zhao Huimin. Artist's signature appears on front

Porcelain

Diameter: 21.6 centimetres (8 ¹/₂ inches)

No hanger

Edition size undisclosed, limited by announced period of issue

Numbered with certificate

10-I50-1.1
1986 *Pao-chai*
Issue price: £ 19.95

10-I50-1.2
1986 *Yuan-chun*
Issue price: £ 19.95

10-I50-1.3
1987 *Hsi-feng*
Issue price unavailable at press time

10-I50-1.4
1987 *Hsi-chun*
Issue price unavailable at press time

10-I50-1.5
1988 *Miau-yu*
Issue price unavailable at press time

TAIWAN, REPUBLIC OF CHINA
PAVILION T'SANG YING-HSÜAN

10-P8-0.0

PAVILION OF T'SANG YING-HSÜAN
Hsin Pu

Chinese porcelain-making reached a high point during the K'ang Hsi Empire (1662-1722). Authorities on Chinese porcelain consider this to be the most remarkable period of multi-colour decoration on pure white porcelain. The Pavilion of T'sang Ying-Hsüan takes its name − and its standards of excellence in porcelain manufacture − from this historic era.

In the seventeenth century, Emperor K'ang Hsi desired porcelain whose beauty would surpass that of all previous ages. To fulfil his dream, the constructed an Imperial porcelain works and appointed T'sang Ying-Hsüan as its director. T'sang recruited the best craftsmen in the country to produce magnificent dragon bowls, delicate figurines and porcelain screens for the Emperor. It has been said that "when T'sang was in charge of the factory, the god laid his finger on the designs and protected the porcelain in the kilns so that it naturally came out perfect".

The Pavilion of T'sang Ying-Hsüan uses the same strict principles to create and judge the quality of its porcelain. Colours must be exceptional, the glaze must be brilliant, the shape of the porcelain must be uniformly proportioned, and when tapped, the porcelain must ring like a bell. If these rigorous tests of artistic quality are passed, the plates are allowed to carry the mark of the Pavilion of T'sang Ying-Hsüan.

The *Chinese Children's Games* series is the first issue of artist Kee Fung Ng for this producer, but it is his second plate series (see United States, ARTISTS OF THE WORLD). Begun in 1986, the series is sponsored by the Hwa Kang Museum of the Chinese Cultural University, under the hallmark of Artists of the World. The *Chinese Children's Games* series depicts scenes of children playing ancient Chinese games and is based on memories of the artist's youth.

Chinese Children's Games Series

Artist: Kee Fung Ng. Artist's signature appears on front

Porcelain

Diameter: 21.6 centimetres (8 ½ inches)

No hanger

Edition size undisclosed, limited by announced period of issue

Numbered with certificate

10-P8-1.1
1986 *Chinese Chess*
Issue price: £ 15.75

10-P8-1.2
1986 *Kite Flying*
Issue price: £ 15.75

10-P8-1.3
1987 *Spinning Tops*
Issue price: £ 19.95

10-P8-1.4
1987 *Rolling Hoops*
Issue price: £ 19.95

DENMARK
BING & GRØNDAHL

14-B36-0.0

KONGELIG HOFLEVERANDØR

BING & GRØNDAHL
Copenhagen

Bing & Grøndahl, Denmark's second oldest existing porcelain maker (after Royal Copenhagen), was established in 1853 by Frederick Vilhelm Grøndahl and Meyer and Jacob Bing. Grøndahl, a young sculptor previously employed by Royal Copenhagen, supplied the artistic talent while the Bing brothers provided financial backing. Although Grøndahl died before the manufactory's third year of operation, his name was retained in honour of his contribution. Bing & Grøndahl has continued under the leadership of the Bing family for five generations.

The world's first collector's plate, "Behind the Frozen Window", was issued by Bing & Grøndahl in 1895. This began its *Christmas* series which has been produced each year without interruption despite wars and economic crises. Plates in this series are now the most widely collected of all plates in the market. In 1969 Bing & Grøndahl issued the first Mother's Day

plate, "Dog and Puppies".

Their *Moments of Truth* series started in 1984.

Besides limited-edition collector's plates, Bing & Grøndahl makes a variety of porcelain articles, including figurines and tableware. Many of their porcelain works can be found in museums arround the world, and they have achieved the distinction of appointment to the royal courts of Denmark, Sweden, and Great Britain. This distinction is symbolized by the crown which is part of their trademark.

The artist for the very first collector's plate was Frans August Hallin, a Swede who moved to Copenhagen in 1885. After Harald Bing named him chief designer in 1895, Hallin created a distinctive item for the maker's Christmas giftware line — "Behind the Frozen Window". Its success assured his niche in history. He also designed the Christmas plates for 1896 and 1897. From 1897 to 1929 he serv-

ed as manager of Bing & Grøndahl's exhibitions abroad and in 1924 rose to the position of Assisting Director of the maker's artware line. Hallin retired in 1934 and died in Copenhagen in 1947.

Artist Henry Thelander's association with Bing & Grøndahl is unparalleled on the collector's plate market. He has been the principal designer of the *Christmas* series, creating 22 consecutive issues between 1963 and 1984 (later issues were designed by Edvard Jensen). He also has designed every Bing & Grøndahl *Mother's Day* issue — eighteen in all.

In 1986, Bing & Grøndahl produced "A Summer at Skagen" series, the first limited edition collector's plate series showing the work of the Danish Impressionist Peter Severin Krøyer. The series depicts idyllic scenes of a turn-of-the-century Scandinavian artists' colony.

Christmas Series

Artist: as indicated

True underglaze-decorated porcelain hand-painted in Copenhagen blue on bas-relief

Diameter: 17.8 centimetres (7 inches)

Pierced foot rim

Edition size undisclosed, limited by year of issue

Not numbered, without certificate; individually initialled on back by each painter

14-B36-1.1
1895 *Behind the Frozen Window*
Artist: Frans August Hallin
Issue price: £ .25

14-B36-1.2
1896 *New Moon over Snow-covered Trees*
Artist: Frans August Hallin
Issue price: £ .25

14-B36-1.3
1897 *Christmas Meal of the Sparrows*
Artist: Frans August Hallin
Issue price: £ .40

14-B36-1.4
1898 *Christmas Roses and Christmas Star*
Artist: Fanny Garde
Issue price: £ .40

14-B36-1.5
1899 *The Crows Enjoying Christmas*
Artist: Dahl Jensen
Issue price: £ .40

14-B36-1.6
1900 *Church Bells Chiming in Christmas*
Artist: Dahl Jensen
Issue price: £ .40

14-B36-1.7
1901 *The Three Wise Man from the East*
Artist: S. Sabra
Issue price: £ .50

14-B36-1.8
1902 *Interior of a Gothic Church*
Artist: Dahl Jensen
Issue price: £ .50

DENMARK
BING & GRØNDAHL
14-B36-1.9

14-B36-1.9
1903 *Happy Expectation of Children*
Artist: Margrethe Hyldahl
Issue price: £ .50

14-B36-1.10
1904 *View of Copenhagen from Frederiksberg Hill*
Artist: Cathinka Olsen
Issue price: £ .50

14-B36-1.11
1905 *Anxiety of the Coming Christmas Night*
Artist: Dahl Jensen
Issue price: £ .50

14-B36-1.12
1906 *Sleighing to Church on Christmas Eve*
Artist: Dahl Jensen
Issue price: £ .50

14-B36-1.13
1907 *The Little Match Girl*
Artist: E. Plockross
Issue price: £ .50

14-B36-1.14
1908 *The St. Petri Curch of Copenhagen*
Artist: Povl Jorgensen
Issue price: £ .50

14-B36-1.15
1909 *Happiness over the Yule Tree*
Artist: Aarestrup
Issue price: £ .75

14-B36-1.16
1910 *The Old Organist*
Artist: C. Ersgaard
Issue price: £ .75

14-B36-1.17
1911 *First It Was Sung by Angels to Shepherds in the Fields*
Artist: H. Moltke
Issue price: £ .75

14-B36-1.18
1912 *Going to Church on Christmas Eve*
Artist: Aar Hansen
Issue price: £ .75

14-B36-1.19
1913 *Bringing Home the Yule Tree*
Artist: Th. Larsen
Issue price: £ .75

14-B36-1.20
1914 *Royal Castle Amalienborg, Copenhagen*
Artist: Th. Larsen
Issue price: £ .75

14-B36-1.21
1915 *Chained Dog Getting Double Meal*
Artist: Dahl Jensen
Issue price: £ .75

14-B36-1.22
1916 *Christmas Prayer of the Sparrows*
Artist: J. Bloch Jorgensen
Issue price: £ .75

14-B36-1.23
1917 *Arrival of the Christmas Boat*
Artist: Achton Friis
Issue price: £ .75

14-B36-1.24
1918 *Fishing Boat Returning Home for Christmas*
Artist: Achton Friis
Issue price: £ .75

14-B36-1.25
1919 *Outside the Lighted Window*
Artist: Achton Friis
Issue price: £ 1.00

14-B36-1.26
1920 *Hare in the Snow*
Artist: Achton Friis
Issue price: £ 1.00

DENMARK
BING & GRØNDAHL
14-B36-1.27

14-B36-1.27
1921 *Pigeons in the Castle Court*
Artist: Achton Friis
Issue price: £ 1.00

14-B36-1.28
1922 *Star of Bethlehem*
Artist: Achton Friis
Issue price: £ 1.00

14-B36-1.29
1923 *Royal Hunting Castle, the Eremitage*
Artist: Achton Friis
Issue price: £ 1.00

14-B36-1.30
1924 *Lighthouse in Danish Waters*
Artist: Achton Friis
Issue price: £ 1.25

14-B36-1.31
1925 *The Child's Christmas*
Artist: Achton Friis
Issue price: £ 1.25

14-B36-1.32
1926 *Churchgoers on Christmas Day*
Artist: Achton Friis
Issue price: £ 1.25

14-B36-1.33
1927 *Skating Couple*
Artist: Achton Friis
Issue price: £ 1.25

14-B36-1.34
1928 *Eskimo Looking at Village Church in Greenland*
Artist: Achton Friis
Issue price: £ 1.25

14-B36-1.35
1929 *Fox outside Farm on Christmas Eve*
Artist: Achton Friis
Issue price: £ 1.25

14-B36-1.36
1930 *Yule Tree in Town Hall Square of Copenhagen*
Artist: H. Flugenring
Issue price: £ 1.25

14-B36-1.37
1931 *Arrival of the Christmas Train*
Artist: Achton Friis
Issue price: £ 1.25

14-B36-1.38
1932 *Lifeboat at Work*
Artist: H. Flugenring
Issue price: £ 1.25

14-B36-1.39
1933 *The Korsor-Nyborg Ferry*
Artist: H. Flugenring
Issue price: £ 1.50

14-B36-1.40
1934 *Church Bell in Tower*
Artist: Immanuel Tjerne
Issue price: £ 1.50

14-B36-1.41
1935 *Lillebelt Bridge Connecting Funen with Jutland*
Artist: Ove Larsen
Issue price: £ 1.50

14-B36-1.42
1936 *Royal Guard Outside Amalienborg Castle in Copenhagen*
Artist: Ove Larsen
Issue price: £ 1.50

14-B36-1.43
1937 *Arrival of Christmas Guests*
Artist: Ove Larsen
Issue price: £ 1.50

14-B36-1.44
1938 *Lighting the Candles*
Artist: Immanuel Tjerne
Issue price: £ 1.50

DENMARK
BING & GRØNDAHL
14-B36-1.45

14-B36-1.45
1939 *Ole Lock-Eye, the Sandman*
Artist: Immanuel Tjerne
Issue price: £ 1.50

14-B36-1.46
1940 *Delivering Christmas Letters*
Artist: Ove Larsen
Issue price: £ 2.00

14-B36-1.47
1941 *Horses Enjoying Christmas Meal in Stable*
Artist: Ove Larsen
Issue price: £ 2.00

14-B36-1.48
1942 *Danish Farm on Christmas Night*
Artist: Ove Larsen
Issue price: £ 2.00

14-B36-1.49
1943 *The Ribe Cathedral*
Artist: Ove Larsen
Issue price: £ 2.50

14-B36-1.50
1944 *Sorgenfri Castle*
Artist: Ove Larsen
Issue price: £ 2.50

14-B36-1.51
1945 *The Old Water Mill*
Artist: Ove Larsen
Issue price: £ 2.50

14-B36-1.52
1946 *Commemoration Cross in Honour of Danish Sailors Who Lost Their Lives in World War II*
Artist: Margrethe Hyldahl
Issue price: £ 2.50

14-B36-1.53
1947 *Dybbol Mill*
Artist: Margrethe Hyldahl
Issue price: £ 2.50

14-B36-1.54
1948 *Watchman, Sculpture of Town Hall, Copenhagen*
Artist: Margrethe Hyldahl
Issue price: £ 2.75

14-B36-1.55
1949 *Landsoldaten, 19th Century Danish Soldier*
Artist: Margrethe Hyldahl
Issue price: £ 2.75

14-B36-1.56
1950 *Kronborg Castle at Elsinore*
Artist: Margrethe Hyldahl
Issue price: £ 2.75

14-B36-1.57
1951 *Jens Bang, New Passenger Boat Running Between Copenhagen and Aalborg*
Artist: Margrethe Hyldahl
Issue price: £ 3.00

14-B36-1.58
1952 *Old Copenhagen Canals at Wintertime with Thorvaldsen Museum in Background*
Artist: Borge Pramvig
Issue price: £ 3.00

14-B36-1.59
1953 *Royal Boat in Greenland Waters*
Artist: Kjeld Bonfils
Issue price: £ 3.25

14-B36-1.60
1954 *Birthplace of Hans Christian Andersen, with Snowman*
Artist: Borge Pramvig
Issue price: £ 3.25

14-B36-1.61
1955 *Kalundborg Church*
Artist: Kjeld Bonfils
Issue price: £ 3.25

14-B36-1.62
1956 *Christmas in Copenhagen*
Artist: Kjeld Bonfils
Issue price: £ 3.25

DENMARK
BING & GRØNDAHL
14-B36-1.63

14-B36-1.63
1957 *Christmas Candles*
Artist: Kjeld Bonfils
Issue price: £ 3.50

14-B36-1.64
1958 *Santa Claus*
Artist: Kjeld Bonfils
Issue price: £ 3.50

14-B36-1.65
1959 *Christmas Eve*
Artist: Kjeld Bonfils
Issue price: £ 3.50

14-B36-1.66
1960 *Danish Village Church*
Artist: Kjeld Bonfils
Issue price: £ 3.50

14-B36-1.67
1961 *Winter Harmony*
Artist: Kjeld Bonfils
Issue price: £ 3.50

14-B36-1.68
1962 *Winter Night*
Artist: Kjeld Bonfils
Issue price: £ 3.75

14-B36-1.69
1963 *The Christmas Elf*
Artist: Henry Thelander
Issue price: £ 3.75

14-B36-1.70
1964 *The Fir Tree and Hare*
Artist: Henry Thelander
Issue price: £ 3.75

14-B36-1.71
1965 *Bringing Home the Christmas
Tree*
Artist: Henry Thelander
Issue price: £ 3.75

14-B36-1.72
1966 *Home for Christmas*
Artist: Henry Thelander
Issue price: £ 3.75

14-B36-1.73
1967 *Sharing the Joy of Christmas*
Artist: Henry Thelander
Issue price: £ 3.75

14-B36-1.74
1968 *Christmas in Church*
Artist: Henry Thelander
Issue price: £ 3.95

14-B36-1.75
1969 *Arrival of the Christmas Guests*
Artist: Henry Thelander
Issue price: £ 3.95

14-B36-1.76
1970 *Pheasants in the Snow at Christmas*
Artist: Henry Thelander
Issue price: £ 4.50

14-B36-1.77
1971 *Christmas at Home*
Artist: Henry Thelander
Issue price: £ 4.95

14-B36-1.78
1972 *Christmas in Greenland*
Artist: Henry Thelander
Issue price: £ 5.95

14-B36-1.79
1973 *Country Christmas*
Artist: Henry Thelander
Issue price: £ 5.95

14-B36-1.80
1974 *Christmas in the Village*
Artist: Henry Thelander
Issue price: £ 6.95

DENMARK
BING & GRØNDAHL
14-B36-1.81

14-B36-1.81
1975 *The Old Water Mill*
Artist: Henry Thelander
Issue price: £ 8.50

14-B36-1.82
1976 *Christmas Welcome*
Artist: Henry Thelander
Issue price: £ 9.95

14-B36-1.83
1977 *Copenhagen Christmas*
Artist: Henry Thelander
Issue price: £ 11.00

14-B36-1.84
1978 *A Christmas Tale*
Artist: Henry Thelander
Issue price: £ 12.80

14-B36-1.85
1979 *White Christmas*
Artist: Henry Thelander
Issue price: £ 14.00

14-B36-1.86
1980 *Christmas in the Wood*
Artist: Henry Thelander
Issue price: £ 18.65

14-B36-1.87
1981 *Christmas Peace*
Artist: Henry Thelander
Issue price: £ 19.95

14-B36-1.88
1982 *The Christmas Tree*
Artist: Henry Thelander
Issue price: £ 21.00

14-B36-1.89
1983 *Christmas in the Old Town*
Artist: Henry Thelander
Issue price: £ 21.00

14-B36-1.90
1984 *The Christmas Letter*
Artist: Henry Thelander
Issue price: £ 21.00

14-B36-1.91
1985 *Christmas Eve at the Farmhouse*
Artist: Edvard Jensen
Issue price: £ 21.50

14-B36-1.92
1986 *Silent Night, Holy Night*
Artist: Edvard Jensen
Issue price: £ 23.00

14-B36-1.93
1987 *Snowman's Christmas Eve*
Artist: Edvard Jensen
Issue price: £ 27.50

Mother's Day Series

Artist: Henry Thelander

True underglaze-decorated porcelain hand-painted in Copenhagen blue on bas-relief

Diameter: 15.2 centimetres (6 inches)

Pierced foot rim

Edition size undisclosed, limited by year of issue

Not numbered, without certificate; individually initialed on back by each painter

14-B36-3.1
1969 *Dog and Puppies*
Issue price: £ 2.50

14-B36-3.2
1970 *Bird and Chicks*
Issue price: £ 2.50

DENMARK
BING & GRØNDAHL
14-B36-3.3

14-B36-3.3
1971 *Cat and Kitten*
Issue price: £ 3.95

14-B36-3.4
1972 *Mare and Foal*
Issue price: £ 3.95

14-B36-3.5
1973 *Duck and Ducklings*
Issue price: £ 5.50

14-B36-3.6
1974 *Bear and Cubs*
Issue price: £ 6.50

14-B36-3.7
1975 *Doe and Fawns*
Issue price: £ 7.50

14-B36-3.8
1976 *Swan Family*
Issue price: £ 8.00

14-B36-3.9
1977 *Squirrel and Young*
Issue price: £ 8.44

14-B36-3.10
1978 *Heron*
Issue price: £ 10.00

14-B36-3.11
1979 *Fox and Cubs*
Issue price: £ 10.90

14-B36-3.12
1980 *Woodpecker and Young*
Issue price: £ 13.35

14-B36-3.13
1981 *Hare and Young*
Issue price: £ 14.20

14-B36-3.14
1982 *Lioness and Cubs*
Issue price: £ 16.10

14-B36-3.15
1983 *Raccoon and Young*
Issue price: £ 16.10

14-B36-3.16
1984 *Stork and Nestings*
Issue price: £ 16.90

14-B36-3.17
1985 *Bear with Cubs*
Issue price: £ 16.90

14-B36-3.18
1986 *Elephant with Calf*
Issue price: £ 16.90

14-B36-3.19
1987 *Sheep with Lambs*
Issue price: £ 16.90

DENMARK
BING & GRØNDAHL

14-B36-7.1

Moments of Truth Series

Artist: Kurt Ard. Artist's signature appears on front

Porcelain

Diameter: 21.1 centimetres (8 ⁵/₁₆ inches)

Pierced foot rim

Edition size undisclosed, limited by announced period of issue

Numbered, with certificate

14-B36-7.1
1984 *Home Is Best*
Issue price: £ 20.85

14-B36-7.2
1984 *The Road to Virtuosity*
Issue price: £ 20.85

14-B36-7.3
1985 *First Things First*
Issue price: £ 22.95

14-B36-7.4
1985 *Unfair Competition*
Issue price: £ 22.95

14-B36-7.5
1986 *Bored Sick*
Issue price: £ 22.95

14-B36-7.6
1986 *First Crush*
Issue price: £ 22.95
Serie Closed

Children's Day Series

Artistin: Carole Roller

True underglaze-decorated porcelain hand-painted in Copenhagen blue on bas-relief

Diameter: 13 centimetres (5 ¹/₈ inches)

Pierced foot rim

Edition size undisclosed, limited by year of issue

Not numbered, without certificate; individually initialled on back by each painter

14-B36-13.1
1985 *The Magical Tea Party*
Issue price: £ 13.70

14-B36-13.2
1986 *A Joyful Flight*
Issue price: £ 14.60

14-B36-13.3
1987 *The Little Gardener*
Issue price: £ 15.50

DENMARK
BING & GRØNDAHL

14-B36-20.1

Family Portraits Series

Artist: Kurt Ard. Artist's signature appears on front

Porcelain

Diameter: 21.1 centimetres (8 ⁵/₁₆ inches)

Pierced foot rim

Edition size undisclosed, limited by announced period of issue

Numbered, with certificate

14-B36-20.1
1987 *The Card Sharks*
Issue price: £ 26.95

14-B36-20.2
1987 *The Intruder*
Issue price: £ 26.95

14-B36-20.3
1987 *Midnight Serenade*
Issue price: £ 26.95

A Summer at Skagen Series

Artist: Peter Severin Krøyer. Artist's signature appears on front

Porcelain

Diameter: 21.3 centimetres (8 ³/₈ inches)

Pierced foot rim

Edition size undisclosed, limited by announced period of issue

Numbered, with certificate

14-B36-22.1
1986 *Summer Evening at Skagen, the Artist's Wife with a Dog on the Beach*
Issue price: £ 21.95

14-B36-22.2
1987 *Luncheon at the Krøyers'*
Issue price: £ 21.95

14-B36-22.3
1987 *Hip-Hip-Hurrah!*
Issue price: £ 24.95

14-B36-22.4
1987 *The Artist's Wife Resting in the Garden*
Issue price: £ 24.95
Series Closed

DENMARK
GRANDE COPENHAGEN

14-G65-1.1

GRANDE COPENHAGEN
Copenhagen

Grande Copenhagen plates are produced at the Eslau porcelain factory near Copenhagen. Grande Copenhagen began its *Christmas* series of plates depicting Danish winter scenes in 1975. The series ended in 1984.

Artists for Grande Copenhagen *Christmas* plates prior to 1980 were undisclosed. The artist for the 1980 and subsequent issues was Frode Bahnsen of Aarhus, Jutland, Denmark.

The *Ugly Duckling* series began in 1985; it represents the first Grande Copenhagen series to be created in full colour. The *Ugly Duckling* series is also the first by artist Karen J. Bornholt. The series depicts one of Hans Christian Andersen's most beloved stories.

Christmas Series

Artist: as indicated

True underglaze-decorated porcelain hand-painted in Copenhagen blue on bas-relief

Diameter: 18.4 centimetres (7 ¹/₄ inches)

Pierced foot rim

Edition size undisclosed, limited by year of issue

Not numbered, without certificate through 1979; numbered with certificate therafter

14-G65-1.1
1975 *Alone Together*
Artist: undisclosed
Issue price: £ 11.50

14-G65-1.2
1976 *Christmas Wreath*
Artist: undisclosed
Issue price: £ 11.50

14-G65-1.3
1977 *Fishwives at Gammelstrand*
Artist: undisclosed
Issue price: £ 12.50

14-G65-1.4
1978 *Hans Christian Andersen*
Artist: undisclosed
Issue price: £ 15.50

14-G65-1.5
1979 *Pheasants in the Snow*
Artist: undisclosed
Issue price: £ 16.50

14-G65-1.6
1980 *The Snow Queen in the Tivoli*
Artist: Frode Bahnsen
Issue price: £ 18.50

14-G65-1.7
1981 *Little Match Girl in Nyhavn*
Artist: Frode Bahnsen
Issue price: £ 18.50

14-G65-1.8
1982 *The Shepherdess and the
Chimney Sweep*
Artist: Frode Bahnsen
Issue price: £ 18.50

14-G65-1.9
1983 *The Little Mermaid Near Kronborg*
Artist: Frode Bahnsen
Issue price: £ 20.35

14-G64-1.10
1984 *The Sandman at Amalienborg*
Artist: Frode Bahnsen
Issue price: £ 22.40
Series Closed

DENMARK
GRANDE COPENHAGEN

14-G65-2.1

Ugly Ducking Series

Artist: Karen J. Bornholt.
Artist's signature appears on
front

Porcelain

Diameter: 19 centimetres
(7 ½ inches)

Pierced foot rim

Edition size undisclosed,
limited by announced period of
issue

Numbered with certificate

14-G65-2.1
1985 *Not Like the Others*
Issue price: £ 16.95

14-G65-2.2
1986 *He Will Grow Up Strong*
Issue price: £ 16.95

14-G65-2.3
1986 *Come with Us*
Issue price: £ 16.95

14-G65-2.4
1986 *You Don't Understand Me*
Issue price: £ 18.65

14-G65-2.5
1986 *What Beautiful Birds*
Issue price: £ 18.65

14-G65-2.6
1986 *Most Beautiful of All*
Issue price: £ 18.65
Series Closed

14-R59-1.1 „Madonna and Child"
1908 Royal Copenhagen *Christmas*
The first limited-edition plate to be
produced by Denmark's oldest
porcelain house. "Madonna and Child"
began an annual series that continues
uninterrupted to this day. The blue
underglaze artwork depicts an unusual
figure of the Madonna in that she is not
wearing a head mantle. Only one other
image of the Madonna, this time
hooded, appears in the entire series; it
occurs on the 1920 issue.

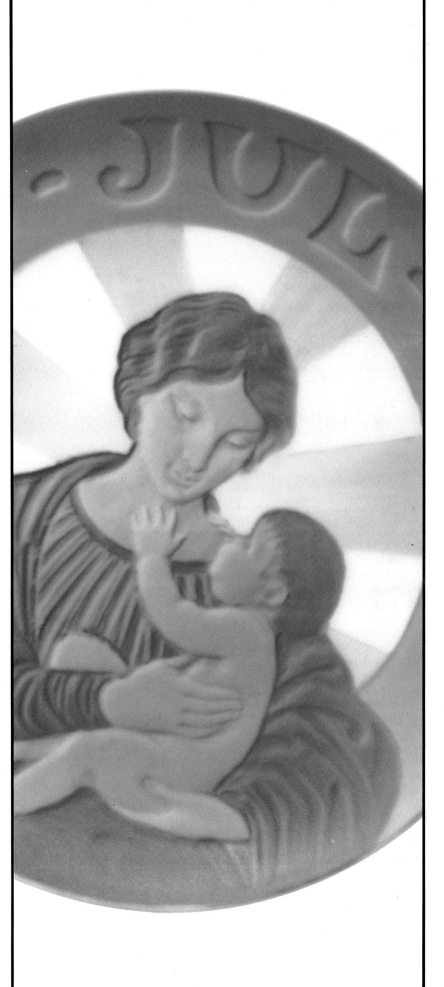

DENMARK
ROYAL COPENHAGEN

14-R59-0.0

ROYAL COPENHAGEN
Copenhagen

The Royal Copenhagen Porcelain Manufactory, Denmark's oldest existing porcelain maker, was established by Franz Henrich Muller with the support of Denmark's queen dowager, Juliane Marie, in January 1775. Since the 1760s, members of the Danish royal family had been interested in the white hard-paste porcelain made in China, but it was not until 1772 that Muller, a Danish pharmacist and chemist, was able to duplicate the fine porcelain. In 1779 "The Danish Porcelain Factory", as Royal Copenhagen was then called, came under royal control.

The Danish Court controlled the firm from 1779 to 1867, a period in its history that is still symbolized by the crown in its trademark. The three wavy lines under the crown, part of the factory, trademark since 1775, pay tribute to Denmark's tradition as a seafaring nation and represent Denmark's three ancient waterways: the Sound, the Great Belt and the Little Belt. In 1867 the factory was sold and has since been under private ownership. It is still a supplier to the royal court in Denmark.

The first Royal Copenhagen *Christmas* plate was issued in 1908, and the series has continued every year since then. From the beginning, the motif for each year's *Christmas* plate has been selected from suggestions submitted by employees of the Royal Copenhagen factory. Until 1941, small quantities of plates in the *Christmas* series were created with the world "Christmas" translated into other languages to meet the demand from non-Danish collectors.

In 1982, the Royal Copenhagen *Motherhood* series started with artwork by Sven Vestergaard.

Christian Thomsen, designer of the first Royal Copenhagen collector's plate, served an apprenticeship as a woodcarver before joining the firm in 1898. His porcelain creations won a silver medal in a Milan exhibit in 1908 and a gold medal in a Brussels exhibit in 1910. His work now hangs in the Museum of Decorative Arts in Copenhagen. Arnold Krog innovated the famed cobalt-blue underglaze design technique which has become a tradition in Danish plate making. He worked for Royal Copenhagen from 1884 to 1916, rising to art director and taking the Grand Prix for decorative art in Paris in 1900. Krog's most famous creation is his fountain located in The Hague, The Netherlands. Artist Kai Lange has been with Royal Copenhagen since the age of 17 and, after more than half a century with the firm, is regarded as one of the most knowledgeable artists working in the porcelain medium today. The first Kai Lange design selected for the annual *Christmas* plate was for the 1940 issue, and since 1963 every plate, except the 1976 issue, has been a Kai Lange creation.

Christmas Series

Artist: as indicated. Artist's name appears on back since 1955

True underglaze-decorated porcelain hand-painted in Copenhagen blue on bas-relief

Diameter: 15.2 centimetres (6 inches) for 1908 through 1910; 17.8 centimetres (7 inches) thereafter

Pierced foot rim

Edition size undisclosed, limited by year of issue

Not numbered, without certificate; individually initialled on back by each painter

14-R59-1.1
1908 *Madonna and Child*
Artist: Christian Thomsen
Issue price: £ .50

14-R59-1.2
1909 *Danish Landscape*
Artist: St. Ussing
Issue price: £ .50

14-R59-1.3
1910 *The Magi*
Artist: Christian Thomsen
Issue price: £ .50

14-R59-1.4
1911 *Danish Landscape*
Artist: Oluf Jensen
Issue price: £ .50

14-R59-1.5
1912 *Elderly Couple by Christmas Tree*
Artist: Christian Thomsen
Issue price: £ .50

14-R59-1.6
1913 *Spire of Frederik's Church, Copenhagen*
Artist: A. Boesen
Issue price: £ .75

14-R59-1.7
1914 *Sparrows in Tree at Church of the Holy Spirit, Copenhagen*
Artist: A. Boesen
Issue price: £ .75

14-R59-1.8
1915 *Danish Landscape*
Artist: Arnold Krog
Issue price: £ .75

DENMARK
ROYAL COPENHAGEN
14-R59-1.9

14-R59-1.9
1916 *Shepherd in the Field on
Christmas Night*
Artist: Ricard Böcher
Issue price: £ .75

14-R59-1.10
1917 *Tower of Our Savior's Church,
Copenhagen*
Artist: Oluf Jensen
Issue price: £ 1.00

14-R59-1.11
1918 *Sheep and Shepherds*
Artist: Oluf Jensen
Issue price: £ 1.00

14-R59-1.12
1919 *In the Park*
Artist: Oluf Jensen
Issue price: £ 1.00

14-R59-1.13
1920 *Maria with the Child Jesus*
Artist: G. Rode
Issue price: £ 1.00

14-R59-1.14
1921 *Aabenraa Marketplace*
Artist: Oluf Jensen
Issue price: £ 1.00

14-R59-1.15
1922 *Three Singing Angels*
Artist: Ellinor Selschau
Issue price: £ 1.00

14-R59-1.16
1923 *Danish Landscape*
Artist: Oluf Jensen
Issue price: £ 1.00

14-R59-1.17
1924 *Christmas Star over the Sea and
Sailing Ship*
Artist: Benjamin Olsen
Issue price: £ 1.00

14-R59-1.18
1925 *Street Scene from Christians-*
havn, Copenhagen
Artist: Oluf Jensen
Issue price: £ 1.00

14-R59-1.19
1926 *View of Christianshavn Canal,*
Copenhagen
Artist: Ricard Böcher
Issue price: £ 1.00

14-R59-1.20
1927 *Ship's Boy at the Tiller on*
Christmas Night
Artist: Benjamin Olsen
Issue price: £ 1.00

14-R59-1.21
1928 *Vicar's Family on Way to*
Church
Artist: G. Rode
Issue price: £ 1.00

14-R59-1.22
1929 *Grundtvig Church, Copenhagen*
Artist: Oluf Jensen
Issue price: £ 1.00

14-R59-1.23
1930 *Fishing Boat on the Way to the*
Harbour
Artist: Benjamin Olsen
Issue price: £ 1.25

14-R59-1.24
1931 *Mother and Child*
Artist: G. Rode
Issue price: £ 1.25

14-R59-1.25
1932 *Frederiksberg Gardens with*
Statue of Frederik VI.
Artist: Oluf Jensen
Issue price: £ 1.25

14-R59-1.26
1933 *The Great Belt Ferry*
Artist: Benjamin Olsen
Issue price: £ 1.25

DENMARK
ROYAL COPENHAGEN
14-R59-1.27

14-R59-1.27
1934 *The Hermitage Castle*
Artist: Oluf Jensen
Issue price: £ 1.25

14-R59-1.28
1935 *Fishing Boat off Kronborg Castle*
Artist: Benjamin Olsen
Issue price: £ 1.25

14-R59-1.29
1936 *Roskilde Cathedral*
Artist: Ricard Böcher
Issue price: £ 1.25

14-R59-1.30
1937 *Christmas Scene in Main Street, Copenhagen*
Artist: Nils Thorsson
Issue price: £ 1.25

14-R59-1.31
1938 *Round Church in Osterlars on Bornholm*
Artist: Herne Nielsen
Issue price: £ 1.50

14-R59-1.32
1939 *Expeditionary Ship in the Pack-Ice of Greenland*
Artist: Sv. Nic. Nielsen
Issue price: £ 1.50

14-R59-1.33
1940 *The Good Shepherd*
Artist: Kai Lange
Issue price: £ 1.50

14-R59-1.34
1941 *Danish Village Church*
Artist: Th. Kjolner
Issue price: £ 1.50

14-R59-1.35
1942 *Bell Tower of Old Church in Jutland*
Artist: Nils Thorsson
Issue price: £ 2.00

14-R59-1.36
1943 *Flight of the Holy Family into Egypt*
Artist: Nils Thorsson
Issue price: £ 2.00

14-R59-1.37
1944 *Typical Danish Winter Scene*
Artist: Viggo Olsen
Issue price: £ 2.00

14-R59-1.38
1945 *A Peaceful Motif*
Artist: Ricard Böcher
Issue price: £ 2.00

14-R59-1.39
1946 *Zealand Village Church*
Artist: Nils Thorsson
Issue price: £ 2.00

14-R59-1.40
1947 *The Good Shepherd*
Artist: Kai Lange
Issue price: £ 2.25

14-R59-1.41
1948 *Nodebo Church at Christmastime*
Artist: Th. Kjolner
Issue price: £ 2.25

14-R59-1.42
1949 *Our Lady's Cathedral, Copenhagen*
Artist: Hans H. Hansen
Issue price: £ 2.50

14-R59-1.43
1950 *Boeslunde Church, Zealand*
Artist: Viggo Olsen
Issue price: £ 2.50

14-R59-1.44
1951 *Christmas Angel*
Artist: Ricard Böcher
Issue price: £ 2.50

DENMARK
ROYAL COPENHAGEN
14-R59-1.45

14-R59-1.45
1952 *Christmas in the Forest*
Artist: Kai Lange
Issue price: £ 2.50

14-R59-1.46
1953 *Frederiksberg Castle*
Artist: Th. Kjolner
Issue price: £ 3.00

14-R59-1.47
1954 *Amalienborg Palace,*
Copenhagen
Artist: Kai Lange
Issue price: £ 3.00

14-R59-1.48
1955 *Fano Girl*
Artist: Kai Lange
Issue price: £ 3.50

14-R59-1.49
1956 *Rosenborg Castle, Copenhagen*
Artist: Kai Lange
Issue price: £ 3.50

14-R59-1.50
1957 *The Good Shepherd*
Artist: Hans H. Hansen
Issue price: £ 4.00

14-R59-1.51
1958 *Sunshine over Greenland*
Artist: Hans H. Hansen
Issue price: £ 4.50

14-R59-1.52
1959 *Christmas Night*
Artist: Hans H. Hansen
Issue price: £ 4.50

14-R59-1.53
1960 *The Stag*
Artist: Hans H. Hansen
Issue price: £ 5.00

14-R59-1.54
1961 *Training Ship Danmark*
Artist: Kai Lange
Issue price: £ 5.00

14-R59-1.55
1962 *The Little Mermaid at Winter-time*
Artist: Undisclosed
Issue price: £ 5.50

14-R59-1.56
1963 *Hojsager Mill*
Artist: Kai Lange
Issue price: £ 5.50

14-R59-1.57
1964 *Fetching the Christmas Tree*
Artist: Kai Lange
Issue price: £ 5.00

14-R59-1.58
1965 *Little Skaters*
Artist: Kai Lange
Issue price £ 6.00

14-R59-1.59
1966 *Blackbird at Christmastime*
Artist: Kai Lange
Issue price £ 6.00

14-R59-1.60
1967 *The Royal Oak*
Artist: Kai Lange
Issue price: £ 6.50

14-R59-1.61
1968 *The Last Umiak*
Artist: Kai Lange
Issue price: £ 6.50

14-R59-1.62
1969 *The Old Farmyard*
Artist: Kai Lange
Issue price: £ 6.50

DENMARK
ROYAL COPENHAGEN
14-R59-1.63

14-R59-1.63
1970 *Christmas Rose and Cat*
Artist: Kai Lange
Issue price: £ 7.00

14-R59-1.64
1971 *Hare in Winter*
Artist: Kai Lange
Issue price: £ 7.00

14-R59-1.65
1972 *In the Desert*
Artist: Kai Lange
Issue price: £ 7.50

14-R59-1.66
1973 *Train Homeward Bound for Christmas*
Artist: Kai Lange
Issue price: £ 8.50

14-R59-1.67
1974 *Winter Twilight*
Artist: Kai Lange
Issue price £ 9.00

14-R59-1.68
1975 *Queen's Palace*
Artist: Kai Lange
Issue price £ 10.00

14-R59-1.69
1976 *Danish Water Mill*
Artist: Sven Vestergaard
Issue price: £ 10.00

14-R59-1.70
1977 *Immervad Bridge*
Artist: Kai Lange
Issue price: £ 13.50

14-R59-1.71
1978 *Greenland Scenery*
Artist: Kai Lange
Issue price: £ 14.00

14-R59-1.72
1979 *Choosing the Christmas Tree*
Artist: Kai Lange
Issue price: £ 16.50

14-R59-1.73
1980 *Bringing Home the Christmas Tree*
Artist: Kai Lange
Issue price: £ 19.50

14-R59-1.74
1981 *Admiring the Christmas Tree*
Artist: Kai Lange
Issue price: £ 17.50

14-R59-1.75
1982 *Waiting for Christmas*
Artist: Kai Lange
Issue price: £ 19.85

14-R59-1.76
1983 *Merry Christmas*
Artist: Kai Lange
Issue price: £ 21.50

14-R59-1.77
1984 *Jingle Bells*
Artist: Kai Lange
Issue price: £ 21.50

14-R59-1.78
1985 *The Snowman*
Artist: Sven Vestergaard
Issue price: £ 24.50

14-R59-1.79
1986 *Christmas Vacation*
Artist: Sven Vestergaard
Issue price: £ 26.50

14-R59-1.80
1987 *Winter Birds*
Artist: Sven Vestergaard
Issue price: £ 27.50

DENMARK
ROYAL COPENHAGEN

14-R59-2.1

Mother's Day Series

Artist: As indicated

True underglaze-decorated porcelain hand-painted in Copenhagen blue on bas-relief

Diameter: 15.9 centimetres (6 ¼ inches)

Pierced foot rim

Edition size unannounced, limited by year of issue

Not numbered, without certificate; individually initialled on back by each painter

14-R59-2.1
1971 *American Mother*
Artist: Kamma Svensson
Issue price: £ 7.60

14-R59-2.2
1972 *Oriental Mother*
Artist: Kamma Svensson
Issue price: £ 8.50

14-R59-2.3
1973 *Danish Mother*
Artist: Arne Ungermann
Issue price: £ 9.70

14-R59-2.4
1974 *Greenland Mother*
Artist: Arne Ungermann
Issue price: £ 10.00

14-R59-2.5
1975 *Bird in Nest*
Artist: Arne Ungermann
Issue price: £ 12.15

14-R59-2.6
1976 *Mermaids*
Artist: Arne Ungermann
Issue price: £ 12.15

14-R59-2.7
1977 *The Twins*
Artist: Arne Ungermann
Issue price: £ 14.55

14-R59-2.8
1978 *Mother and Child*
Artist: Ib Spang Olsen
Issue price: £ 15.80

14-R59-2.9
1979 *A Loving Mother*
Artist: Ib Spang Olsen
Issue price: £ 17.90

14-R59-2.10
1980 *An Outing with Mother*
Artist: Ib Spang Olsen
Issue price: £ 22.75

14-R59-2.11
1981 *Reunion*
Artist: Ib Spang Olsen
Issue price: £ 23.65

14-R59-2.12
1982 *Childrens Hour*
Artist: Ib Spang Olsen
Issue price: £ 23.65
Series Closed

DENMARK
ROYAL COPENHAGEN
14-R59-4.1

Motherhood Series

Artist: Sven Vestergaard

True underglaze-decorated porcelain hand-painted in Copenhagen blue on bas-relief

Diameter: 15.2 centimetres (6 inches)

Pierced foot rim

Edition size undisclosed, limited by year of issue

Not numbered, without certificate

14-R59-4.1
1982 *Mother Robin and Her Young Ones*
Issue price: £ 16.00

14-R59-4.2
1983 *Mother Cat and Kitten*
Issue price: £ 17.00

14-R59-4.3
1984 *Mare with Foal*
Issue price: £ 18.00

14-R59-4.4
1985 *Mother Rabbit with Bunny*
Issue price: £ 18.50

14-R59-4.5
1986 *Dog and Puppies*
Issue price: £ 20.50

14-R59-4.6
1987 *Goat and Kid*
Issue price: £ 20.50

16-A69-1.1 „Vainamoinen's Sowing"
1976 Arabia Kalevala
This series bears the name of the Finnish national epic, the Kalevala, whose heroes it depicts. The series, much like the saga, has run continuously since 1976. Arabia is famous for the density and durability of its stoneware, which is fired three times like fine china; ordinary stoneware is fired only twice.

FINLAND
ARABIA
16-A69-1.1

ARABIA
Helsinki

In 1873, Arabia was founded as a subsidiary of the Swedish firm Rörstrand (see Sweden, RÖR-STRAND). The factory was located on the outskirts of Helsinki, a site chosen in hopes of supplying the growing markets for ceramics in Finland and the Russian Empire. Early products included dinner services, pitchers and mugs, almost all based on Rörstrand designs.

In 1884 Arabia was reorganized as a Finnish company, Arabia Aktiefabrik, and developed its own designs from that time on. The company won a gold medal at the Paris World Exhibition in 1900 and is the only company producing both household and art ceramics in Finland today.

To celebrate the 100th anniversary of the firm in 1973, Arabia produced a limited-edition anniversary plate. Its success, in turn, led to the introduction in 1976 of an annual limited-edition series bases on the Finnish national epic, the *Kalevala,* by artist Raija Uosikkinen.

Kalevala Series

Artist: Raija Uosikkinen

Stoneware

Diameter: 19 centimetres square (7 ¹/₂ inches)

Pierced foot rim

Edition size undisclosed

Not numbered, without certificate

16-A69-1.1
1976 *Vainamoinen's Sowing*
Issue price: £ 14.90

16-A69-1.2
1977 *Aino's Fate*
Issue price: £ 14.90

84

16-A69-1.3
1978 *Lemminkainen's Chase*
Issue price: £ 18.90

16-A69-1.4
1979 *Kullervo's Revenge*
Issue price: £ 19.50

16-A69-1.5
1980 *Vainamoinen's Rescue*
Issue price: £ 21.00

16-A69-1.6
1981 *Vainamoinen's Magic*
Issue price: £ 22.00

16-A69-1.7
1982 *Joukahainen Shoots Horse*
Issue price: £ 24.50

16-A69-1.8
1983 *Lemminkainen's Escape*
Issue price: £ 26.00

16-A69-1.9
1984 *To the North Pole*
Issue price: £ 28.00

16-A69-1.10
1985 *Vainamoinen Fishing*
Issue price: £ 28.00

16-A69-1.11
1986 *Osmotar*
Issue price: £ 28.00

FINLAND
ARABIA
16-A69-1.12

16-A69-1.12
1987 *Vainamoinen's Tricks*
Issue price: £ 28.00

Arabia Christmas

Artist: Raja Uosikkinen

Stoneware

Diameter: 23.2 centimetres
(9¹/₆ inches)

Attached back hanger

Edition size undisclosed,
limited by year of issue

Not numbered, without
certificate

16-A69-2.1
1978 *Sleigh-Ride*
Issue price: £ 18.90

16-A69-2.2
1979 *Forest Work in Wintertime*
Issue price: £ 19.50

16-A69-2.3
1980 *Icefisher*
Issue price: £ 21.00

16-A69-2.4
1981 *Severity of the Winter*
Issue price: £ 22.00

16-A69-2.5
1982 *Winter Fun*
Issue price: £ 24.00

16-A69-2.6
1983 *Winter Atmosphere*
Issue price: £ 24.50

16-A69-2.7
1984 *Winter in the City*
Issue price: £ 26.00

16-A69-2.8
1985 *City Park*
Issue price: £ 50.00

16-A69-2.9
1986 *Christmas in the City*
Issue price: £ 50.00

16-A69-2.10
1987 *Around the Church*
Issue price: £ 57.75

FRANCE
PORCELAINE GEORGES BOYER
18-B61-0.0

PORCELAINE

LIMOGES

PORCELAINE GEORGES BOYER
Limoges

Porcelaine Georges Boyer of Limoges, France, was founded in 1933 by Georges Boyer; his is the second generation of Boyers to work in porcelain. His father, Jean Boyer, originally worked for the house of Haviland before forming his own company in which Georges worked as technical director. Today, the firm is managed by Gerard Boyer, son of Georges, thus continuing the family tradition.

Porcelaine Georges Boyer is the third-ranking company in the renowned porcelain centre of Limoges, producing porcelain dinnerware as well as limited-edition collector's plates. The firm numbers among its efforts the production of extremely small limited-edition plate series based upon the works of Pierre Auguste Renoir and Maurice Utrillo. In 1982, Porcelaine Georges Boyer introduced its first collector's series for the United States market under its own name — the *Alice in Wonderland* series by British artist Sandy Nightingale.

Alice in Wonderland Series

Artist: Sandy Nightingale

Overglaze-decorated porcelain banded in 24k gold

Diameter: 21.6 centimetres (8 ½ inches)

Attached back hanger

Edition size undisclosed, limited by announced period of issue

Numbered with certificate

18-B61-1.1
1982 *Alice and the White Rabbit*
Issue price: £ 17.95

18-B61-1.2
1983 *Alice and the Caterpillar*
Issue price: £ 17.95

18-B61-1.3
1983 *Alice and the Cheshire Cat*
Issue price: £ 17.95

18-B61-1.4
1983 *Alice and the Mad Hatter*
Issue price: £ 17.95

18-B61-1.5
1984 *Painting the Roses*
Issue price: £ 17.95

18-B61-1.6
1984 *Alice and the Croquet Game*
Issue price: £ 17.95

18-B61-1.7
1984 *The Gryphon and Mock Turtle*
Issue price: £ 17.95

18-B61-1.8
1984 *The Knave of Hearts*
Issue price: £ 17.95
Series Closed

FRANCE
D'ARCEAU-LIMOGES

18-D15-0.0

D'ARCEAU-LIMOGES
Limoges

The hallmark of Henri d'Arceau L. & Fils is one of the most prestigious in the famous porcelain centre of Limoges. The firm, which claims to adhere to the original "Grellet Standard" of 1768 for handcraftsmanship, is today directed by Gerard Boyer, a descendant of the founder.

The firm was commissioned by L'Association l'Esprit de Lafayette to produce the six-plate bicentennial series *Collection Le Patrimoine de Lafayette (Lafayette Legacy Collection),* 1973-1975, which chronicles the role of the Marquis de Lafayette in America's War of Independence. The D'Arceau-Limoges *Christmas* series, *Noël Vitrail,* begun in 1975, was inspired by the stained-glass windows of the cathedral at Chartres. It ended in 1982. *Les Femmes du Siècle (Women of the Century),* a twelve-plate series commissioned by the Chambre Syndicale de la Couture Parisienne, began in 1976 and ended in 1979. This series, recognized by the United Nations, depicts Western women's fashions from 1865 to 1965. Introduced in 1978 was Les Jeunes Filles des Saisons Girls of the Seasons), which ended in 1981, and in 1979 *Les Très Riches Heures (The Very Rich Hours),* which adapts its artwork from an early fifteenth-century illuminated manuscript. This series ended in 1984. In 1980, the firm, in collaboration with La Société de Paris et Son Histoire, issued Louis Dali's *Les Douze Sites Parisiens de Louis Dali (The Twelve Parisian Places of Louis Dali)* series, a collection of the artist's unique impressions of the famous city. The series closed in 1983. In 1984 *Josephine et Napoléon* was introduced with artwork by Claude Boulmé. The series ended in 1986. The *Cambier Mother's Day* series began in 1983 with artwork by French classicist Guy Cambier. In early 1985, D'Arceau-Limoges introduced its first series relating to a classic motion picture, *Gigi,* by Jean-Claude-Guidou. In 1986, Guidou began his second series for the firm, a contemporary Christmas series titled *Les Noëls de France.*

In 1986, D'Arceau-Limoges introduced *Les Femmes de la Belle Epoque (The Women of the Beautiful Era)* series, an historic tribute to the women of the grand couture of Paris at the turn of the century. The artist for the series is Pierre-Laurent Brenot. The year 1987 saw the introduction of the series *Paysages de France (French Country Landscapes),* painted in the difficult *lavis* technique by Michel Julien.

Among the artists who have designed works for D'Arceau-Limoges are the late André Restieau, world authority on the techniques of re-creating medieval stained glass colouration in porcelain; neo-Classicist Guy Cambier, and the late François Ganeau, resident consultant to the Theatre Comédie Française, as well as Louis Dali.

Collection Le Patrimoine de Lafayette

(The Lafayette Legacy Collection)

Artist: André Restieau. Artist's signature appears on front, initials on back

Underglaze-decorated porcelain

Diameter: 21.6 centimetres (8 ½ inches)

Attached back hanger

Edition size undisclosed, limited by announced period of issue

Numbered with certificate

18-D15-1.1
1973 *The Secret Contract*
Issue price: £ 9.00

18-D15-1.2
1973 *The Landing at North Island*
Issue price: £ 12.00

18-D15-1.3
1974 *The Meeting at City Tavern*
Issue price: £ 12.00

18-D15-1.4
1974 *The Battle of Brandywine*
Issue price: £ 12.00

18-D15-1.5
1975 *The Message of Franklin*
Issue price: £ 12.00

18-D15-1.6
1975 *The Siege at Yorktown*
Issue price: £ 12.00
Series Closed

FRANCE
D'ARCEAU-LIMOGES
18-D15-2.1

Noël Vitrail

Artist: André Restieau. Artist's signature appears on front, initials on back

Overglaze-decorated porcelain

Diameter: 21.6 centimetres (8 ¹/₂ inches)

Attached back hanger

Edition size undisclosed, limited by announced period of issue

Numbered with certificate

18-D15-2.1
1975 *La Fuite en Egypte*
(Flight into Egypt)
Issue price: £ 11.95

18-D15-2.2
1976 *Dans la Crèche*
(In the Manger)
Issue price: £ 11.95

18-D15-2.3
1977 *Le Refus d'Hébergement*
(No Room at the Inn)
Issue price: £ 11.95

18-D15-2.4
1978 *La Purification*
(The Purification)
Issue price: £ 13.40

18-D15-2.5
1979 *L'Adoration des Rois*
(The Adoration of Kings)
Issue price: £ 13.40

18-D15-2.6
1980 *Joyeuse Nouvelle*
(Tidings of Great Joy)
Issue price: £ 14.50

18-D15-2.7
1981 *Giudés par l'Etoile*
(Guided by the Star)
Issue price: £ 14.50

18-D15-2.8
1982 *L'Annonciation*
(The Annunciation)
Issue price: £ 15.50
Series Closed

Les Femmes du Siècle

(The Women of the Century)

Artist: François Ganeau.
Artist's signature appears on front, initials on back

Overglaze-decorated porcelain

Diameter: 21.6 centimetres
(8 ½ inches)

Attached back hanger

Edition size undisclosed, limited by announced period of issue

Numbered with certificate

18-D15-3.1
1977 *Scarlet en Crinoline*
Issue price: £ 11.80

18-D15-3.2
1978 *Sarah en Tournure*
Issue price: £ 13.05

18-D15-3.3
1978 *Colette, la Femme Sportive*
Issue price: £ 13.05

18-D15-3.4
1979 *Léa, la Femme Fleur*
Issue price: £ 13.05

18-D15-3.5
1979 *Albertine, la Femme Liane*
Issue price: £ 13.05

18-D15-3.6
1980 *Edith, La Femme Pratique*
Issue price: £ 13.05

18-D15-3.7
1980 *Daisy, la Garçonne*
Issue price: £ 13.05

18-D15-3.8
1980 *Marlène, la Vamp*
Issue price: £ 13.05

FRANCE
D'ARCEAU-LIMOGES
18-D15-3.9

18-D15-3.9
1980 *Hélène*
Issue price: £ 13.05

18-D15-3.10
1981 *Sophie*
Issue price: £ 13.05

18-D15-3.11
1981 *Françoise*
Issue price: £ 13.05

18-D15-3.12
1981 *Brigitte*
Issue price: £ 13.05
Series Closed

Les Jeunes Filles des Saisons

(The Girls of the Seasons)
Artist: Guy Cambier
Overglaze-decorated porcelain
banded in gold
Diameter: 24.8 centimetres
(9 ³/₄ inches)
No hanger
Edition size limited to 15,000
Numbered with certificate

18-D15-4.1
1978 *La Jeune Fille d'Eté*
(Summer Girl)
Issue price: £ 55.00

18-D15-4.2
1979 *La Jeune Fille d'Hiver*
(Winter Girl)
Issue price: £ 55.00

18-D15-4.3
1980 *La Jeune Fille du Printemps*
(Spring Girl)
Issue price: £ 55.00

18-D15-4.4
1981 *La Jeune Fille d'Automne*
(Autumn Girl)
Issue price: £ 55.00
Series Closed

Les Très Riches Heures

(The Book of Hours Series)
Artist: Jean Dutheil
Overglaze porcelain
Diameter: 24.8 centimetres
(9 ³/₄ inches)
Attached back hanger
Edition size unannounced
Numbered with certificate

18-D15-5.1
1979 *Janvier (January)*
Issue price: £ 32.00

18-D15-5.2
1980 *Avril (April)*
Issue price: £ 32.00

18-D15-5.3
1981 *Août (August)*
Issue price: £ 33.00

18-D15-5.4
1982 *Juin (June)*
Issue price: £ 33.00

18-D15-5.5
1983 *Mai (May)*
Issue price: £ 33.00

FRANCE
D'ARCEAU-LIMOGES
18-D15-5.6

18-D15-5.6
1984 *Octobre (October)*
Issue price: £ 33.00

18-D15-5.7
1987 *Février (February)*
Issue price: £ 33.00

18-D15-5.8
1986 *Mars (March)*
Issue price: £ 33.00

Les Douze Sites Parisiens de Louis Dali

(The Twelve Parisian Places of Louis Dali)

Artist: Louis Dali. Artist's signature appears on front

Overglaze-decorated porcelain

Diameter: 21.6 centimetres (8 ¹/₂ inches)

Attached back hanger

Edition size undisclosed, limited by announced period of issue

Numbered with certificate

18-D15-6.1
1980 *L'Arc de Triomphe
(The Arch of Triumph)*
Issue price: £ 12.80

18-D15-6.2
1981 *La Cathédrale Notre-Dame
(Notre Dame Cathedral)*
Issue price: £ 12.80

18-D15-6.3
1981 *La Place de la Concorde
(Concord Place)*
Issue price: £ 14.30

18-D15-6.4
1981 *L'Eglise Saint-Pierre et le Sacré-
Coeur de Montmartre
(St. Peter's Church and Sacred Heart
Basilica)*
Issue price: £ 14.30

18-D15-6.5
1982 *Le Marché aux Fleurs et la
Conciergerie
(The Flower Market and the
Conciergerie)*
Issue price: £ 15.80

18-D15-6.6
1982 *La Pointe du Vert Galant et le Pont Neuf (Vert Galant Point and the New Bridge)*
Issue price: £ 15.80

18-D15-6.7
1983 *Le Jardin des Tuileries (The Garden of the Tuileries)*
Issue price: £ 15.80

18-D15-6.8
1983 *Le Moulin Rouge (The Moulin Rouge)*
Issue price: £ 15.80

18-D15-6.9
1983 *Le Pont Alexandre III (The Alexander III Bridge)*
Issue price: £ 17.30

18-D15-6.10
1983 *L'Opéra (The Opera)*
Issue price: £ 17.30

18-D15-6.11
1983 *La Tour Eiffel (The Eiffel Tower)*
Issue price: £ 17.30

18-D15-6.12
1983 *L'Hôtel de Ville de Paris (The Hotel de Ville de Paris)*
Issue price: £ 17.30
Series Closed

FRANCE
D'ARCEAU-LIMOGES

18-D15-7.1

Joséphine et Napoléon

(Josephine and Napoleon)

Artist: Claude Boulmé. Artist's signature appears on front

Overglaze-decorated porcelain

Diameter: 21.6 centimetres (8 ¹/₂ inches)

Attached back hanger

Edition size undisclosed, limited by announced period of issue

Numbered with certificate

18-D15-7.1
1984 *L'Impératrice Joséphine*
(The Empress Josephine)
Issue price: £ 14.99

18-D15-7.2
1984 *Bonaparte traversant les Alpes*
(Bonaparte Crossing the Alps)
Issue price: £ 14.99

18-D15-7.3
1984 *La Rencontre*
(The Meeting)
Issue price: £ 16.45

18-D15-7.4
1985 *Sacre de Napoléon*
(The Coronation)
Issue price: £ 16.45

18-D15-7.5
1985 *Le Divorce*
(The Divorce)
Issue price: £ 16.45

18-D15-7.6
1986 *Le Souvenir*
(The Memory)
Issue price: £ 16.45

Cambier Mother's Day Series

Artist: Guy Cambier. Artist's signature appears on front

Overglaze-decorated porcelain

Diameter: 21.6 centimetres (8 ¹/₂ inches)

Attached back hanger

Edition size undisclosed, limited by year of issue

Numbered with certificate

18-D15-8.1
1983 *Michèle et Sylvie*
Issue price: £ 20.95

18-D15-8.2
1984 *Marie et Jacqueline*
Issue price: £ 20.95

18-D15-8.3
1985 *Monique et François*
Issue price: £ 22.95

18-D15-8.4
1986 *Marianne et Thérèse*
Issue price: £ 22.95
Series Closed

Gigi Series

Artist: Jean-Claude Guidou. Artist's signature appears on front

Overglaze-decorated porcelain

Diameter: 21.6 centimetres (8 ¹/₂ inches)

Attached back hanger

Edition size undisclosed, limited by announced period of issue

Numbered with certificate

18-D15-9.1
1985 *Gigi*
Issue price: £ 20.95

18-D15-9.2
1985 *The Night They Invented Champagne*
Issue price: £ 20.95

FRANCE
D'ARCEAU-LIMOGES
18-D15-9.3

18-D15-9.3
1986 *I Remember It Well*
Issue price: £ 20.95

18-D15-9.4
1986 *Gigi Is in Love*
Issue price: £ 20.95
Series Closed

Les Femmes de la Belle Epoque Series

(The Women of the Beautiful Era)

Artist: Pierre-Laurent Brenot. Artist's signature appears on front

Overglaze-decorated porcelain

Diameter: 21.6 centimetres (8 ¹/₂ inches)

Attached back hanger

Edition size undisclosed, limited by announced period of issue

Numbered with certificate

18-D15-10.1
1986 *Sarah Bernhardt as Marguerite in "The Lady of the Camellias"*
Issue price: £ 18.55

18-D15-10.2
1986 *Liane de Pougy Makes Her Entrance at Maxim's*
Issue price: £ 18.55

18-D15-10.3
1986 *Caroline Otéro Pauses in Front of the Opera at Monte Carlo*
Issue price: £ 19.85

18-D15-10.4
1987 *Anna Pavlova Greets an Admirer at the Ballet Russes*
Issue price: £ 19.85

Les Noëls de France

(Christmas in France)

Artist: Jean-Claude Guidou. Artist's signature appears on front

Overglaze-decorated porcelain

Diameter: 21.6 centimetres (8 ¹/₂ inches)

Attached back hanger

Edition size undisclosed, limited by announced period of issue

Numbered with certificate

18-D15-11.1
1986 *The Magical Window*
Issue price: £ 17.55

18-D15-11.2
1987 *The Starlit Chèche*
Issue price: £ 17.55

Paysages de France Series

(French Country Landscapes)

Artist: Michel Julien. Artist's signature appears on front

Overglaze-decorated porcelain

Diameter: 21.6 centimetres (8 ¹/₂ inches)

Attached back hanger

Edition size undisclosed, limited by announced period of issue

Numbered with certificate

18-D15-12.1
1987 *Along the Riverside*
Issue price: £ 14.95

18-D15-12.2
1987 *Sunday in a Village*
Issue price: £ 14.95

18-D15-12.3
1987 *Harvest in the Champagne*
Issue price: £ 14.95

FRANCE
HAVILAND

18-H6-0.0

HAVILAND
Limoges

In 1839 David Haviland of New York City became the first American importer of Limoges porcelain made from white kaolin clay. When, in 1842, he realized that French factories would not adjust methods to meet the tastes of his American market, Haviland established his own pottery in Limoges.

In 1892 his son, Theodore, left the firm but remained in Limoges to set up Theodore Haviland & Company for production of porcelain dinnerware and decorative pieces. In the 1930s, Theodore Haviland & Company opened an American Haviland factory to produce tableware; the firm also bought the original Haviland & Company established by David Haviland.

All Haviland collector's plates are produced in Limoges, France. *The Twelve Days of Christmas* series, begun in 1970, is based on the carol of the same title. The five-plate *Bicentennial* series, introduced in 1972, commemorates events leading to the American Declaration of Independence. In 1973, the *Mother's Day* series of seven plates, entitled *The French Collection,* was started.

And 1979 marked the beginning of the *Mille et Une Nuits* series based on the literary classic *One Thousand One Arabian Nights.*

Adept in a variety of styles, French painter Remy Hétreau is the principal artist for Haviland collector's plates, with three distinctively different series to his credit — from historical chronicle to whimsical sketches of modern family life. Noted watercolourist Liliane Tellier, creator of the *Mille et Une Nuits* series, has an extensive following among connoisseurs of the medium. A native Parisienne, she studied watercolour and gouache at *L'Ecole Camond* in Paris and refined her techniques in Sweden. Later she worked for the International Society for Education through Art as a consultant for UNESCO.

The Twelve Days of Christmas Series

Artist: Remy Hétreau. Artist's signature appears on front

Overglaze-decorated porcelain

Diameter: 21.3 centimetres (8 ³/₈ inches)

No hanger

Edition size limited to announced quantity of 30.000

Not numbered, without certificate

18-H6-1.1
1970 *A Partridge in a Pear Tree*
Issue price: £ 15.15

18-H6-1.2
1971 *Two Turtle Doves*
Issue price: £ 15.15

18-H6-1.3
1972 *Three French Hens*
Issue price: £ 16.70

18-H6-1.4
1973 *Four Colly Birds*
Issue price: £ 17.30

18-H6-1.5
1974 *Five Golden Rings*
Issue price: £ 18.20

18-H6-1.6
1975 *Six Geese A'Laying*
Issue price: £ 19.70

18-H6-1.7
1976 *Seven Swans A'Swimming*
Issue price: £ 23.10

18-H6-1.8
1977 *Eight Maids A'Milking*
Issue price: £ 24.25

FRANCE
HAVILAND
18-H6-1.9

18-H6-1.9
1978 *Nine Ladies Dancing*
Issue price: £ 27.30

18-H6-1.10
1979 *Ten Lords A'Leaping*
Issue price: £ 30.30

18-H6-1.11
1980 *Eleven Pipers Piping*
Issue price: £ 33.35

18-H6-1.12
1981 *Twelve Drummers Drumming*
Issue price: £ 36.40
Series Closed

Mille et Une Nuits

(1001 Arabian Nights)

Artist: Liliane Tellier. Artist's signature appears on front

Porcelain banded in gold

Diameter: 24.1 centimetres
(9 ½ inches)

No hanger

Edition size undisclosed, limited by announced period of issue

Numbered with certificate

18-H6-4.1
1979 *Le Cheval Magique*
(The Magic Horse)
Issue price: £ 27.90

18-H6-4.2
1980 *Aladin et la Lampe Merveilleuse*
(Aladin and the Wonderful Lamp)
Issue price: £ 27.90

18-H6-4.3
1981 *Scheherazade*
Issue price: £ 30.70

18-H6-4.4
1982 *Sindbad the Sailor*
Issue price: £ 30.70
Series Closed

18-H8-1.1 "Unicorn in Captivity"
1971 Haviland & Parlon
Tapestry
This series captures the delightful
mythical quality and great detail of
"The Hunt of the Unicorn", a series of
French medieval tapestries now
hanging in The Cloisters of New York's
Metropolitan Museum of Art.

HAVILAND & PARLON
Limoges

Haviland & Parlon is a chapter in the intricate Haviland porcelain story. In 1853 Robert Haviland left New York City to work for his brother David Haviland in Limoges (see France, HAVILAND). In 1870 Robert's son Charles Field Haviland also established a porcelain factory in Limoges and used "Ch. Field Haviland" as his trade name. After he retired in 1881, the firm was known by several different names until 1942, when Robert Haviland (Robert's great-grandson) purchased it. The firm is now known as Robert Haviland & C. Parlon but retains the "Ch. Field Haviland" trademark.

The *Tapestry* series, begun in 1971, reproduced six scenes from the French medieval tapestries, "The Hunt of the Unicorn", now hanging in the Cloisters of New York's Metropolitan Museum of Art. The *Christmas* series of famous Renaissance Madonnas began in 1972 and ended in 1979; a second *Tapestry* series of six plates began in 1977, reproducing scenes, from "The Lady and the Unicorn" tapestries hanging in the Cluny Museum in Paris.

Designs for the *Christmas* series are taken from works by the great masters as indicated.

Tapestry Series

Artist: unknown. Reproduced from French medieval tapestries

Overglaze-decorated porcelain banded in gold

Diameter: 25.4 centimetres (10 inches)

No hanger

Edition size limited to announced quantity of 10,000

Not numbered, without certificate

18-H8-1.1
1971 *The Unicorn in Captivity*
Issue price: £ 17.50

18-H8-1.2
1972 *Start of the Hunt*
Issue price: £ 17.50

18-H8-1.3
1973 *Chase of the Unicorn*
Issue price: £ 17.50

18-H8-1.4
1974 *End of the Hunt*
Issue price: £ 17.95

18-H8-1.5
1975 *The Unicorn Surrounded*
Issue price: £ 19.95

18-H8-1.6
1976 *The Unicorn Is Brought to the Castle*
Issue price: £ 21.50
Series Closed

FRANCE
HAVILAND & PARLON

18-H8-2.1

Christmas Series

Artist: as indicated

Overglaze-decorated porcelain banded in gold

Diameter: 25.4 centimetres (10 inches)

No hanger

Edition size: as indicated

Numbered without certificate

18-H8-2.1
1972 *Madonna and Child*
Artist: Raphael/Edition: 5,000
Issue price: £ 21.25

18-H8-2.2
1973 *Madonnina*
Artist: Feruzzi/Edition: 5,000
Issue price: £ 24.25

18-H8-2.3
1974 *Cowper Madonna and Child*
Artist: Raffael/Edition: 5,000
Issue price: £ 25.75

18-H8-2.4
1975 *Madonna and Child*
Artist: Murillo/Edition: 7,500
Issue price: £ 25.75

18-H8-2.5
1976 *Madonna and Child*
Artist: Botticelli/Edition: 7,000
Issue price: £ 27.30

18-H8-2.6
1977 *Madonna and Child*
Artist: Bellini/Edition: 7,500
Issue price: £ 29.10

18-H8-2.7
1978 *Madonna and Child*
Artist: Fra Filippo Lippi/Edition: 7,500
Issue price: £ 29.10

18-H8-2.8
1979 *Madonna of the Eucharist*
Artist: Botticelli/Edition: 7,500
Issue price: £ 30.00

The Lady and the Unicorn Series

Artist: unknown. Reproduced from French medieval tapestries

Overglaze-decorated porcelain banded in gold

Diameter: 25.4 centimetres (10 inches)

No hanger

Edition size: as indicated

Not numbered, without certificate

18-H8-4.1
1977 *To My Only Desire*
Edition size: 20,000
Issue price: £ 22.50

18-H8-4.2
1978 *Sight*
Edition size: 20,000
Issue price: £ 22.50

18-H8-4.3
1979 *Sound*
Edition size: 20,000
Issue price: £ 24.50

18-H8-4.4
1980 *Touch*
Edition size: 15,000
Issue price: £ 26.50

18-H8-4.5
1981 *Scent*
Edition size: 10,000
Issue price: £ 29.50

18-H8-4.6
1982 *Taste*
Edition size: 10,000
Issue price: £ 35.00
Series Closed

FRANCE
LALIQUE
18-L3-0.0

LALIQUE
Alsace

René Lalique, founder of the firm that bears his name, began his career as a goldsmith and jeweller in the late nineteenth century. His clients included such notables as Sarah Bernhardt and the dealers Cartier and Boucheron.

In 1902 his interests turned to glassmaking and be acquired a small glassworks at Clairfontaine, France. In 1909 he opened a glass factory near Paris where he produced bottles for the leading Parisian *parfumeurs,* and in 1918 he opened the present Lalique factory in Alsace. Here he began to produce glass items in the Art Deco style. His designs, usually created in pressed glass, are noted for the frosted and satin effects of the glass. Until his death in 1945, Lalique produced numerous commercial glass objects such as perfume bottles, vases and figurines.

Upon René's death in 1945, his son Marc – himself a noted artist – inherited the firm and served as its president until his death in 1977. The firm is currently headed by Marc's daughter, Marie-Claude. Als Lalique's chief designer she sreated the *Annual* series of Lalique crystal collector's plates which began in 1965 and ended in 1976.

Annual Series

Artist: Marie-Claude Lalique

Full lead crystal with incised designs

Diameter: 21.6 centimetres (8 ¹/₂ inches)

No hanger

Edition size: as indicated. Announced between 5,000 and 8,000 from 1967 through 1976

Not numbered, without certificate; engraved "Lalique-France" on back

18-L3-1.1
1965 *Deux Oiseaux (Two Birds)*
Edition: 2,000
Issue price: £ 15.15

18-L3-1.2
1966 *Rose de Songerie (Dream Rose)*
Edition: 5,000
Issue price: £ 15.15

18-L3-1.3
1967 *Ballet de Poisson (Fish Ballet)*
Issue price: £ 15.15

18-L3-1.4
1968 *Gazelle Fantaisie (Gazelle Fantasy)*
Issue price: £ 15.15

18-L3-1.5
1969 *Papillon (Butterfly)*
Issue price: £ 18.20

18-L3-1.6
1970 *Paon (Peaock)*
Issue price: £ 18.20

18-L3-1.7
1971 *Hibou (Owl)*
Issue price: £ 21.25

18-L3-1.8
1972 *Coquillage (Shell)*
Issue price: £ 24.25

FRANCE
LALIQUE
18-L3-1.9

18-L3-1.9
1973 *Petit Geai (Jayling)*
Issue price: £ 25.80

18-L3-1.10
1974 *Sous d'Argent (Silver Pennies)*
Issue price: £ 28.80

18-L3-1.11
1975 *Duo de Poisson (Fish Duett)*
Issue price: £ 30.30

18-L3-1.12
1976 *Aigle (Eagle)*
Issue price: £ 36.40
Series Closed

18-L52-2.1 „Cinderella"
1983 Limoges-Turgot
Quellier's Morals of Perrault
Many of today's most beloved
children's tales began as serious
examples of morality for adults. Such
was true of "Cinderella", a tale with
origins in 17th century France, here
interpreted in the graceful style of that
period by Andre Quellier.

LIMOGES-TURGOT
Limoges

The porcelain house of Limoges-Turgot draws upon a tradition of porcelain making which began with A.-R.-J. Turgot, Baron de l'Aulne, Louis XVI's administrator for the Limousin province of which Limoges was the capital. When kaolin clay, the key ingredient in true hard-fire porcelain, was discovered in 1768 at the nearby town of Saint-Yrieix, it was largely due to Turgot's efforts that the Limoges porcelain industry was established and achieved world renown.

Les Enfants de Durand, (Durand's Children Collection), by Paul Durand, began in 1978 and is the first proprietary series by Limoges-Turgot. The series ended in 1980. *Quellier's Morals of Perrault* series, by André Quellier, began in 1983. Their third series, entitled *Children of the Turn of the Century,* was created by Bernard Peltriaux.

Les Elefants de Durand

(Durand's Children)

Artist: Paul Durand. Artist's signature appears on front

Overglaze-decorated porcelain

Diameter: 20.3 centimetres (8 inches)

Attached back hanger

Edition size undisclosed, limited by year of issue

Numbered with certificate

18-L52-1.1
1978 *Marie-Ange*
Issue price: £ 13.95

18-L52-1.2
1979 *Emilie et Philippe*
Issue price: £ 14.95

18-L52-1.3
1980 *Christiane et Fifi*
Issue price: £ 14.95

18-L52-1.4
1980 *Cécile et Raoul*
Issue price: £ 14.95
Series Closed

Quellier's Morals of Perrault Series

Artist: André Quellier. Artist's signature appears on front

Overglaze-decorated porcelain

Diameter: 21.6 centimetres (8 ¹/₂ inches)

Attached back hanger

Edition size undisclosed, limited by announced period of issue

Numbered with certificate

18-L52-2.1
1983 *Cinderella*
Issue price: £ 21.00

18-L52-2.2
1984 *Little Tom Thumb*
Issue price: £ 21.00

FRANCE
LIMOGES-TURGOT

18-L52-2.3

18-L52-2.3
1984 *Little Red Riding Hood*
Issue price: £ 21.00

18-L52-2.4
1985 *Sleeping Beauty*
Issue price: £ 21.00
Series Closed

Les Elefants de la Fin du Siècle de Peltriaux

(Peltriaux's Children of the Turn of the Century)

Artist: Bernard Peltriaux. Artist's signature appears on front

Overglaze-decorated porcelain

Diameter: 21.6 centimetres (8 ¹/₂ inches)

Attached back hanger

Edition size undisclosed, limited by announced period of issue

Numbered with certificate

18-L52-3.1
1985 *Patinage au Trocadéro (Skating at the Trocadéro)*
Issue price: £ 21.45

18-L52-3.2
1985 *Petits Voiliers au Bassin des Tuileries (Setting Sail at the Tuileries)*
Issue price: £ 21.45

18-L52-3.3
1985 *Guignol au Luxembourg (At the Puppet Show in Luxemburg)*
Issue price: £ 21.45

18-L52-3.4
1986 *Manège aux Champs-Elysées (Merry Go Round on the Champs-Elysées)*
Issue price: £ 21.45

22-A3-3.1-1 „Gabriel"
1979 Anna-Perenna Triptych
This issue is one of a three-plate set
entitled "The Byzantine Triptych". A
modern interpretation of the three-
panelled altarpieces of the 14th century,
called triptychs, it is the work of
husband-and-wife artist team Frank
Russell and Gertrude Barrer.

GERMANY
ANNA PERENNA

22-A3-3.1-1

ANNA PERENNA
Stuttgart

Named for Anna Perenna, the Roman goddess associated with health, abundance and the rebirth of spring, Anna Perenna, Inc. was founded in 1977 by its president, Klaus D. Vogt, exclusively to produce high-quality limited-edition plates in hard-paste porcelain.

Two *Triptych* sets, inspired by the portable altar-pieces of the Middle Ages, were issued in 1979 and 1980. Each three-plate set reinterprets ancient Byzantine religious motifs. In 1979, Anna Perenna introduced *Romantic Loves,* a four-plate series celebrating great romantic loves of histo-ry. Their four-plate series, *Uncle Tad's Cats,* began in 1979 and ended in 1981.

Frank Russell and Gertrude Barrer, the creators of the "Triptych and the *Romantic Loves* series, are husband-and-wife co-workers who have blended their talents to become a successful art-producing team. Thaddeus Krumeich ("Uncle Tad") is the artist for the *Uncle Tad's Cats* series.

In 1986, Anna Perenna introduced *Uncle Tad's Golden Oldies* series, again with artwork by Thaddeus-Krumeich.

The Triptych Series

Artist: Frank Russell and Gertrude Barrer. Artist's signature appears on front

Hard-paste porcelain with hinged frame

Diameter: plates one and three, 21.6 cm (8 $^1/_2$ in.); plate two, 24.8 cm (9 $^3/_4$ in.); overall Triptych, 88.9 cm x 45.7 cm. (35 in. x 18 in.) for 1979 set; 83.8 cm x 38.1 cm. (33 in. x 15 in.) for 1980 set

Attached back hanger

Edition size limited to 5,000 sets

Individually hand-numbered with certificate

22-A3-3.1-1
1979 *Gabriel*
The Byzantine Triptych
Issue price: £ 175.00 (the set)

22-A3-3.1-2
1979 *Madonna and Child*

22-A3-3.1-3
1979 *Michael*

22-A3-3.2-1
1980 *Saul*
The Jerusalem Triptych
Issue price: £ 175.00 (the set)

22-A3-3.2-2
1980 *David*

22-A3-3.2-3
1980 *Salomon*

Romantic Love Series

Artist: Frank Russell and Gertrude Barrer. Artist's signature appears on front

Hard-paste porcelain banded in gold

Diameter: 25 centimetres (9 $^7/_8$ inches)

Attached back hanger

Edition size limited to 7,500

Numbered with certificate

22-A3-4.1
1979 *Romeo and Juliet*
Issue price: £ 45.00

22-A3-4.2
1980 *Lancelot and Guinevere*
Issue price: £ 45.00

22-A3-4.3
1981 *Helen and Paris*
Issue price: £ 45.00

119

GERMANY
ANNA PERENNA

22-A3-4.4

22-A3-4.4
1982 *Lovers of the Taj Mahal*
Issue price: £ 45.00
Series Closed

Uncle Tad's Cats Series

Artist: Thaddeus Krumeich.
Artist's signature appears on front

Hard-past porcelain

Diameter: 24.8 centimetres
(9 ³/₄ inches)

Attached back hanger

Edition size limited to 5,000

Individually hand-numbered with certificate

22-A3-5.1
1979 *Oliver's Birthday*
Issue price: £ 37.50

22-A3-5.2
1980 *Peaches and Cream*
Issue price: £ 37.50

22-A3-5.3
1981 *Princess Aurora, Queen of the Night*
Issue price: £ 37.50

22-A3-5.4
1981 *Walter's Window*
Issue price: £ 37.50
Series Closed

Flowers of Bernadotte

Artist: Garie von Schunck.
Artist's signature appears on front

Porcelain banded in gold

Diameter: 24.1 centimetres
(9 ¹/₂ inches)

Pierced foot rim

Edition size limited to 17,800

Numbered with certificate

22-A3-20.1
1984 *Iris*
Issue price: £ 40.00

22-A3-20.2
1984 *Lily*
Issue price: £ 40.00

22-A3-20.3
1984 *Orchid*
Issue price: £ 40.00

22-A3-20.4
1984 *Tulip*
Issue price: £ 40.00

22-A3-20.5
1984 *Rose*
Issue price: £ 40.00

22-A3-20.6
1984 *Chrysanthemum*
Issue price: £ 40.00
Series Closed

Uncle Tad's Golden Oldies Series

Artist: Thaddeus Krumeich. Artist's signature appears on front

Hard-paste porcelain

Diameter: 20.3 centimetres (8 inches)

Pierced foot rim

Edition size undisclosed, limited by announced period of issue

Individually hand-numbered with certificate

22-A3-26.1
1986 *My Merry Oldsmobile*
Issue price: £ 37.75

22-A3-26.2
1986 *Down by the Old Mill Stream*
Issue price: £ 37.75

22-A3-26.3
1986 *Ramona*
Issue price: £ 37.75

22-A3-26.4
1987 *Paddlin' Madeline Home*
Issue price: £ 37.75
Series Closed

GERMANY
BAREUTHER
22-B7-0.0

BAREUTHER
Waldsassen

The Bareuther & Company porcelain factory began to produce dinnerware, vases and giftware in 1867. The small shop was established with a porcelain kiln and an annular brick kiln by sculptor Johann Matthaeus Ries. In 1884 Ries's son sold the shop to Oskar Bareuther who continued to produce fine tableware.

To observe the 100th anniversary of the factory in 1967, Bareuther began a series of limited-edition *Christmas* plates. A *Father's Day* series depicting to great castles of Germany was started in 1969.

Hans Mueller is the principal artist for all Bareuther series.

Christmas Series

Artist: Hans Mueller, except 1971

Porcelain decorated in cobalt blue underglaze

Diameter: 20.3 centimetres (8 inches)

Pierced foot rim

Edition size limited to announced quantity of 10,000

Not numbered, without certificate

22-B7-1.1
1967 *Stiftskirche*
Issue price: £ 7.25

22-B7-1.2
1968 *Kappl*
Issue price: £ 7.25

22-B7-1.3
1969 *Christkindlesmarkt*
Issue price: £ 7.25

22-B7-1.4
1970 *Chapel in Oberndorf*
Issue price: £ 7.50

22-B7-1.5
1971 *Toys for Sale*
Issue price: £ 7.75

22-B7-1.6
1972 *Christmas in Munich*
Issue price: £ 8.85

22-B7-1.7
1973 *Christmas Sleigh Ride*
Issue price: £ 9.25

22-B7-1.8
1974 *Church in the Black Forest*
Issue price: £ 11.50

GERMANY
BAREUTHER
22-B7-1.9

22-B7-1.9
1975 *Snowman*
Issue price: £ 13.00

22-B7-1.10
1976 *Chapel in the Hills*
Issue price: £ 14.25

22-B7-1.11
1977 *Story Time*
Issue price: £ 14.85

22-B7-1.12
1978 *Mittenwald*
Issue price: £ 16.75

22-B7-1.13
1979 *Winter Day*
Issue price: £ 21.25

22-B7-1.14
1980 *Miltenberg*
Issue price: £ 22.75

22-B7-1.15
1981 *Walk in the Forest*
Issue price: £ 23.95

22-B7-1.16
1982 *Bad Wimpfen*
Issue price: £ 23.95

22-B7-1.17
1983 *The Night Before Christmas*
Issue price: £ 23.95

22-B7-1.18
1984 *Zeil on the River Main*
Issue price: £ 25.75

22-B7-1.19
1985 *Winter Wonderland*
Issue price: £ 25.75

22-B7-1.20
1986 *Market Place in Forchheim*
Issue price: £ 25.75

22-B7-1.21
1987 *Decorating the Christmas Tree*
Issue price: £ 25.75

Father's Day Series

Artist: Hans Müller

Porcelain decorated in cobalt blue underglaze

Diameter: 20.3 centimetres (8 inches)

Pierced foot rim

Edition size limited to announced quantity of 2,500

Not numbered, without certificate

22-B7-2.1
1969 *Castle Neuschwanstein*
Issue price: £ 6,35

22-B7-2.2
1970 *Castle Pfalz*
Issue price: £ 7,50

BAREUTHER

22-B7-2.3

22-B7-2.3
1974 *Castle Heidelberg*
Issue price: £ 7.75

22-B7-2.4
1975 *Castle Hohenschwangau*
Issue price: £ 8.85

22-B7-2.5
1976 *Castle Katz*
Issue price: £ 9.25

22-B7-2.6
1974 *Würzburg Castle*
Issue price: £ 11.50

22-B7-2.7
1975 *Castle Lichtenstein*
Issue price: £ 13.00

22-B7-2.8
1976 *Castle Hohenzollern*
Issue price: £ 14.25

22-B7-2.9
1977 *Castle Eltz*
Issue price: £ 14.85

22-B7-2.10
1978 *Castle Falkenstein*
Issue price: £ 16.75

22-B7-2.11
1979 *Castle Rheinstein*
Issue price: £ 21.25

22-B7-2.12
1980 *Castle Cochem*
Issue price: £ 22.75

22-B7-2.13
1981 *Castle Gutenfels*
Issue price: £ 23.95

22-B7-2.14
1982 *Castle Zwingenberg*
Issue price: £ 23.95

22-B7-2.15
1983 *Castle Lauenstein*
Issue price: £ 23.95

22-B7-2.16
1984 *Castle Neuenstein*
Issue price: £ 25.75

22-B7-2.17
1985 *Castle Wartburg Near Eisenach*
Issue price: £ 25.75

22-B7-2.18
1986 *Castle Hardegg*
Issue price: £ 25.75

22-B7-2.19
1987 *Castle Buerresheim*
Issue price: £ 28.25

GERMANY
BERLIN DESIGN
22-B20-1.1

BERLIN DESIGN
Staffelstein

Berlin Design's limited-edition plates, mugs and other collectibles are manufactured by the Kaiser Porcelain Company (see Germany, KAISER), and are identified by the distinctive bear-and-crown symbol of the city of Berlin.

The *Christmas* series, introduced in 1970, depicts Yule festivities in German towns. Artists for Berlin Design *Christmas* plates are not disclosed.

The *Holiday Week of the Family Kappelmann* series began in 1984. It is by artist Detlev Nitschke.

Christmas Series

Artist: undisclosed

Porcelain decorated in cobalt blue underglaze

Diameter: 19.7 centimetres (7 ³/₄ inches)

Pierced foot rim

Edition size limited to 4,000 in 1970; 20,000 thereafter

Not numbered, without certificate

22-B20-1.1
1970 *Christmas in Bernkastel*
Issue price: £ 9.90

22-B20-1.2
1971 *Christmas in Rothenburg ob der Tauber*
Issue price: £ 10.50

22-B20-1.3
1972 *Christmas in Michelstadt*
Issue price: £ 10.50

22-B20-1.4
1973 *Christmas in Wendelstein*
Issue price: £ 10.95

22-B20-1.5
1974 *Christmas in Bremen*
Issue price: £ 12.95

22-B20-1.6
1975 *Christmas in Dortmund*
Issue price: £ 15.50

22-B20-1.7
1976 *Christmas in Augsburg*
Issue price: £ 16.95

22-B20-1.8
1977 *Christmas in Hamburg*
Issue price: £ 18.50

22-B20-1.9
1978 *Christmas Market at the Dom of Berlin*
Issue price: £ 18.95

22-B20-1.10
1979 *Christmas Eve in Greetsiel*
Issue price: £ 19.95

22-B20-1.11
1980 *Christmas Eve in Miltenberg*
Issue price: £ 21.50

GERMANY
BERLIN DESIGN
22-B20-1.12

22-B20-1.12
1981 *Christmas Eve in Hahnenklee*
Issue price: £ 25.00

22-B20-1.13
1982 *Christmas Eve in Wasserburg*
Issue price: £ 25.00

22-B20-1.14
1983 *The Chapel in Oberndorf*
Issue price: £ 25.00

22-B20-1.15
1984 *Christmas Eve in Ramsau*
Issue price: £ 26.25

22-B20-1.16
1985 *Christmas Eve in Bad Wimpfen*
Issue price: £ 27.50

22-B20-1.17
1986 *Christmas Eve in Gelnhausen*
Issue price: £ 27.50

22-B20-1.18
1987 *Christmas Eve in Goslar*
Issue price: £ 28.50

Mother's Day Series

Artist: undisclosed

Porcelain decorated in cobalt blue underglaze

Diameter: 19.5 centimetres (7²/₃ inches)

Edition size undisclosed, limited by year of issue

Pierced foot rim

Not numbered, without certificate

22-B20-3.1
1971 *Grey Poodles*
Issue price: £ 9.90

22-B20-3.2
1972 *Fledglings*
Issue price: £ 10.50

22-B20-3.3
1973 *Duck Family*
Issue price: £ 10.95

22-B20-3.4
1974 *Squirrels*
Issue price: £ 10.95

22-B20-3.5
1975 *Cats*
Issue price: £ 12.95

22-B20-3.6
1976 *Doe and Her Fawn*
Issue price: £ 15.50

22-B20-3.7
1977 *Storks*
Issue price: £ 16.95

22-B20-3.8
1978 *Mare with Foal*
Issue price: £ 18.50

GERMANY
BERLIN DESIGN
22-B20-3.9

22-B20-3.9
1979 *Swans and Cygnets*
Issue price: £ 18.50

22-B20-3.10
1980 *Goat Family*
Issue price: £ 19.95

22-B20-3.11
1981 *Dachshund Family*
Issue price: £ 21.50

22-B20-3.12
1982 *Partridge Family*
Issue price: £ 25.00

22-B20-3.13
1983 *Swallow Family*
Issue price: £ 25.00

22-B20-3.14
1984 *Mother's Care*
Issue price: £ 26.25

22-B20-3.15
1985 *Flowers for Mother*
Issue price: £ 27.50

22-B20-3.16
1986 *Chickens*
Issue price: £ 27.50

22-B20-3.17
1987 *Foxes*
Issue price: £ 27.50

Holiday Week of the Family Kappelmann Series

Artist: Detlev Nitschke. Artist's signature appears on front

Overglaze-decorated porcelain

Diameter: 19 centimetres (7 ¹/₂ inches)

Pierced foot rim

Edition size undisclosed, limited by announced period of issue

Numbered with certificate

22-B20-4.1
1984 *Monday*
Issue price: £ 14.99

22-B20-4.2
1984 *Tuesday*
Issue price: £ 14.99

22-B20-4.3
1985 *Wednesday*
Issue price: £ 16.50

22-B20-4.4
1985 *Thursday*
Issue price: £ 16.50

22-B20-4.5
1986 *Friday*
Issue price: £ 16.50

22-B20-4.6
1986 *Saturday*
Issue price: £ 18.15

22-B20-4.7
1986 *Sunday*
Issue price: £ 18.15
Series Closed

GERMANY
CHRISTIAN SELTMANN
22-C32-1.1

CHRISTIAN SELTMANN
Weiden / Oberpfalz

The Christian Seltmann porcelain factory was established in 1901 by a talented, 30-year-old porcelain maker of the same name. Seltmann started his porcelain-making career as a young apprentice in a porcelain-making factory near Schlottenhof, Germany. In 1894 he made a special mould that helped his company win an important American contract. To show its gratitude, the company sent him to Teplitz-Schonau, the most prestigious porcelain-making school of the time.

Soon afterwards, Mr. Seltmann was promoted to factory manager, and eventually, the enterprising young man went into business on his own.

Since 1901, Christian Seltmann Porcelain has achieved considerable prestige and esteem by maintaining the high standards of its founder. Throughout its history, the firm has consistently produced exquisitely-wrought porcelain objects, well-known in Europe.

The *Lückel's Idyllic Village Life* series by artist Christian Luckel is produced on true hard-fire German porcelain. This series, which began in 1986, depicts scenes from a typical Bavarian village of the early 19th century.

Lückel's Idyllic Village Life Series

Artist: Christian Lückel. Artist's signature appears on front

Porcelain

Diameter: 19 centimetres
(7 $\frac{1}{2}$ inches)

Pierced foot rim

Edition size undisclosed, limited by announced period of issue

Numbered with certificate

22-C32-1.1
1986 *The Blacksmith*
Issue price: £ 13.25

22-C32-1.2
1986 *Arrival of the Stagecoach*
Issue price: £ 13.25

22-C32-1.3
1986 *Stop at the Village Inn*
Issue price: £ 13.25

22-C32-1.4
1986 *In the Fields at Harvest Time*
Issue price: £ 15.25

22-C32-1.5
1987 *On the Way to the Market*
Issue price: £ 15.25

22-C32-1.6
1987 *At the Village Fountain*
Issue price: £ 15.25

22-C32-1.7
1987 *The Fishermen*
Issue price: £ 16.55

22-C32-1.8
1987 *Daytrip in Summertime*
Issue price: £ 16.55

22-C32-1.9
1987 *The Farmer's Wedding*
Issue price unavailable at press time

22-C32-1.10
1987 *Angler's Pleasure*
Issue price unavailable at press time

GERMANY
CLASSIC ROSE

22-C45-0.0

CLASSIC ROSE

Rosenthal's first traditional Christmas plate appeared in 1910. Since 1974 Classic Rose has been continuing this tradition. Each year a Christmas plate, decorated like its "historical" predecessors by a cobalt-blue sgraffito technique, is issued in limited edition. Classic Rose also manufactures high-quality tableware.

Christmas Series

Artist: Helmut Drexler. Artist's signature appears on front

Porcelain

Diameter: 21.6 centimetres (8 ¹/₂ inches)

Attached back hanger

Edition size undisclosed, limited by year of issue

Not numbered, without certificate

22-C45-1.1
1974 *Memorial Church in Berlin*
Issue price: £ 32.50

22-C45-1.2
1975 *The Freiburg Cathedral*
Issue price: £ 39.35

22-C45-1.3
1976 *Cochem Castle*
Issue price: £ 46.35

22-C45-1.4
1977 *Hannover's Town Hall*
Issue price: £ 53.00

22-C45-1.5
1978 *The Dom in Aachen*
Issue price: £ 62.70

22-C45-1.6
1979 *The Archduice Adolph Bridge*
Issue price: £ 66.00

22-C45-1.7
1980 *Marketplace in Brussels*
Issue price: £ 66.00

22-C45-1.8
1981 *Marketplace in Trier*
Issue price: £ 70.00

GERMANY
CLASSIC ROSE
22-C45-1.9

22-C45-1.9
1982 *Milan Cathedral*
Issue price: £ 73.35

22-C45-1.10
1983 *Castle Church of Wittenberg*
Issue price: £ 76.70

22-C45-1.11
1984 *Town Hall in Stockholm*
Issue price: £ 78.35

22-C45-1.12
1985 *Augsburg "St. Ulrich and Afra"*
Issue price: £ 81.70

22-C45-1.13
1986 *The Old Church Amsterdam*
Issue price: £ 86.50

22-C45-1.14
1987 *National Theatre of Munich*
Issue price: £ 87.50

22-F82-6.1 Muninger's Romantic Winter Impressions
1986 Ice Skaters in the Evening Sun
First plate in the series 'Muninger's Romantic Winter Impressions', created by Ludwig Muninger, whose mentors are the Dutch landscape artists of the seventeenth century.

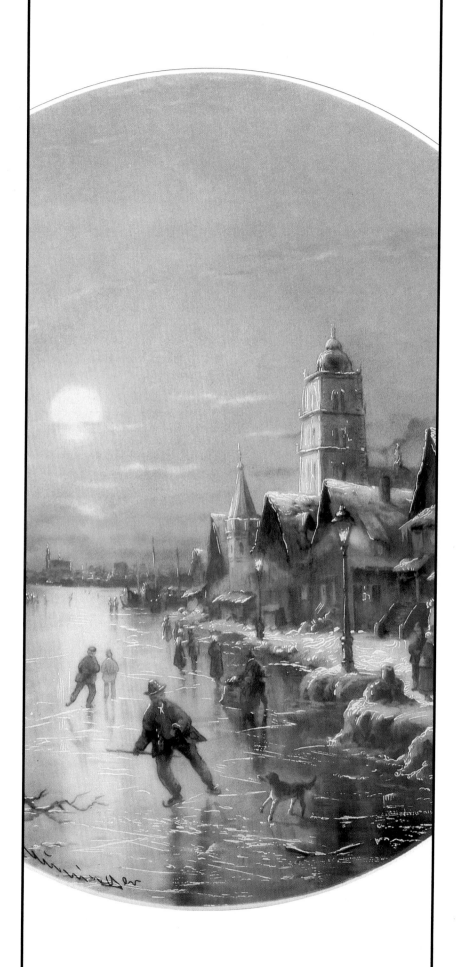

PORZELLANMANUFAKTUR
FÜRSTENBERG
SEIT 1747

FÜRSTENBERG PORZELLAN
Fürstenberg

Furstenberg, West Germany's oldest existing porcelain works, was founded by order of Charles I, Duke of Brunswick, in 1747. The porcelain manufactory took up residence in the 14th-century castle of Furstenberg, high on the banks of the river Weser. To produce the quality of porcelain that in the 18th century was called "white gold", the Duke assembled a blue-ribbon group of artists and craftsmen. Six years later, in 1753, he decreed that each priece of porcelain from the Furstenberg works be marked with a blue "F", which was later enhanced by the addition of a crown.

Through the centuries the Furstenberg logo has changed little, while the porcelain produced there continues to represent the high achievements of the ceramicist's art. However, it was not until 1986 that the firm earned Bradex listing in the United Kingdom with the series titled *Muninger's Romantic Winter Impressions*. The artist for this series, Ludwig Muninger, is German-born and European-trained. Although his work is contemporary, it emulates the outstanding work of the Dutch landscape artists of the 17th century.

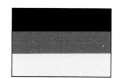

Muninger's Romantic Winter Impressions Series

Artist: Ludwig Muninger. Artist's signature appears on front

Overglaze-decorated porcelain

Diameter: 19 centimetres (7 ¹/₂ inches)

Edition size undisclosed, limited by announced period of issue

Numbered, with certificate

22-F82-6.1
1987 *Ice Skaters in the Evening Sun*
Issue price: £ 21.95

22-F82-6.2
1987 *Ice Fishers on the Village Pond*
Issue price: £ 21.95

22-F82-6.3
1987 *Refreshments after the Winter Fest*
Issue price: £ 23.45

22-F82-6.4
1987 *Visit of the Peddler*
Issue price: £ 23.45

22-F82-6.5
1987 *On the Way to Church*
Issue price unavailable at press time

Goebel

GOEBEL
Rödenthal

W. Goebel Porzellanfabrik was established in 1871 in Oeslau by Franz-Detleff Goebel and his son William. Now headed by Wilhelm Goebel, who represents the fifth generation of the founding family, Goebel produces hand-crafted figurines, plates, dinnerware, and gift items.

In 1935 Goebel introduced the famous M. I. Hummel figurines based on sketches by the Franciscan nun. In 1971, to celebrate the 100th anniversary of the firm, Goebel inaugurated an *Annual* series of limited-edition plates featuring M. I. Hummel motifs.

The three-issue M. I. Hummel *Anniversary* series began in 1975, with the second and third plates issued in 1980 and 1985.

Hummel Annual Series

Artist: Sister M.I. Hummel. Artist's signature incised on front

Porcelain with hand-painted bas-relief

Diameter: 19 centimetres (7 ½ inches)

Pierced foot rim

Edition size undisclosed, limited by year of issue

Not numbered, without certificate

22-G54-1.1
1971 *Heavenly Angel*
Issue price: £ 11.75

22-G54-1.2
1972 *Hear Ye, Hear Ye*
Issue price: £ 13.50

22-G54-1.3
1973 *Globe Trotter*
Issue price: £ 14.75

22-G54-1.4
1974 *Goose Girl*
Issue price: £ 16.50

22-G54-1.5
1975 *Ride into Christmas*
Issue price: £ 26.00

22-G54-1.6
1976 *Apple Tree Girl*
Issue price: £ 29.50

22-G54-1.7
1977 *Apple Tree Boy*
Issue price: £ 34.50

22-G54-1.8
1978 *Happy Pastime*
Issue price: £ 39.50

GERMANY
GOEBEL

22-G54-1.9

22-G54-1.9
1979 *Singing Lesson*
Issue price: £ 43.65

22-G54-1.10
1980 *School Girl*
Issue price: £ 55.25

22-G54-1.11
1981 *Umbrella Boy*
Issue price: £ 55.25

22-G54-1.12
1982 *Umbrella Girl*
Issue price: £ 55.25

22-G54-1.13
1983 *The Postman*
Issue price: £ 55.25

22-G54-1.14
1984 *Little Helper*
Issue price: £ 55.25

22-G54-1.15
1985 *Chick Girl*
Issue price: £ 63.55

22-G54-1.16
1986 *Playmates*
Issue price: £ 74.55

22-G54-1.17
1987 *Feeding Time*
Issue price: £ 81.85

Hummel Anniversary Series

Artist: Sister M.I. Hummel. Artist's signature incised on front

Porcelain with hand-painted bas-relief

Diameter: 25.4 centimetres (10 inches)

Pierced foot rim

Edition size undisclosed, limited by year of issue

Not numbered, without certificate

22-G54-3.1
1975 *Stormy Weather*
Issue price: £ 60.65

22-G54-3.2
1980 *Spring Dance*
Issue price: £ 136.35

22-G54-3.3
1985 *Auf Wiedersehen*
Issue price: £ 136.35
Series Closed

HEINRICH / VILLEROY & BOCH
Selb

The history of Heinrich Porzellan dates from the opening by Franz Heinrich of a porcelain-painting studio in 1896 in Selb, Bavaria, near the Czechoslovakian border. In 1901, Heinrich established his own porcelain factory, Heinrich & Co., which produced fine table- and giftware. The firm remained under the control of the Heinrich family until 1976, when it was purchased by Villeroy & Boch. Heinrich creations are now distributed world-wide through Villeroy & Boch's marketing channels.

From 1980 to 1983, Heinrich issued a 12-plate series of porcelain plates entitled *Russian Fairy Tales*, adapted from the artwork of famous Russian illustrator Boris Zvorykin. The *Fairies of the Fields and Flowers* series began in 1982, with artwork by Cicely Mary Barker. The *Once Upon a Rhyme* series began in 1984, featuring for the first time the work of an American artist, Renée Faure.

The unusual symbolist art of Gero Trauth was introduced in *The Dreams of Katharina* in 1986.

Russian Fairy Tales Series

Artist: Boris Zvorykin

Hard-paste porcelain banded in gold

Diameter: 21 centimetres (8 ¹/₄ inches)

No hanger

Edition size limited to 27,500

Not numbered, without certificate

22-H18-1.1
1980 *The Snow Maiden*
Issue price: £ 29.95

22-H18-1.2
1980 *The Snow Maiden at the Court of Tsar Berendei*
Issue price: £ 29.95

22-H18-1.3
1980 *The Snow Maiden and Lel the Shepherd Boy*
Issue price: £ 29.95

22-H18-1.4
1981 *The Red Knight*
Issue price: £ 29.95

22-H18-1.5
1981 *Vassilissa and Her Stepsisters*
Issue price: £ 29.95

22-H18-1.6
1981 *Vassilissa Is Presented to the Tsar*
Issue price: £ 39.95

22-H18-1.7
1982 *In Search of the Firebird*
Issue price: £ 39.95

22-H18-1.8
1982 *Ivan and Tsarevna on the Grey Wolf*
Issue price: £ 39.95

22-H18-1.9
1982 *The Wedding of Tsarevna Elena the Fair*
Issue price: £ 39.95

22-H18-1.10
1983 *Maria Morevna and Tsarevich Ivan*
Issue price: £ 39.95

22-H18-1.11
1983 *Koshchey Carries off Maria Morevna*
Issue price: £ 39.95

22-H18-1.12
1983 *Tsarevich Ivan and The Beautiful Castle*
Issue price: 39.95
Series Closed

Fairies of the Fields and Flowers Series

Artist: Cicely Mary Barker

Bone china banded in 24k gold

Diameter: 21.6 centimetres (8¹/₂ inches)

Attached back hanger

Edition size undisclosed, limited by announced period of issue

Numbered with certificate

22-H18-3.1
1982 Ragged Robin
Issue price: £ 24.50

22-H18-3.2
1983 Willow
Issue price: £ 24.50

22-H18-3.3
1984 Elderberry
Issue price: £ 24.50

22-H18-3.4
1984 Vetch
Issue price: £ 24.50

22-H18-3.5
1984 Narcissus
Issue price: £ 24.50

22-H18-3.6
1985 Nasturtium
Issue price: £ 24.50

22-H18-3.7
1985 Phlox
Issue price: £ 24.50

22-H18-3.8
1985 Gorse
Issue price: £ 24.50
Series Closed

GERMANY
HEINRICH/VILLEROY & BOCH

22-H18-8.1

Once Upon a Rhyme Series

Artist: Renée Faure. Artist's signature appears on front

Overglaze-decorated porcelain

Diameter: 19.7 centimetres (7 ³/₄ inches)

Attached back hanger

Edition size undisclosed, limited by announced period of issue

Numbered with certificate

22-H18-8.1
1984 *Roses are Red*
Issue price: £ 17.95

22-H18-8.2
1984 *A Tisket, a Tasket*
Issue price: £ 17.95

22-H18-8.3
1984 *Mary had a Little Lamb*
Issue price: £ 17.95

22-H18-8.4
1985 *Star Light, Star Bright*
Issue price: £ 17.95

22-H18-8.5
1985 *Tom, Tom, the Piper's Son*
Issue price: £ 17.95

22-H18-8.6
1985 *Over the River and trough the Woods*
Issue price: £ 17.95
Series Closed

Dreams of Katharina Series

Artist: Gero Trauth. Artist's signature appears on front

Overglaze-decorated porcelain

Diameter: 21.6 centimetres (8 ¹/₂ inches)

Edition size limited to 19,900

Numbered, with certificate

22-H18-12.1
1986 *Katharina Receives a Promise of Love*
Issue price: £ 39.95

22-H18-12.2
1986 *Katharina's Aura and Her Earthly Laments*
Issue price: £ 39.95

22-H18-12.3
1986 *Katharina's Dream Castle*
Issue price: £ 39.95

22-H18-12.4
1986 *Katharina's Blossoming Love*
Issue price: £ 39.95

22-H18-12.5
1987 *Proposal of Marriage for Katharina*
Issue price: £ 39.95

22-H18-12.6
1987 *Katharina's Hour of Bliss*
Issue price: £ 39.95

GERMANY
HEINRICH/VILLEROY & BOCH
22-H18-13.1

*Magic Fairy Tales from
Old Russia*

Artist: Gero Trauth. Artist's
signature appears on front

Porcelain

Diameter: 22 centimetres
(8 ²/₃ inches)

Attached back hanger

Edition size limited to 19,900

Not numbered with certificate

22-H18-13.1
1987 *Tsar Bear*
Issue price: £ 49.95

22-H18-13.2
1987 *Morozko*
Issue price: £ 49.95

22-H18-13.3
1987 *Tsar Saltan*
Issue price: £ 49.95

22-H18-13.4
1988 *The Stone Flower*
Issue price: £ 49.95

22-H18-13.5
1988 *Ruslan and Ludmilla*
Issue price: £ 49.95

22-H18-13.6
1988 *Alyonushka*
Issue price: £ 49.95

22-H54-1.4 „Life Cycle"
1987 Winter
First series of limited-edition plates by
Hoechst Decor, a subsidiary of the
Hoechster Porzellanmanufaktur. For her
first plate collection artist Ilse Besser
created delicate symbols of the four
seasons.

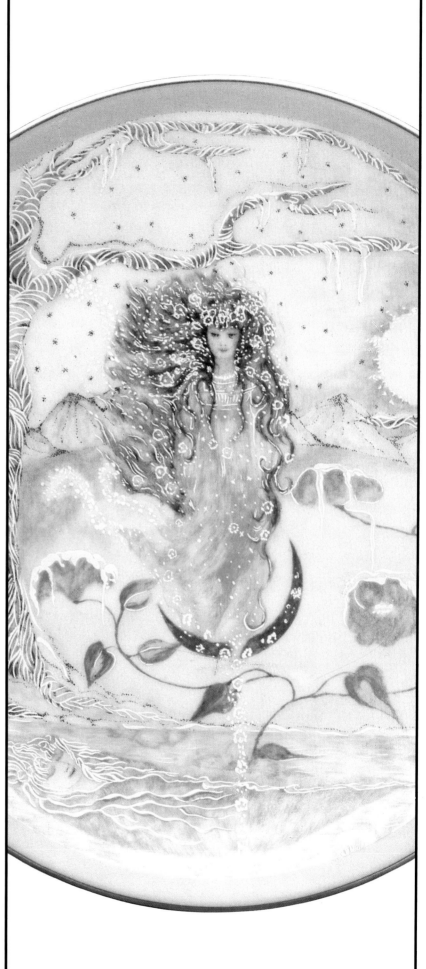

GERMANY
HÖCHST DECOR
22-H54-0.0

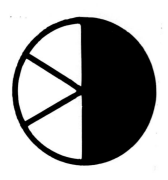

HÖCHST DECOR
Frankfurt

Hoechst Decor is a subsidiary of the Hoechster Porzellanmanufaktur which was founded in 1746 under the patronage of the Elector of Mainz, Friedrich Karl von Ostein, and is the second oldest porcelain manufactory in Germany. Since that date the wheel on the electoral coat of arms has also been the trademark of the "white gold" from Hoechst. The large collection of porcelain figurines produced by the hands of master craftsmen have made the name of Hoechster Porzellanmanufaktur famous worldwide. This tradition of quality craftsmanship is also the criterion on which the subsidiary company, Hoechst Decor, bases its commitment to the creation of outstanding, out-of-the-ordinary designs. And it is in the unusual style and content of Ilse Besser's motifs for the "Life Cycle" collection, begun in 1987, that Hoechst Decor sees its high standards realized in a most outstanding way. Her motifs, in subdued colours that betray a depth of perception, offer the beholder more than just aesthetic appeal.

Life Cycle

Artist: Ilse Besser. Artist's signature appears on front

Porcelain

Diameter: 20 centimetres (7 9/10 inches)

Pierced foot rim

Edition size undisclosed, limited by announced period of issue

Numbered with certificate

22-H54-1.1
1987 *Spring*
Issue price: £ 25.00

22-H54-1.2
1987 *Summer*
Issue price: £ 25.00

22-H54-1.3
1987 *Autumn*
Issue price: £ 25.00

22-H54-1.4
1987 *Winter*
Issue price: £ 25.00

GERMANY
HUTSCHENREUTHER
22-H82-3.1

HUTSCHENREUTHER
GERMANY

HUTSCHENREUTHER
Selb

Hutschenreuther has produced limited-edition collector's plates since 1973, when they introduced their *Canada Christmas* series (not U.K. Bradex-listed). The *Love for All Seasons* series was issued in 1982 and 1983 and depicts six scenes of medieval romance as portrayed by the artist team of Charlotte and William Hallett.

In 1986, Hutschenreuther introduced the *Bouquets of the Seasons* series by noted naturalist painter Ursula Band, who has also produced plates for Tirschenreuth (see Germany, TIRSCHENREUTH).

Year's Plate Series

Artist: not mentioned until 1979, Hans Achtziger thereafter

Porcelain

Diameter: 25.5 cm (10 inches)

Attached back hanger

Edition size undisclosed, limited by year of issue

Not numbered without certificate

22-H82-3.1
1972
Issue price: unknown

22-H82-3.2
1973 *Found*
Issue price: £ 23.30

22-H82-3.3
1974 *Awake*
Issue price: £ 33.25

22-H82-3.4
1975 *The Light*
Issue price: £ 33.25

22-H82-3.5
1976 *The Encounter*
Issue price: £ 33.25

22-H82-3.6
1977 *Long Winter Night*
Issue price: £ 33.25

22-H82-3.7
1978 *Spring Trip*
Issue price: £ 45.95

22-H82-3.8
1979 *Flight to the South*
Issue price: £ 57.00

22-H82-3.9
1980 *Playful Flight*
Issue price: £ 61.70

22-H82-3.10
1981 *Under Tropical Sky*
Issue price: £ 70.35

22-H82-3.11
1982 *Borne by the Wind*
Issue price: £ 70.60

GERMANY
HUTSCHENREUTHER
22-H82-3.12

22-H82-3.12
1983 *Meeting the Sun*
Issue price: £ 75.30

22-H82-3.13
1984 *Over Land and Sea*
Issue price: £ 79.60

Mother and Child

Artist: Ole Winther. Artist's signature appears on front

Porcelain

Diameter: 21x21 centimetres (8 1/4 x 8 1/4 inches)

Attached back hanger

Edition size undisclosed, limited by year of issue

Not numbered without certificate

22-H82-4.1
1978 *Mother and Child*
Issue price: £ 19.20

22-H82-4.2
1979 *Tender Confidence*
Issue price: £ 19.20

22-H82-4.3
1980 *Bond of Love*
Issue price: £ 19.85

22-H82-4.4
1981 *Bonds*
Issue price: £ 25.00

22-H82-4.5
1982 *Loving Harmony*
Issue price: £ 25.00

22-H82-4.6
1983 Mother and Child
Issue price: £ 25.00
Series Closed

Band's Bouquets of the Seasons Series

Artist: Ursula Band. Artist's signature appears on front

Porcelain banded in gold

Diameter: 19 centimetres (7 1/2 inches)

Pierced foot rim

Edition size undisclosed, limited by announced period of issue

Numbered, with certificate

22-H82-26.1
1986 Spring Morning
Issue price: £ 15.55

22-H82-26.2
1987 Easter Bouquet
Issue price: £ 15.55

22-H82-26.3
1987 Summer Promise
Issue price: £ 17.85

22-H82-26.4
1987 Summer Glory
Issue price: £ 17.85

22-H82-26.5
1987 Autumn Tints
Issue price: £ 17.85

GERMANY
KAISER
22-K4-1.1

KAISER
Staffelstein

Kaiser porcelain dates to 1872 when porcelain painter August Alboth set up his own workshop in Coburg. When he retired in 1899, his son Ernst moved the pottery to Bavaria. Marriage, united the Alboth and Kaiser families in 1922, resulting in the ALKA trademark – a combination of the first two letters of both names.

In 1938 the firm purchased the old Bavarian pottery of Silbermann Brothers, which had been awarded a royal diploma in 1882 for its "magnificent" cobalt blue underglaze. The company opened its modern factory in Staffelstein in 1953 and in 1970 the trademark was changed to Kaiser Porcelain.

Long a producer of porcelain coffee sets, dinnerware, and figurines, Kaiser introduced its first series of limited-edition plates, the *Christmas* series, in 1980. The series ended in 1982. The *Mother's Day* series began in 1971 and ended in 1983. These series feature the artwork of Toni Schoener and Nori Peter. The *Classic Fairy Tales Collection* began in 1982, with artwork by Gerda Neubacher. The series ended in 1984.

In 1985, Kaiser introduced the *Classic Lullabies of the World* series, also designed by Gerda Neubacher. *Classic Lullabies of the World* is a tribute to the beloved melodies shared by parents and children all over the world.

Christmas Series

Artist: as indicated

Porcelain decorated in cobalt-blue underglaze

Diameter: 19 centimetres (7 ¹/₂ inches)

Pierced foot rim

Edition size undisclosed, limited by year of issue except 1974

Not numbered, without certificate

22-K4-1.1
1970 *Waiting for Santa Claus*
Artist: Toni Schoener
Issue price: £ 7.50

22-K4-1.2
1971 *Silent Night*
Artist: Kurt Bauer
Issue price: £ 8.25

22-K4-1.3
1972 *Welcome Home*
Artist: Kurt Bauer
Issue price: £ 10.00

22-K4-1.4
1973 *Holy Night*
Artist: Toni Schoener
Issue price: £ 10.95

22-K4-1.5
1974 *Christmas Carolers*
Artist: Kurt Bauer
Edition: 8,000
Issue price: £ 15.25

22-K4-1.6
1975 *Bringing Home the Christmas Tree*
Artist: Joann Northcott
Issue price: £ 15.25

22-K4-1.7
1976 *Christ the Saviour is Born*
Artist: Carlo Maratti
Issue price: £ 15.25

22-K4-1.8
1977 *The Three Kings*
Artist: Toni Schoener
Issue price: £ 15.25

22-K4-1.9
1978 *Shepherd in the Field*
Artist: Toni Schoener
Issue price: £ 18.25

22-K4-1.10
1979 *Christmas Eve*
Artist: Hannelore Blum
Issue price: £ 19.45

22-K4-1.11
1980 *Joys of Winter*
Artist: Hannelore Blum
Issue price: £ 24.25

GERMANY
KAISER
22-K4-1.12

22-K4-1.12
1981 *Most Holy Night*
Artist: Kurt Bauer
Issue price: £ 24.25

22-K4-1.13
1982 *Bringing Home the Christmas Tree*
Artist: Kurt Bauer
Issue price: £ 24.25
Series Closed

Mother's Day Series

Artist: as indicated

Porcelain decorated in cobalt blue underglaze

Diameter: 19 centimetres (7 ¹/₂ inches)

Pierced foot rim

Edition size undisclosed, limited by year of issue except 1974

Not numbered, without certificate

22-K4-2.1
1971 *Mare and Foal*
Artist: Toni Schoener
Issue price: £ 7.95

22-K4-2.2
1972 *Flowers for Mother*
Artist: Toni Schoener
Issue price: £ 10.00

22-K4-2.3
1973 *Cats*
Artist: Toni Schoener
Issue price: £ 10.35

22-K4-2.4
1974 *Fox*
Artist: Toni Schoener
Edition: 7,000
Issue price: £ 13.35

22-K4-2.5
1975 *German Shepherd*
Artist: Toni Schoener
Issue price: £ 15.25

22-K4-2.6
1976 *Swan and Cygnets*
Artist: Toni Schoener
Issue price: £ 15.15

22-K4-2.7
1977 *Mother Rabbit and Young*
Artist: Toni Schoener
Issue price: £ 15.15

22-K4-2.8
1978 *Hens and Chicks*
Artist: Toni Schoener
Issue price: £ 18.25

22-K4-2.9
1979 *A Mother's Devotion*
Artist: Nori Peter
Issue price: £ 19.45

22-K4-2.10
1980 *Raccoon Family*
Artist: Joann Northcott
Issue price: £ 24.25

22-K4-2.11
1981 *Safe Near Mother*
Artist: Hannelore Blum
Issue price: £ 24.25

22-K4-2.12
1982 *Pheasant Family*
Artist: Kurt Bauer
Issue price: £ 24.25

22-K4-2.13
1983 *Tender Care*
Artist: Kurt Bauer
Issue price: £ 24.25
Series Closed

GERMANY
KAISER

22-K4-5.1

Classic Fairy Tales Collection

Artist: Gerda Neubacher. Artist's signature appears on front

Porcelain banded in 24 k gold

Diameter: 19.7 centimetres (7 ³/₄ inches)

Pierced foot rim

Edition size undisclosed, limited by announced period of issue

Numbered with certificated booklet

22-K4-5.1
1982 *The Frog King*
Issue price: £ 19.00

22-K4-5.2
1983 *Puss in Boots*
Issue price: £ 20.90

22-K4-5.3
1983 *Little Red Riding Hood*
Issue price: £ 23.00

22-K4-5.4
1983 *Hansel and Gretel*
Issue price: £ 23.00

22-K4-5.5
1984 *Cinderella*
Issue price: £ 23.00

22-K4-5.6
1984 *Sleeping Beauty*
Issue price: £ 23.00
Series Closed

Classic Lullabies of the World Series

Artist: Gerda Neubacher. Artist's signature appears on front

Porcelain banded in gold

Diameter: 19.7 centimetres (7 ¹/₄ inches)

Pierced foot rim

Edition size undisclosed, limited by announced period of issue

Numbered with certificated booklet

22-K4-22.1
1985 *Sleep, Baby, Sleep*
Issue price: £ 26.25

22-K4-22.2
1986 *Rock-a-bye-Baby*
Issue price: £ 26.25

22-K4-22.3
1986 *The Mocking-Bird*
Issue price: £ 26.25

22-K4-22.4
1986 *Au Clair de la Lune*
Issue price: £ 28.95

22-K4-22.5
1986 *All Through the Night*
Issue price: £ 28.95

22-K4-22.6
1987 *Brahms Lullaby*
Issue price: £ 28.95
Series Closed

GERMANY
KÖNIGSZELT BAYERN

22-K46-0.0

KÖNIGSZELT BAYERN
Waldsassen

Königszelt Bayern entered the collector's plate market in 1979 with the first issue in its *Hedi Keller Christmas* series, more than a century after the creation on the first porcelain bearing the hallmark of Königszelt of Silesia. The likeness of Wilhelm I (1797-1888), king of Prussia and first sovereign of a united Germany, is incorporated in the hallmark of Königszelt Bayern — a tribute to his early patronage under which Bavarian porcelain began its rise to prominence among the porce-lain creations of the world. In 1981 the *Grimm's Fairy Tales* series began in commemoration of the two-hundredth anniversary of the Grimm brothers' birth, with art by Charles Gehm. *Sulamith's Love Song* series, created by Sulamith Wülfing, began in 1982. Her *Christmas* series made its debut in 1985. In 1986, *A Woman's Love and Life* series was introduced, with artwork by this same artist. The *German Half-Timbered Houses* series, by Karl Bedal, was introduced in 1984.

Hedi Keller Christmas Series

Artist: Hedi Keller. Artist's signature appears on front

Overglaze-decorated porcelain

Diameter: 24 centimetres (9 ¹/₂ inches)

Pierced foot rim

Edition size undisclosed, limited by year of issue

Numbered with certificate

22-K46-1.1
1979 *The Adoration*
Issue price: £ 14.95

22-K46-1.2
1980 *Flight into Egypt*
Issue price: £ 14.95

22-K46-1.3
1981 *Return into Galilee*
Issue price: £ 14.95

22-K46-1.4
1982 *Following the Star*
Issue price: £ 14.95

22-K46-1.5
1983 *Rest on the Flight*
Issue price: £ 16.45

22-K46-1.6
1984 *The Nativity*
Issue price: £ 16.45

22-K46-1.7
1985 *Gift of the Magi*
Issue price: £ 17.45

22-K46-1.8
1986 *The Annunciation*
Issue price: £ 17.45
Series Closed

GERMANY
KÖNIGSZELT BAYERN
22-K46-2.1

Grimm's Fairy Tales Series

Artist: Charles Gehm. Artist's signature appears on front

Overglaze-decorated porcelain

Diameter: 19 centimetres (7 ¹/₂ inches)

Pierced foot rim

Edition size undisclosed, limited by announced period of issue

Numbered with certificate

22-K46-2.1
1981 *Rumpelstilzchen*
Issue price: £ 12.95

22-K46-2.2
1982 *Rapunzel*
Issue price: £ 12.95

22-K46-2.3
1982 *Hänsel and Gretel*
Issue price: £ 14.25

22-K46-2.4
1983 *The Shoemaker and the Elves*
Issue price: £ 14.25

22-K46-2.5
1984 *The Golden Goose*
Issue price: £ 14.25

22-K46-2.6
1985 *The Shoes That Were Danced to Pieces*
Issue price: £ 15.75

22-K46-2.7
1986 *Sleeping Beauty*
Issue price: £ 15.75

22-K46-2.8
1987 *Snow White and the Seven Dwarves*
Issue price: £ 15.75
Series Closed

Sulamith's Love Song Series

Artist: Sulamith Wülfing. Artist's signature appears on front

Overglaze-decorated porcelain

Diameter: 19 centimetres (7 $\frac{1}{2}$ inches)

Pierced foot rim

Edition size undisclosed, limited by announced period of issue

Numbered with certificate

22-K46-3.1
1982 *The Music*
Issue price: £ 12.50

22-K46-3.2
1983 *The Pledge*
Issue price: £ 12.50

22-K46-3.3
1983 *The Vision*
Issue price: £ 13.50

22-K46-3.4
1983 *The Gift*
Issue price: £ 13.50

22-K46-3.5
1984 *The Circle*
Issue price: £ 13.50

22-K46-3.6
1984 *The Centre*
Issue price: £ 14.50

22-K46-3.7
1984 *The Journey*
Issue price: £ 14.50

22-K46-3.8
1984 *The Completion*
Issue price: £ 14.50
Series Closed

GERMANY
KÖNIGSZELT BAYERN

22-K46-4.1

Deutsches Fachwerk

(German Half-Timbered Houses)

Artist: Karl Bedal. Artist's signature appears on front

Overglaze-decorated porcelain

Diameter: 19 centimetres (7 ¹/₂ inches)

Pierced foot rim

Edition size undisclosed, limited by announced period of issue

Numbered with certificate

22-K46-4.1
1984 *Bauernhaus in Fronhausen*
Issue price: £ 13.65

22-K46-4.2
1984 *Niedersachsenhaus bei Thedinghausen*
Issue price: £ 13.65

22-K46-4.3
1985 *Moselhaus in Rißbach*
Issue price: £ 14.95

22-K46-4.4
1985 *Westfalenhaus aus Delbrück*
Issue price: £ 14.95

22-K46-4.5
1985 *Mittelfrankenhaus in Ernhofen*
Issue price: £ 15.95

22-K46-4.6
1986 *Bodenseehaus in Immenstaad*
Issue price: £ 15.95

Sulamith's Christmas Series

Artist: Sulamith Wülfing. Artist's signature appears on front

Overglaze-decorated porcelain double-banded in 24k gold

Diameter: 24.1 centimetres (9 ¹/₂ inches)

No hanger

Edition size undisclosed, limited by year of issue

Numbered with certificate

22-K46-5.1
1985 *The Angels' Vigil*
Issue price: £ 14.65

22-K46-5.2
1986 *The Christmas Child*
Issue price: £ 15.75

22-K46-5.3
1987 *The Christmas Angels*
Issue price: £ 19.55

GERMANY
KÖNIGSZELT BAYERN
22-K46-6.1

A Woman's Love and Life Series

Artist: Sulamith Wülfing. Artist's signature appears on front

Overglaze-decorated porcelain

Diameter: 19 centimetres (7 ¹/₂ inches)

Pierced foot rim

Edition size undisclosed, limited by announced period of issue

Numbered with certificate

22-K46-6.1
1986 *Since I First Saw Him*
Issue price: £ 15.95

22-K46-6.2
1986 *He, the Noblest of All*
Issue price: £ 15.95

22-K46-6.3
1986 *I Can't Understand It*
Issue price: £ 16.95

22-K46-6.4
1987 *You, Ring on my Finger*
Issue price: £ 16.95

Wülfing Mother's Day Series

Artist: Sulamith Wülfing

Overglaze-decorated porcelain

Diameter: 19 centimetres
(7 ¹/₂ inches)

Pierced foot rim

Edition size undisclosed, limited by announced period of issue

Numbered with certificate

22-K46-8.1
1987 *Spring's New Life*
Issue price: £ 18.95

Historic German Water Mills

Artist: Karl Bedal

Overglaze-decorated porcelain

Diameter: 19 centimetres
(7 ¹/₂ inches)

Pierced foot rim

Edition size undisclosed, limited by announced period of issue

Numbered, with certificate

22-K46-9.1
1987 *Water Mill in the Swabian Forest*
Issue price unavailable at press time

22-K46-9.2
1987 *The Strötzbacher Mills*
Issue price unavailable at press time

Rosenthal
studio-linie

ROSENTHAL

Selb, Landstuhl, Speichersdorf, Woodershof,
Kronach, Atberg, Neusorg, Espelkamp

Philipp Rosenthal, Sr. began his business in 1879 in the town of Selb in Bavaria. He initially purchased "white ware" from various porcelain manufacturers in Selb (including Hutschenreuther) and painted it with his own designs.

In 1895 he established his own factory in Kronach where he produced fine porcelain signed *Rosenthal* on the back, making him one of the first porcelain makers to use his name rather than a symbol. Philipp died in 1937 and the business was taken over by his son, Philipp, Jr., who still heads the firm.

Rosenthal's *Traditional Classic Rose Christmas* series began in 1910 and continues through 1984. In 1974, Rosenthal changed its backstamp to reflect their Classic Rose Collection. From 1969 to 1971 some of the earlier plates were reissued in small quantities (no more than 500 per reissue). Reissued plates, regardless of the year depicted, have a post-1957 backstamp and their foot rims are not pierced. After 1971, the firm discontinued the practice of reissuing plates from previous years, and each Rosenthal collector's plate is now produced only during its current year. The *Traditional Classic Rose Christmas* plates now qualify as limited editions.

In 1971 Rosenthal began the first of its Studio-Linie collections with the *Wiinblad Christmas* series, by noted designer Bjørn Wiinblad. These plates carry intricate modern designs partially hand-painted in as many as eighteen colours and are embellished with platinum and 18k gold. The *Nobility of Children* series and the *Oriental Gold* series also began in 1976 and carried Rosenthal's Classic Rose Collection backstamp. Both series ended in 1979. They featured the artwork of Edna Hibel.

Traditional Classic Rose Christmas Series

Artist: as indicated. Artist's name appears on back

Overglaze-decorated porcelain, many in series have gold inner rim and lettering

Diameter: 21.5 centimetres (8 ¹/₂ inches)

Pierced foot rim until 1971; attached back hanger thereafter

Edition size undisclosed

Not numbered, without certificate

22-R55-1.1
1910 *Winter Peace*
Artist: Jul. V. Guldbrandson
Issue price: £ 0.81

22-R55-1.2
1911 *The Three Wise Men*
Artist: Heinrich Vogler
Issue price: £ 0.81

22-R55-1.3
1912 *Shooting Stars*
Artist: Paul Rieth
Issue price: £ 0.62

22-R55-1.4
1913 *Christmas Lights*
Artist: Julius Dietz
Issue price: £ 0.89

22-R55-1.5
1914 *Christmas Song*
Artist: Prof. L. von Zumbusch
Issue price: £ 0.89

22-R55-1.6
1915 *Walking to Church*
Artist: Jul. V. Guldbrandson
Issue price: £ 0.89

22-R55-1.7
1916 *Christmas During War*
Artist: Jul. V. Guldbrandson
Issue price: £ 0.89

22-R55-1.8
1917 *Angel of Peace*
Artist: Prof. Mermagen
Issue price: £ 0.89

GERMANY
ROSENTHAL
22-R55-1.9

22-R55-1.9
1918 *Peace on Earth*
Artist: K. Pfeiffer
Issue price: £ 0.89

22-R55-1.10
1919 *St. Christopherus with the Christ Child*
Artist: Dr. W. Schertel
Issue price: £ 3.61

22-R55-1.11
1920 *The Manger in Bethlehem*
Artist: Dr. W. Schertel
Issue price: £ 3.61

22-R55-1.12
1921 *Christmas in the Mountains*
Artist: Jupp Wiertz
Issue price: £ 3.61

22-R55-1.13
1922 *Advent Branch*
Artist: Friedrich Nicolai
Issue price: 3.61

22-R55-1.14
1923 *Children in the Winter Wood*
Artist: Ernst Höfer
Issue price: 3.61

22-R55-1.15
1924 *Deer in the Woods*
Artist: Theo Karner
Issue price: £ 1.81

22-R55-1.16
1925 *The Three Wise Men*
Artist: Otto Tauschek
Issue price: £ 1.81

22-R55-1.17
1926 *Christmas in the Mountains*
Artist: Theo Schmutz-Baudiss
Issue price: £ 1.81

22-R55-1.18
1927 *Station on the Way*
Artist: Theo Schmutz-Baudiss
Issue price: £ 1.81

22-R55-1.19
1928 *Chalet Christmas*
Artist: Heinrich Fink
Issue price: £ 1.81

22-R55-1.20
1929 *Christmas in the Alps*
Artist: Heinrich Fink
Issue price: £ 1.81

22-R55-1.21
1930 *Group of Deer under the Pines*
Artist: Theo Karner
Issue price: £ 1.81

22-R55-1.22
1931 *Path of the Magi*
Artist: Heinrich Fink
Issue price: £ 1.87

22-R55-1.23
1932 *Christ Child*
Artist: Otto Koch
Issue price: £ 1.87

22-R55-1.24
1933 *Through the Night to Light*
Artist: Hans Schiffner
Issue price: £ 1.87

22-R55-1.25
1934 *Christmas Peace*
Artist: Heinrich Fink
Issue price: £ 1.87

22-R55-1.26
1935 *Christmas by the Sea*
Artist: Heinrich Fink
Issue price: £ 1.87

GERMANY
ROSENTHAL
22-R55-1.27

22-R55-1.27
1936 *Nurnberg Angel*
Artist: Heinrich Fink
Issue price: £ 1.87

22-R55-1.28
1937 *Berchtesgaden*
Artist: Heinrich Fink
Issue price: £ 1.87

22-R55-1.29
1938 *Christmas in the Alps*
Artist: Heinrich Fink
Issue price: £ 1.87

22-R55-1.30
1939 *Schneekoppe Mountain*
Artist: Heinrich Fink
Issue price: £ 1.87

22-R55-1.31
1940 *Marien Church in Danzig*
Artist: Walter Mutze
Issue price: £ 1.87

22-R55-1.32
1941 *Strassburg Cathedral*
Artist: Walter Mutze
Issue price: £ 1.87

22-R55-1.33
1942 *Marianburg Castle*
Artist: Walter Mutze
Issue price: £ 1.87

22-R55-1.34
1943 *Winter Idyll*
Artist: Amadeus Dier
Issue price: £ 1.87

22-R55-1.35
1944 *Wood Scape*
Artist: Willi Hein
Issue price: £ 1.87

22-R55-1.36
1945 *Christmas Peace*
Artist: Alfred Mundel
Issue price: £ 1.87

22-R55-1.37
1946 *Christmas in an Alpine Valley*
Artist: Willi Hein
Issue price: £ 1.87

22-R55-1.38
1947 *The Dillingen Madonna*
Artist: Louis Hagen
Issue price: £ 3.64

22-R55-1.39
1948 *Message to the Shepherds*
Artist: Richard Hoffman
Issue price: £ 3.64

22-R55-1.40
1949 *The Holy Family*
Artist: Prof. Karl
Issue price: £ 3.64

22-R55-1.41
1950 *Christmas in the Forest*
Artist: Willi Hein
Issue price: £ 3.18

22-R55-1.42
1951 *Star of Bethlehem*
Artistin: Anne v. Groote
Issue price: £ 3.48

22-R55-1.43
1952 *Christmas in the Alps*
Artist: Willi Hein
Issue price: £ 3.48

22-R55-1.44
1953 *The Holy Light*
Artist: Willi Hein
Issue price: £ 3.48

GERMANY
ROSENTHAL
22-R55-1.45

22-R55-1.45
1954 *Christmas Eve*
Artist: Willi Hein
Issue price: £ 3.79

22-R55-1.46
1955 *Christmas in a Village*
Artist: Willi Hein
Issue price: £ 3.79

22-R55-1.47
1956 *Christmas in the Alps*
Artist: Willi Hein
Issue price: £ 3.79

22-R55-1.48
1957 *Christmas by the Sea*
Artist: Willi Hein
Issue price: £ 3.79

22-R55-1.49
1958 *Christmas Eve*
Artist: Willi Hein
Issue price: £ 3.94

22-R55-1.50
1959 *Midnight Mass*
Artist: Willi Hein
Issue price: £ 4.09

22-R55-1.51
1960 *Christmas in a small Village*
Artist: Willi Hein
Issue price: £ 4.39

22-R55-1.52
1961 *Solitary Christmas*
Artist: Willi Hein
Issue price: £ 4.70

22-R55-1.53
1962 *Christmas Eve*
Artist: Willi Hein
Issue price: £ 5.30

22-R55-1.54
1963 *Silent Night*
Artist: Willi Hein
Issue price: £ 5.30

22-R55-1.55
1964 *Christmas Market in Nürnberg*
Artist: Georg Küspert
Issue price: £ 5.30

22-R55-1.56
1965 *Christmas in Munich*
Artist: Georg Küspert
Issue price: £ 6.67

22-R55-1.57
1966 *Christmas in Ulm*
Artist: Georg Küspert
Issue price: £ 6.67

22-R55-1.58
1967 *Christmas in Regensburg*
Artist: Georg Küspert
Issue price: £ 6.67

22-R55-1.59
1968 *Christmas in Bremen*
Artist: Georg Küspert
Issue price: £ 6.67

22-R55-1.60
1969 *Christmas in Rothenburg*
Artist: Georg Küspert
Issue price: £ 9.55

22-R55-1.61
1970 *Christmas in Cologne*
Artist: Georg Küspert
Issue price: £ 9.70

22-R55-1.62
1971 *Christmas in Garmisch*
Artist: Georg Küspert
Issue price: £ 40.00

GERMANY
ROSENTHAL
22-R55-1.63

22-R55-1.63
1972 *Christmas Celebration in Franconia*
Artist: Georg Küspert
Issue price: £ 44.00

22-R55-1.64
1973 *Christmas in Lübeck-Holstein*
Artist: Georg Küspert
Issue price: £ 50.90

22-R55-1.65
1974 *Christmas in Wurzburg*
Artist: Georg Küspert
Issue price: £ 51.50
Series Closed

Wiinblad Christmas Series

Artist: Bjørn Wiinblad. Artist's signature appears on front

Overglaze-decorated porcelain partially hand-painted in 18 colours with 18k gold design on border

Diameter: 29.2 centimetres (11 ¹/₂ inches)

Attached back hanger

Edition size undisclosed

Not numbered, without certificate

22-R55-2.1
1971 *Maria and Child*
Issue price: £ 50.00

22-R55-2.2
1972 *Caspar*
Issue price: £ 55.00

22-R55-2.3
1973 *Melchior*
Issue price: £ 59.00

22-R55-2.4
1974 *Balthasar*
Issue price: £ 65.00

22-R55-2.5
1975 *The Annunciation*
Issue price: £ 75.00

22-R55-2.6
1976 *Angel with Trumpet*
Issue price: £ 85.00

22-R55-2.7
1977 *Adoration of Shepherds*
Issue price: £ 97.00

22-R55-2.8
1978 *Angel with Harp*
Issue price: £ 103.00

22-R55-2.9
1979 *Exodus from Egypt*
Issue price: £ 109.00

22-R55-2.10
1980 *Angel with a Glockenspiel*
Issue price: £ 112.00

22-R55-2.11
1981 *Christ Child Visits Temple*
Issue price: £ 112.00

22-R55-2.12
1982 *Christening of Christ*
Issue price: £ 115.00
Series Closed

Wiinblad Christmas Series

(Glas)

Artist: Bjørn Wiinblad

Decorated crystal with 18k gold hand-painted overlay

Diameter: 31.3 centimetres (12 ¹/₄ inches)

Attached back hanger

Edition size undisclosed

Not numbered, without certificate

22-R55-12.1
1976 *Maria and Child*
Issue price: £ 57.00

22-R55-12.2
1977 *The Annunciation*
Issue price: £ 86.00

22-R55-12.3
1978 *The Three Wise Men*
Issue price: £ 87.50

22-R55-12.4
1979 *Mary, Joseph and Child*
Issue price: £ 87.50

22-R55-12.5
1980 *Angel and Shepherds*
Issue price: £ 97.00

22-R55-12.6
1981 *Adoration of the Shepherds*
Issue price: £ 97.00

Artist Plates

Artist: as indicated

Porcelain

Diameter: 26 centimetres
(10 ¹/₄ inches)

Attached back hanger

Edition up to No. 19 limited to
5,000; No. 20 to 22 3,000;
No. 23 limited by year of issue

22-R55-13.1
No. 1 Günter Grass
Issue price: £ 12.70

22-R55-13.2
No. 2 Jean Cocteau
Issue price: £ 16.00

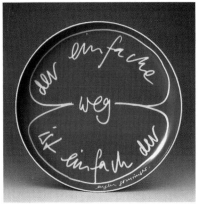

22-R55-13.3
No. 3 Eugen Gomringer
Issue price: £ 16.00

22-R55-13.4
No. 4 Otto Piene
Issue price: £ 55.65

22-R55-13.5
No. 5 Max Bill
Issue price: £ 13.20

22-R55-13.6
No. 6 Hans-Werner Henze
Issue price: £ 19.35

22-R55-13.7
No. 7 Bjørn Wiinblad
Issue price: £ 32.70

22-R55-13.8
No. 8 Kriwet
Issue price: £ 19.35

22-R55-13.9
No. 9 Hildegard Knef
Issue price: £ 32.70

22-R55-13.10
No. 10 Yehudi Menuhin
Issue price: £ 39.35

22-R55-13.11
No. 11 Emilio Pucci
Issue price: £ 39.35

GERMANY
ROSENTHAL
22-R55-13.12

22-R55-13.12
No. 12 Salvadoro Dali
Issue price: £ 160.00

22-R55-13.13
No. 13 Victor Vasarely
Issue price: £ 66.00

22-R55-13.14
No. 14 Almir Mazignier
Issue price: £ 49.35

22-R55-13.15
No. 15 Ivan Rapuzin
Issue price: £ 78.35

22-R55-13.16
No. 16 Otmar Alt
Issue price: £ 45.00

22-R55-13.17
No. 17 Ernst Fuchs
Issue price: £ 61.70

22-R55-13.18
No. 18 O.H. Hajek
Issue price: £ 52.70

22-R55-13.19
No. 19 Paul Wunderlich
Issue price: £ 48.35

22-R55-13.20
No. 20 Eduardo Paolozzi
Issue price: £ 48.35

22-R55-13.21
No. 21 Tom Wesselmann
Issue price: £ 48.35

22-R55-13.22
No. 22 Salomé
Issue price: £ 48.35

22-R55-13.23
No. 23 Gilbert Portanier
Issue price: £ 65.00

Satire Plates

Artist: Ernst Maria Lange.
Artist's signature appears on front

Porcelain

Diameter: 26 centimetres
(10 ¹⁄₄ inches)

Attached back hanger

Edition size limited to 5,000

Numbered without certificate

22-R55-14.1
No. 1 *Konrad Adenauer*
Issue price: £ 13.20

22-R55-14.2
No. 2 *Willi Brandt*
Issue price: £ 13.20

22-R55-14.3
No. 3 *Theodor Heuss*
Issue price: £ 13.20

22-R55-14.4
No. 4 *Walter Scheel*
Issue price: £ 13.20

22-R55-14.5
No. 5 *Helmut Schmidt*
Issue price: £ 13.20

GERMANY
ROSENTHAL
22-R55-14.6

22-R55-14.6
No. 6 *Franz-Josef Strauß*
Issue price: £ 13.20

22-R55-14.7
No. 7 *Helmut Kohl*
Issue price: £ 13.20

22-R55-14.8
No. 8 *Heinz Rühmann*
Issue price: £ 13.20

22-R55-14.9
No. 9 *Herbert von Karajan*
Issue price: £ 13.20

22-R55-14.10
No. 10 *Marlene Dietrich*
Issue price: £ 15.35

22-R55-14.11
No. 11 *Mao-Tse-Tung*
Issue price: £ 15.35

22-R55-14.12
No. 12 *Bruno Kreisky*
Issue price: £ 16.35

22-R55-14.13
No. 13 *Philip Rosenthal*
Issue price: £ 22.70

Christmas Songs on Porcelain

Artist: Bjørn Wiinblad. Artist's signature appears on front
Porcelain

Diameter: 27.5 centimetres (10 ⁴/₅ inches)

Pierced foot rim

Edition size undisclosed, limited by year of issue

Not numbered, with certificate

22-R55-15.1
1983 *Silent Night*
Issue price: £ 131.70

22-R55-15.2
1984 *Jingle Bells*
Issue price: £ 131.70

22-R55-15.3
1985 *We Three Kings*
Issue price: £ 141.70

22-R55-15.4
1986 *The Christmas Tree*
Issue price: £ 141.70

22-R55-15.5
1987 *Hark, the Herald Angels Sing*
Issue price: £ 155.00

GERMANY

KGL. PRIVILEGIERT TETTAU

22-R73-0.0

ANNO 1794

Royal Tettau

BAVARIA
GERMANY

KÖNIGLICH PRIVILEGIERTE PORZELLANFABRIK TETTAU

Tettau

The "Königlich Privilegierte Porzellanfabrik Tettau" was founded in Tettau, Upper Franconia, in 1794. It was the first porcelain manufactory to be founded in Bavaria under pirvate ownership of this company. The *Christmas* Series was begun in 1972.

Under the trademark "Königlich Bayreuth" (Royal Bayreuth) the company launched a *Mother's Day* series in 1973. The series ran until 1982.

Christmas Series

Artist: undisclosed

Porcelain

Diameter: 19 centimetres
(7 1/2 inches)

Attached back hanger

Edition size undisclosed,
limited by year of issue

Not numbered, without
certificate

22-R73-1.1
1972 *Arrival of the Stagecoach*
Issue price: £ 15.00

22-R73-1.2
1973 *Wintertrip*
Issue price: £ 15.00

22-R73-1.3
1974 *The Old Mill*
Issue price: £ 15.00

22-R73-1.4
1975 *Christmas Market*
Issue price: £ 15.00

22-R73-1.5
1976 *Magdeburg's Marketplace*
Issue price: £ 15.00

22-R73-1.6
1977 *Bamberger Tor in Kronach*
Issue price: £ 15.00

22-R73-1.7
1978 *Wallfahrt's Church*
Issue price: £ 15.00

22-R73-1.8
1979 *Moritz Church*
Issue price: £ 15.00

GERMANY
KGL. PRIVILEGIERT TETTAU

22-R73-1.9

22-R73-1.9
1980 *Marketplace in Trier*
Issue price: £ 15.00

22-R73-1.10
1981 *Cathedral and St. John's
Church in Essen*
Issue price: £ 15.00

22-R73-1.11
1982 *Castle Lauenstein*
Issue price: £ 15.00

22-R73-1.12
1983 *Christmas Players*
Issue price: £ 15.00

22-R73-1.13
1984 *Christmas Eve in the Mountain
Village*
Issue price: £ 15.00

22-R73-1.14
1985 *Leineschloss*
Issue price: £ 15.00

22-R73-1.15
1986 *Old Forester's House*
Issue price: £ 17.50

22-R73-1.16
1987 *St. Bartholomew's Church*
Issue price: £ 18.50

22-S77-1.13 Annunciation Angel
1981 Staatliche Porzellanmanufaktur
Berlin (KPM)
Christmas Series
This series, which began 1969, shows
stylized symbols of Christmas.

GERMANY
STAATL. PORZELLAN-MANUFAKTUR BERLIN (KPM)

22-S77-0.0

STAATLICHE PORZELLAN-MANUFAKTUR BERLIN (KPM)
Berlin

The first "Manufacture de Porcelaine de Berlin" was founded in 1751 by the wool manufacturer Wilhelm Caspar Wegely under a privilege granted by the King of Prussia. In 1763 Frederick the Great took over the manufactory for the Prussian State. The Königliche Porzellan-Manufaktur Berlin has been state-owned ever since (it was renamed "Staatliche Porzellan-Manufaktur" in 1918).

The King of Prussia granted the manufactory permission to use the sceptre as its trademark. Since 1832 the Imperial orb in conjunction with the initials KPM has been the distinguishing mark of the manufactory's a products. 1969 saw the beginning of the Christmas Plate Series with stylized depicitions of Christmas motifs.

Christmas Series

Artist: as indicated

Porcelain decorated in cobalt blue with gold

Diameter: 19.7 centimetres (7 ³/₄ inches)

Pierced foot rim

Edition size undisclosed, limited by year of issue

Not numbered, without certificate

22-S77-1.1
1969 *Christmas Star*
Issue price: £ 9.83

22-S77-1.2
1970 *Three Kings*
Issue price: £ 9.83

22-S77-1.3
1971 *Christmas Tree*
Issue price: £ 9.83

22-S77-1.4
1972 *Christmas Angel*
Issue price: £ 11.00

22-S77-1.5
1973 *Christmas Child*
Issue price: £ 11.70

22-S77-1.6
1974 *Angel and Horn*
Issue price: £ 13.20

22-S77-1.7
1975 *Shepherds*
Issue price: £ 14.20

22-S77-1.8
1976 *Star of Bethlehem*
Issue price: £ 15.50

GERMANY
STAATLICHE PORZELLANMANUFAKTUR BERLIN (KPM)
22-S77-1.9

22-S77-1.9
1977 *Mary at Crib*
Issue price: £ 16.50

22-S77-1.10
1978 *The Three Wise Men*
Issue price: £ 17.35

22-S77-1.11
1979 *At the Manger*
Issue price: £ 18.35

22-S77-1.12
1980 *Shepherds on the Field*
Issue price: £ 19.70

22-S77-1.13
1981 *Annunciation Angel*
Issue price: £ 21.35

22-S77-1.14
1982 *Mother and Child*
Issue price: £ 23.00

22-S77-1.15
1983 *The Flight*
Issue price: £ 25.00

22-S77-1.16
1984 *The Angel*
Issue price: £ 26.00

22-S77-1.17
1985 *In the Angel's Care*
Issue price: £ 27.35

22-S77-1.18
1986 *Christmas Forest*
Issue price: £ 27.35

22-S77-1.19
1987 *Guardian Angels*
Issue price: £ 34.50

GERMANY (DDR)
VEB STAATLICHE PORZELLANMANUFAKTUR MEISSEN

22-S79-0.0

VEB STATTLICHE PORZELLAN-MANUFAKTUR MEISSEN
Meissen

The history of the Staatliche Porzellan-Manufaktur Meissen, which was founded by royal decree on the 23rd January 1710, is closely bound up with the history of porcelain manufacture itself. Johann Friedrich Böttger was the manufactory's first administrator.

The formuls for making porcelain was hitherto unknown in Europe. It was not until the alchemist Johann Friedrich Böttger carried out exhaustive experiments under the patronage of Frederick Augustus I, known as "Augustus the Strong", Elector of Saxony and King of Poland, that the desired result was produced: a brilliant and pure white, hard-fired porcelain. Böttger died in 1719, whereupon a commission was appointed to manage the manufactory. In 1720 the management was taken over by the painter Johann Gregorius Hoeroldt, under whom the Meissen manufactory reached its first artistic zenith.

It is under the sign of the "Blue Swords" that many great artists have created exquisite porcelain for the royalty and nobility of Europe, porcelain with through its very uniqueness is today still much sought after all over the world. The House of Meissen, too, has a Christmas plate tradition which goes back as far as 1910.

The first artists to design a Christmas — most probably for a customer — were Rudolph Hentschel and Otto Eduard Voigt. Although between the years of 1910 and 1968 — with intervals of several years' duration — Christmas plates were indeed produced, they were for the most part commissioned by customers. This is the reason for the considerable differences which exist between the individual motifs. The plates are decorated by an aquatinta process invented by Jean-Baptiste le Prince in 1768.

Year's Plate

Artist: undisclosed

Porcelain

Diameter: 25 centimetres
(9 ⁴/₅ inches)

Attached back hanger

Edition size undisclosed,
limited by year of issue

Not numbered, without
certificate

22-S79-1.1
1974 *Sleeping Beauty*
Issue price: £ 66.00

22-S79-1.2
1975 *Archway to Albrecht's Castle*
Issue price: £ 73.50

22-S79-1.3
1976 *Doge's Palace in Venice*
Issue price: £ 73.50

22-S79-1.4
1977 *Frau Holle*
Issue price: £ 79.50

22-S79-1.5
1978 *Singing Children*
Issue price: £ 75.00

22-S79-1.6
1979 *Winter Fair Tale*
Issue price: £ 86.00

22-S79-1.7
1980 *Puss in Boots*
Issue price: £ 96.50

22-S79-1.8
1981 *"Sterntaler"*
Issue price: £ 105.00

GERMANY (DDR)
MEISSEN
22-S79-1.9

22-S79-1.9
1982 *The Frog King*
Issue price: £ 110.00

22-S79-1.10
1983 *The Little Mermaid*
Issue price: £ 65.00

22-S79-1.11
1984 *Rumpelstiltskin*
Issue price: £ 65.00

22-S79-1.12
1985 *Pinocchio*
Issue price: £ 63.50

22-S79-1.13
1986 *Little 'Muck'*
Issue price: £ 63.50

22-S79-1.14
1987 *"Däumelinchen"*
Issue price: £ 63.50

22-T40-1.1 „Blue Titmouse"
1985 Tirschenreuth Band's
Songbirds of Europe
Evolving from her many years as a
porcelain artist of some renown,
German artist Ursula Band's approach
to nature painting is scrupulously
accurate, yet highly personal. This is
her first work in the medium of
collector's plates.

GERMANY
ALT TIRSCHENREUTH

22-T40-1.1

ALT TIRSCHENREUTH
Tirschenreuth

Since production of Tirschenreuth china began in 1838, Porzellanfabrik Tirschenreuth has continued to create magnificent porcelain objects for discerning collectors on five continents, including royalty and heads of state.

Their first entry into the limited-edition plate field is the series entitled *Band's Songbirds of Europe.*

It was created by artist Ursula Band, a native of Meissen, Germany, who received her professional training at the prestigious Painting and Drawing School of the Meissen State Porcelain Factory. In her first series, Frau Band has chosen to portray the songbirds which surround her home in Germany.

The series is the first depicting birds in their natural habitats to be produced under the auspices of the World Wildlife Fund, whose international president is H.R.H. The Duke of Edinburgh, Prince Philip, of Great Britain.

Band's Songbirds of Europe Series

Artist: Ursula Band. Artist's signature appears on front

Overglaze-decorated porcelain banded in 22k gold

Diameter: 19 centimetres
(7 ¹/₂ inches)

Pierced foot rim

Edition size undisclosed, limited by announced period of issue

Numbered, with certificate

22-T40-1.1
1985 *Blue Titmouse*
Issue price: £ 12.25

22-T40-1.2
1986 *Firecrest*
Issue price: £ 12.25

22-T40-1.3
1986 *Corsican Nuthatch*
Issue price: £ 12.25

22-T40-1.4
1986 *Golden Oriole*
Issue price: £ 13.95

22-T40-1.5
1987 *Great Titmouse*
Issue price: £ 13.95

22-T40-1.6
1987 *Red Robin*
Issue price: £ 13.95

22-T40-1.7
1987 *Chaffinch*
Issue price: £ 15.55

22-T40-1.8
1987 *Redstart*
Issue price: £ 15.55

Ancient Giants

Artist: Ernst Wetteroth. Artist's
signature appears on front

Porcelain

Diameter: 19 centimetres
(7 ¹/₂ inches)

Pierced foot rim

Edition size undisclosed,
limited by announced period of
issue

Numbered with certificate

22-T40-2.1
1987 *The Fat Mary*
Issue price: £ 17.95

22-T40-2.2
1988 *The Bavarian Beech*
Issue price: £ 17.95

Aynsley China Ltd

AYNSLEY CHINA LTD.
Staffordshire

John Aynsley & Sons Limited has a long established tradition in the history of English pottery making. It was founded by John Aynsley in 1775 at Longton and has been owned for five generations by the same family. The firm initially specialised in beer and cider mugs but in the early nineteenth century became widely known for its bone china tea services and dinnerware. Aynsley creations were personally selected by Queen Victoria for the royal yacht *H.M.S. Osborne.*
Subsequent pieces have been created for Queen Mary, the Duchess of Kent and the Duchess of Gloucester. Queen Elizabeth II selected Aynsley china as the service used on the occasion of her marriage to the Duke of Edinburgh in 1948.
In 1979 Aynsley introduced its *A Christmas Carol Series* based on memorable scenes from the Charles Dickens classic.

Artwork is by Lawrence Woodhouse who studied art at the Blackpool School of Art and the Stoke-on-Trent College of Art.

A Christmas Carol Series

Artist: Lawrence Woodhouse
Artist's signature appears on front

Bone China

Diameter: 21 centimetres (8 ¹/₄ inches)

No hanger

Edition size undisclosed, limited by year of issue

Not numbered, without certificate

26-A97-2.1
1979 *Mr. Fezziwig's Ball*
Artist: Lawrence Woodhouse
Issue price: £ 8.95

26-A97-2.2
1980 *Marley's Ghost*
Artist: Lawrence Woodhouse
Issue price: £ 10.50

26-A97-2.3
1981 *The Cratehit Family*
Artist: Lawrence Woodhouse
Issue price: £ 11.50

26-A97-2.4
1982 *Christmas Day*
Artist: Lawrence Woodhouse
Issue price: £ 12.95
Series Closed

GREAT BRITAIN
BELLEEK

26-B18-0.0

BELLEEK
Belleek, Grafschaft Fermanagh

Belleek Pottery Ltd., maker of thin, translucent parian china, was established in 1857 by David McBirney and Robert W. Armstrong on the banks of the River Erne near the small village of Belleek in Country Fermanagh, Northern Ireland. The site is near deposits of clay discovered when the owner of Castle Caldwell in Fermanagh became interested in the brilliant whitewash used on local cottages and found that his entire estate lay on a bed of feldspar clay.

When combined with metallic washes, this clay produces the unique iridescent effect for which Belleek is known — a mother-of-pearl lustre that is used on tea sets, figurines, and tableware. Queen Victoria and her son, the Prince of Wales, are among those who commissioned elaborate table services from the firm. Belleek ware is still made today much as it was a century ago.

Belleek's *Christmas* series, based on Irish subjects, began in 1970 and ended in 1977. The *Irish Wildlife Christmas* series began in 1978.

Artists for Belleek plates are not disclosed.

Christmas Series

Artist: undisclosed

Parian china

Diameter: 21.6 centimetres (8 ½ inches)

No hanger

Edition size limited to announced quantity of 7,500

Not numbered, without certificate

26-B18-1.1
1970 *Castle Caldwell*
Issue price: £ 15.15

26-B18-1.2
1971 *Celtic Cross*
Issue price: £ 15.15

26-B18-1.3
1972 *Flight of the Earls*
Issue price: £ 18.20

26-B18-1.4
1973 *Tribute to W.B. Yeats*
Issue price: £ 23.35

26-B18-1.5
1974 *Devenish Island*
Issue price: £ 27.30

26-B18-1.6
1975 *The Celtic Cross*
Issue price: £ 29.10

26-B18-1.7
1976 *Dove of Peace*
Issue price: £ 33.35

26-B18-1.8
1977 *Wren*
Issue price: £ 33.35
Series Closed

GREAT BRITAIN

BELLEEK

26-B18-2.1

*Irish Wildlife
Christmas Series*

Artist: undisclosed

Parian china

Diameter: 22.9 centimetres
(9 inches)

No hanger

Edition size undisclosed

Not numbered, without
certificate

26-B18-2.1
1978 *A Leaping Salmon*
Issue price: £ 18.40

26-B18-2.2
1979 Hare at Rest
Issue price: £ 19.80

26-B18-2.3
1980 *Hedgehog*
Issue price: £ 21.00

26-B18-2.4
1981 *Red Squirrel*
Issue price: £ 20.95

26-B18-2.5
1982 *Irish Seal*
Issue price: £ 20.95

26-B18-2.6
1983 *Red Fox*
Issue price: £ 20.95
Series Closed

26-C58-1.1 Christmas Eve
1976 Coalport Christmas Series by
Jessie Austin

GREAT BRITAIN
COALPORT
26-C58-1.1

COALPORT

COALPORT
Stoke-on-Trent, Staffordshire

Coalport Pottery was founded by John Rose at Ironbridge, Shropshire, in 1780. It gained note for faithfully reproducing tableware based on the designs of Sevres, Dresden and Chelsea – and was particularly well known for its creations in the rose Pompadour style. Rose received the Society of Art Medal Award in 1820 for his achievements in lead-free china. In 1926 the firm relocated to its present site in Staffordshire where is now specialises in intri-cately designed bone china.

The Coalport *Christmas Series* began in 1976 bearing designs of Pratt Potlids. These potlids were prized possessions of Victorian noblemen who used them to contain the precious bear's grease used to pomade their hair. In 1978 Coalport started a *Mother's Day Series* with designs based on flowers.

Artists for Coalport plates are not disclosed.

Christmas Series

Engraver: Jessie Austin, from Pratt Prints

Bone china

Diameter: 22.9 centimetres (9 inches)

No hanger

Edition size undisclosed, limited by year of issue

Not numbered, without certificate

26-C58-1.1
1976 *Christmas Eve*
Engraver: Jessie Austin
Issue price: £ 6.95

26-C58-1.2
1977 *Dangerous Skating*
Engraver: Jessie Austin
Issue price: £ 8.10

26-C58-1.3
1978 *Alas! Poor Bruin*
Engraver: Jessie Austin
Issue price: £ 8.90

26-C58-1.4
1979 *Christmas Morning*
Engraver: Jessie Austin
Issue price: £ 9.80

26-C58-1.5
1980 *Blind Man's Bluff*
Engraver: Jessie Austin
Issue price: £ 11.75

26-C58-1.6
1981 *Skating*
Engraver: Jessie Austin
Issue price: £ 12.90

26-C58-1.7
1982 *Snapdragon*
Engraver: Jessie Austin
Issue price: £ 13.95

26-C58-1.8
1983 *Trafalgar Square*
Engraver: Jessie Austin
Issue price: £ 13.95

26-C58-1.9
1984 *Peace*
Engraver: Jessie Austin
Issue price: £ 13.95

26-C58-1.10
1985 *Hide and Seek*
Engraver: Jessie Austin
Issue price: £ 14.95

26-C58-1.11
1986 *Snowdrift*
Engraver: Jessie Austin
Issue price: £ 15.95

GREAT BRITAIN
COALPORT
26-C58-1.12

26-C58-1.12
1987 *God Bless Us Everyone*
Engraver: Jessie Austin
Issue price: £ 16.95

Mother's Day Series

Artist: Undisclosed

Bone china

Diameter: 22.9 centimetres
(9 inches)

No hanger

Edition size undisclosed,
limited by year of issue

Not numbered, without
certificate

26-C58-2.1
1978 *Clematis*
Artist: Undisclosed
Issue price: £ 8.10

26-C58-2.2
1979 *Orchid*
Artist: Undisclosed
Issue price: £ 9.20

26-C58-2.3
1980 *Peony*
Artist: Undisclosed
Issue price: £ 11.75

26-C58-2.4
1981 *Rose*
Artist: Undisclosed
Issue price: £ 12.90

26-C73-2.4 Vigilance
1984 Crown Staffordshire
Wildlife in Winter by Kevin Platt

GREAT BRITAIN
CROWN STAFFORDSHIRE

26-C73-0.0

CROWN STAFFORDSHIRE
Staffordshire

Internationally acclaimed as a manufacturer of fine bone china, Crown, Staffordshire was founded in 1801 by Thomas Green – a Staffordshire potter who had served a long apprenticeship gaining a high degree of craft ability through working at the Etruria factory of Josiah Wedgwood, 'father of English potters'. Working unter Wedgwood's son Josiah II, Thomas established his pottery at the Minerva works in Fenton, – one of the six towns of Stoke-on-Trent, where it sill remains today as the home of Crown Staffordshire. The present factory has now been extensively enlarged and modernised, employing over 600 craftsmen and women.

Crown Staffordshire was the first English company to introduce the exquisite floral studies in fine bone china towards the end of the nineteenth century, which along with a range of giftware, tableware, bird models and limited edition studies, comprise a range of expertise that is so well known today.

Wildlife in Winter

Artist: Kevin Platt

Fine bone china

Diameter: 23.5 centimetres
(9 ¼ inches)

No hanger

Edition size limited to 10,000

Numbered, with certificate

26-C73-2.1
1983 *Tranquillity*
Issue price: £ 18.95

26-C73-2.2
1983 *Winter's Orphan*
Issue price: £ 19.95

26-C73-2.3
1983 *Early Awakening*
Issue price: £ 19.95

26-C73-2.4
1984 *Vigilance*
Issue price: £ 19.95
Series Closed

Heroes of the Sea

Artist: Kevin Platt

Minervaware

Diameter: 20.4 centimetres
(8 inches)

No hanger

Edition size undisclosed,
limited by announced period of
issue

Numbered, with certificate

26-C73-3.1
1984 *Off the Slipway*
Issue price: £ 15.95

26-C73-3.2
1984 *At the Rescue*
Issue price: £ 15.95

26-C73-3.3
1984 *Safe Return*
Issue price: £ 15.95
Series Closed

GREAT BRITAIN
DAVENPORT POTTERY

26-D8-1.1

DAVENPORT POTTERY
Staffordshire

The Davenport Pottery was founded by Arthur Wood and Son, descendants of esteemed potters who made their name and fortune by crafting Toby jugs at the close of the eighteenth century. Davenport is committed to preserving the tradition of fine British pottery, still relying on techniques that have been carefully handed down through generations of craftsmen.

With its move into the medium of limited-edition plates, The Davenport Pottery introduced, in 1983, the first collector's plate series based on the 200-year-old Toby tradition with "Toby Fillpot",

the first issue in the Toby Plate Collection. Each plate in this edition is hand-cast and hand-painted by artisans using techniques that date back to the eighteenth century.

W. A. Blandford was commissioned as master modeller to design the "Toby Fillpot" plate. Subsequent plates have been modelled by Douglas Tootle.

In 1986, Davenport Pottery introduced the *Treasury of Classic Children's Verse* series, with artwork by Linda Worrall. Sponsored by the Poetry Society of London, the series depicts scenes from classic children's poems.

Toby Plate Collection

Artist: as indicated. Artist's signature appears on front

Earthenware

Diameter: 21.6 centimetres (8 ½ inches)

No hanger

Edition size undisclosed, limited by announced period of issue

Numbered, with certificate

26-D8-1.1
1984 *Toby Fillpot*
Artist: Wilfred Blandford
Issue price: £ 18.25

26-D8-1.2
1984 *Falstaff*
Artist: Douglas Tootle
Issue price: £ 18.25

26-D8-1.3
1985 *Jack Tar*
Artist: Douglas Tootle
Issue price: £ 19.95

26-D8-1.4
1986 *Mr. Pickwick*
Artist: Douglas Tootle
Issue price: £ 19.95

26-D8-1.5
1986 *Friar Tuck*
Artist: Douglas Tootle
Issue price: £ 19.95

26-D8-1.6
1986 *Long John Silver*
Artist: Douglas Tootle
Issue price: £ 19.95

Treasury of Classic Children's Verse Series

Artist: Linda Worrall. Artist's signature appears on front

Earthenware

Diameter: 21.6 centimetres (8 ½ inches)

No hanger

Edition size undisclosed, limited by announced period of issue

Numbered, with certificate

26-D8-2.1
1986 *All Things Bright and Beautiful*
Issue price: £ 13.55

26-D8-2.2
1986 *Pirate's Story*
Issue price: £ 13.55

26-D8-2.3
1986 *The Star*
Issue price: £ 14.95

26-D8-2.4
1987 *Animal Crackers*
Issue price: £ 14.95

GREAT BRITAIN
HORNSEA
26-H58-1.1

HORNSEA
Hornsea, Yorkshire

Hornsea Pottery was founded in 1949 by two enterprising brothers, Desmond and Colin Rawson. From its humble origins, a converted pigsty, Hornsea emerged into one of the most progressive potteries in Europe. In 1973 the firm expanded with a second pottery located in Lancaster, Lancashire. Today both sites, while remaining a full production, serve as public parks featuring guided tours, a cafeteria, playgrounds for children, and giftshops.

Hornsea's initial works were simple kiln creations such as Toby Jugs and 'Francies' which included a variety of bowls, vases and trinkets. Later, more sophisticated products, have included dinnerware designs such as Heirloom, Saffron, Bronte and Concept.
The Concept design inspired Hornsea's first *Christmas Series*, introduced in 1979, which is stoneware in 24-carat burnished gold. Each issue illustrates a letter from the word 'CHRISTMAS'.

Christmas Series

Artist: Ian Taylor

Vitrified unglazed stoneware

Diameter: 22 centimetres
(8 ¹/₂ inches)

No hanger

Edition size undisclosed, limited by year of issue

Not numbered, without certificate

26-H58-1.1
1979 'C' – *The Nativity*
Issue price: £ 9.50

26-H58-1.2
1980 'H' – *Mary and Child*
Issue price: £ 11.00

26-H58-1.3
1981 'R' – Three Wise Men
Issue price: £ 12.50

26-H58-1.4
1982 'I' – At the Inn
Issue price: £ 13.75

26-H58-1.5
1983 'S' – The Shepherds
Issue price: £ 14.00

26-H58-1.6
1984 'T' – The Trinity
Issue price: £ 16.80

26-H58-1.7
1985 'M' – Mary
Issue price: £ 17.95

26-H58-1.8
1986 'A' – The Angel
Issue price: £ 18.90

26-H58-1.9
1987 'S' – The Star
Issue price: £ 19.99

GREAT BRITAIN
LONGTON CROWN POTTERY

26-L46-0.0

LONGTON CROWN POTTERY
Longton, Stoke-on-Trent, Staffordshire

Longton Crown Pottery maintains a long tradition of quality English bone china manufacture. Josiah Spode perfected the process by which animal bone ash is added to china clay to produce bone china, which is creamy white and translucent. His formula came to be known as English bone china and remains the standard today.

Longston Crown Pottery began its first Baronet bone china collector's plate series in 1981 with *The Canterbury Tales* collection, interpreting Geoffrey Chaucer's literary classic of the same name, and with the sponsorship of the Centre for Medieval & Renaissance Studies of Oxford, England. The series ended in 1982.

The artist for the series was G. A. Hoover.

The Canterbury Tales Collection

Artist: G.A. Hoover. Artist's signature appears on front

Baronet bone china

Diameter: 21.6 centimetres (8 ½ inches)

No hanger

Edition size undisclosed, limited by announced period of issue

Numbered, with certificate

22-L46-1.1
1981 *The Man of Law's Tale*
Issue price: £ 12.00

22-L46-1.2
1982 *The Franklin's Tale*
Issue price: £ 12.00

22-L46-1.3
1982 *The Knight's Tale*
Issue price: £ 13.00

22-L46-1.4
1982 *The Wife of Bath's Tale*
Issue price: £ 14.30
Series Closed

Mason's Ironstone

MASON'S IRONSTONE, STOKE-ON-TRENT
Staffordshire

Mason traces its history to 1798, when Miles Mason established his firm in Lane Delph, Staffordshire. A dealer in Oriental trade, he responded to increasingly prohibitive tariffs on Far Eastern china ware by producing his own. Mason emphasised durability in his product and, in 1804, devised the famed 'Ironstone China', a hardened earthenware, which became the firm's hallmark and was impressed on Mason's work as early as 1813.

In 1975 Mason introduced a *Christmas Series* made in ironstone with a heavy scroll border.

Christmas Series

Artist: As indicated

Ironstone patent china

Diameter: 25 centimetres
(9 ¼ inches)

No hanger

Edition size undisclosed,
limited by year of issue

Not numbered, without
certificate

26-M6-1.1
1975 *Windsor Castle*
Artist: James Cutts
Issue price: £ 8.75

26-M6-1.2
1976 *Holyrood House*
Artist: James Cutts
Issue price: £ 8.75

26-M6-1.3
1977 *Buckingham Palace*
Artist: James Cutts
Issue price: £ 10.56

26-M6-1.4
1978 *Balmoral Castle*
Artist: James Cutts
Issue price: £ 11.90

26-M6-1.5
1979 *Hampton Court*
Artist: Undisclosed
Issue price: £ 12.95

26-M6-1.6
1980 *Sandringham House*
Artist: Undisclosed
Issue price: £ 15.95
Series Closed

GREAT BRITAIN
ROYAL DOULTON

26-R62-0.0

ROYAL DOULTON
Burslem, Stoke-on-Trent, Staffordshire

Royal Doulton dates from 1815, when a potter named John Doulton invested his life savings of £ 100 in a one-kiln pottery in the Lambeth section of London.

At the International Exhibition of 1871, John's son Henry Doulton exhibited many of his experimental art pieces. Their favourable reception led to the development of decorative ceramics whose extensive range of colours and decorative techniques ultimately established Doulton Lambethware as an art form.

In 1877, Henry Doulton turned his attention to the development of tableware. At a small earthenware factory in Burslem, Staffordshire, table services for everyday use were produced along with more costly services with raised gold and acid-etched decorations, often combined with the finest of hand painting. Queen Victoria conferred knighthood upon Henry Doulton in 1887 for his accomplishments in the area of ceramic techniques, thus making him the first potter in England to receive such an honour. In 1901 the company received its first Royal warrant, and was henceforth known, by Royal Command, as *Royal Doulton*.

The *Beswick Christmas* series, sponsored by Royal Doulton's Beswick Potteries from 1972 to 1978, depicted Christmas traditions from around the world. The Collector's International Gallery of "Fine Art on Fine China" began with the *Mother and Child* series in 1973. These plates show mothers and children of various countries. Other series in the Collector's International group are by contemporary artists and include the *Commedia Dell' Arte* series begun in 1974 and ended in 1978, and *The Log of the "Dashing Wave"* series which began in 1976 and ended in 1982. The *Valentine's Day* series also began in 1976 with artwork from Victorian prints. The series ended in 1985. In 1980 Royal Doulton began the *Portraits of Innocence* series. The series ended in 1983.

Royal Doulton has recruited several important artists to design its collector's plates. Among them are John Stobart, Edna Hibel, LeRoy Neiman and Francisco J. J. C. Masseria.

Beswick Christmas Series

Artist: as indicated

Earthenware in hand-cast bas-relief, hand-painted in 15 colours

Diameter: 20.5 centimetres (8 inches)

Pierced foot rim

Edition size limited to 15,000

Not numbered, without certificate

26-R62-1.1
1972 *Christmas in England*
Artist: Harry Sales
Issue price: £ 21.25

26-R62-1.2
1973 *Christmas in Mexico*
Artist: Chavela Castrejon
Issue price: £ 22.75

26-R62-1.3
1974 *Christmas in Bulgaria*
Artist: Dimitri Yordanov
Issue price: £ 22.75

26-R62-1.4
1975 *Christmas in Norway*
Artist: Alton Toby
Issue price: £ 27.30

26-R62-1.5
1976 *Christmas in Holland*
Artist: Alton Toby
Issue price: £ 30.30

26-R62-1.6
1977 *Christmas in Poland*
Artist: Alton Toby
Issue price: £ 30.30

26-R62-1.7
1978 *Christmas in America*
Artist: Alton Toby
Issue price: £ 33.35
Series Closed

GREAT BRITAIN
ROYAL DOULTON

26-R62-7.1

Valentine's Day Series

Artist: unknown. Reproduced from ninetheenth-century Victorian prints

Bone china banded in gold

Diameter: 21 centimetres (8 ¹/₄ inches)

No hanger

Edition size undisclosed, limited by announced period of issue

Not numbered, without certificate

26-R62-7.1
1976 *Victorian Boy and Girl*
Issue price: £ 6.95

26-R62-7.2
1977 *My Sweetest Friend*
Issue price: £ 7.95

26-R62-7.3
1978 *If I Loved You*
Issue price: £ 8.95

26-R62-7.4
1979 *My Valentine*
Issue price: £ 9.95

26-R62-7.5
1980 *On A Swing*
Issue price: £ 11.95

26-R62-7.6
1981 *Sweet Music*
Issue price: £ 13.95

26-R62-7.7
1982 *From My Heart*
Issue price: £ 14.95

26-R62-7.8
1983 *Cherub's Song*
Issue price: £ 14.95

26-R62-7.9
1984 *Love in Bloom*
Issue price: £ 14.95

26-R62-7.10
1985 *With Loving Care*
Issue price: £ 14.95
Series Closed

Christmas Series

Artist: Unknown. Reproduced from nineteenth-century Victorian prints

Bone china banded in gold

Diameter: 21 centimetres (8 ¹/₄ inches)

No hanger

Edition size undisclosed, limited by period of issue

Not numbered, without certificate

26-R62-10.1
1977 *The Skater*
Issue price: £ 8.95

26-R62-10.2
1978 *Victorian Girl*
Issue price: £ 9.95

26-R62-10.3
1979 *Sleigh Rides*
Issue price: £ 11.95

26-R62-10.4
1980 *Santa's Gifts*
Issue price: £ 13.95

26-R62-10.5
1981 *The Carollers*
Issue price: £ 14.95

26-R62-10.6
1982 *Santa Claus*
Issue price: £ 14.95
Series Closed

26-R65-0.0

ROYAL GRAFTON CHINA
Longton, Stoke-on-Trent

It was in 1876 that Albert B. Jones started his first factory, Grafton China Works. Demand for his products was so strong that on January 1, 1900, Jones took into partnership his two sons and, at the same time, moved to a new factory on the present site in Longton, Stoke-on-Trent.

The firm, which had changed its name to A. B. Jones & Sons, then announced that it "still makes tea and breakfast sets for the Home, Colonial and American market". By 1906, A. B. Jones & Sons had diversified, making a special line of miniature coat-of-arms china. The demand for these hand-painted commemorative items lasted well into the 1920s; today, they are still highly sought-after as collector's pieces.

During the next thirty years, the firm specialized in quality tea sets and distinctive hand-painted decorated items. In 1956, a line of dinnerware was reintroduced, Today, the firm is recognized as an established maker of fine English bone china dinnerware and giftware. Royal Grafton offered its first limited-edition collector's plate series to the worldwide market with the 1987 introduction of the *Braithwaite Game Birds Collection* by the accomplished British wildlife illustrator Derek Braithwaite.

Christmas Series

Artist: Harry Colelough

Bone China

Diameter: 21.6 centimetres
(8 ½ inches)

Attached back hanger

Edition size undisclosed,
limited by year of issue

Numbered, with certificate

26-R65-1.1
1976 *Partrige in a Pear Tree*
Issue price: £ 4.95

26-R65-1.2
1977 *Two Turtle Doves*
Issue price: £ 5.50

26-R65-1.3
1978 *Three French Hens*
Issue price: £ 5.86

26-R65-1.4
1979 *Four Colly Birds*
Issue price: £ 6.00

26-R65-1.5
1980 *Five Gold Rings*
Issue price: £ 7.50

26-R65-1.6
1981 *Six Geese A-Laying*
Issue price: £ 8.65

26-R65-1.7
1982 *Seven Swans A-Swimming*
Issue price: £ 9.50

26-R65-1.8
1983 *Eight Maids A-Milking*
Issue price: £ 9.95

GREAT BRITAIN
ROYAL GRAFTON

26-R65-1.9

26-R65-1.9
1984 *Nine Ladies Dancing*
Issue price: £ 10.95

26-R65-1.10
1985 *Ten Lords A-Leaping*
Issue price: £ 11.95

26-R65-1.11
1986 *Eleven Pipers Piping*
Issue price: £ 12,95

26-R56-1.12
1987 *Twelve Drummers Drumming*
Issue price: £ 13.50
Series Closed

Braithwaite's Game Birds Collection

Artist: Derek Braithwaithe.
Artist's signature appears on front

Overglaze-decorated bone china

Diameter: 21.6 centimetres
(8 ¹/₂ inches)

No hanger

Edition size undisclosed,
limited by announced period of
issue

Numbered, with certificate

26-R65-2.1
1987 *Pheasants in Flight*
Issue price: £ 18,95

26-R65-2.2
1987 *Red Legged Partridge*
Issue price: £ 18.95

26-R76-1.1 Redstarts and Beech
1972 Royal Worcester
Bird Series by Dorothy Doughty

GREAT BRITAIN
ROYAL WORCESTER

26-R76-0.0

ROYAL
WORCESTER
CROWN WARE
ENGLAND

MADE IN ENGLAND

ROYAL WORCESTER
Worcester

The Worcester Porcelain Company, the oldest porcelain manufactory in England today, was established in Worcester, England, in 1751. Two of its original stockholders – Dr. John Wall, a physician and an amateur artist, and William Davis, an apothecary – are credited with perfecting a formula for making soft-paste porcelain from soapstone (steatite). Their formula was used until the introduction of bone china in the 19th century.

In 1788, King George III gave the company permission to call itself "Manufacturers to Their Majesties". After undergoing a number of changes in ownership, the firm was reorganized in 1862 as the Royal Worcester Porcelain Company in recognition of its long history of royal patronage. More recently, in 1976, Royal Worcester merged with Spode; however, each company has retained its own trademark.

In the early days of limited-edition plate collecting, Royal Worcester produced a few series for the U.S. market, which can now be found in the OVER-THE-COUNTER SECTION at the back of this book. The firm's newest plate series, begun in 1987, is titled *Happy England* and features scenes of 19th-century country life, created with a light touch by artist Helen Allingham.

Doughty Bird Series

Artist: Dorothy Doughty.
Artist's signature appears on front

Bone china with hand-painted bas-relief and gold scalloped rim

Diameter: 22.9 centimetres (9 inches)

No hanger

Edition size: As indicated

Not numbered, without certificate

26-R76-1.1
1972 *Redstarts and Beech*
Edition: 2,750
Issue price: £ 45.00

26-R76-1.2
1973 *Myrtle Warbler*
Edition: 3,000
Issue price: £ 52.50

26-R76-1.3
1974 *Blue-Grey Gnatcatchers*
Edition: 3,000
Issue price: £ 58.50

26-R76-1.4
1975 *Blackburnian Warbler*
Edition: 3,000
Issue price: £ 58.50

26-R76-1.5
1976 *Blue-winged Sivas*
Edition: 3,000
Issue price: £ 58.50

26-R76-1.6
1977 *Paradise Wydah*
Edition: 3,000
Issue price: £ 58.50

26-R76-1.7
1978 *Bluetits and Witch Hazel*
Edition: 3,000
Issue price: £ 67.00

26-R76-1.8
1979 *Mountain Bluebird and Pine*
Edition: 3,000
Issue price: £ 69.00

Happy England

Artist: Helen Allingham
Bone china
Diameter: 21 centimetres
(8 ¹/₄ inches)
No hanger
Edition size: As indicated
Numbered, with certificate

26-R76-4.1
1987 *Pausing at the Stile*
Issue price: unavailable at press time
Series Closed

SPODE
Stoke-on-Trent, Staffordshire

Josiah Spode I established the Spode Works at Stoke-on-Trent, England, in 1776 after spending nearly 30 years learning every facet of the pottery business. From the beginning, the Spode name was highly respected, and the firm has been awarded the Royal warrant by each English monarch since George III.

Joseah Spode perfected the process by which animal bone ash is added to china clay to produce bone china, which is creamy white and translucent. His formula came to be known as English bone china and remains the standard to this day.

Upon Spode's death 1797, his son, Josiah Spode II, continued the trade with William Copeland in charge of sales. Josiah Spode III in turn headed the business but upon his death, Copeland became sole owner. From 1827 his descendants operated the firm.

Under their direction it was called W. T. Copeland & Sons, Ltd., but retained the Spode trademark. Between 1967 and 1976, the firm was owned by Carborundum Company, but in 1976 Spode merged with Royal Worcester of England. The Spode trademark has been retained and the present factory is located on the site of the original pottery.

Spode's bone china *Christmas* series, which began in 1970 and ended in 1981, is based on old English carols. The plate body itself reproduces an original 18th-century Spode model; the designs are based on work by Gillian West, a prominent 19th-century British ceramics artist. The 1970 and 1971 plates are decorated in gold; thereafter, decorations are in gold plus a second colour which is changed every two years.

Christmas Series

Artist: Gillian West

Bone china decorated in gold

Diameter: 20.3 centimetres (8 inches)

No hanger

Edition size undisclosed, limited by year of issue

Not numbered, without certificate

26-S63-1.1
1970 *Partridge in a Pear Tree*
Issue price: £ 5.50

26-S63-1.2
1971 *In Heaven the Angels Singing*
Issue price: £ 5.50

26-S63-1.3
1972 *We Saw Three Ships A'Sailing*
Issue price: £ 6.00

26-S63-1.4
1973 *We Three Kings of Orient Are*
Issue price: £ 6.15

26-S63-1.5
1974 *Deck the Halls*
Issue price: £ 6.45

26-S63-1.6
1975 *Christbaum*
Issue price: £ 7.95

26-S63-1.7
1976 *Good King Wenceslas*
Issue price: £ 9.15

26-S63-1.8
1977 *The Holly and the Ivy*
Issue price: £ 9.95

GREAT BRITAIN

SPODE

26-S63-1.9

26-S63-1.9
1978 *While Shepherds Watched*
Issue price: £ 11.50

26-S63-1.10
1979 *Away in a Manger*
Issue price: £ 14.50

26-S63-1.11
1980 *Bringing in the Boar's Head*
Issue price: £ 15.45

26-S63-1.12
1981 *Make We Merry*
Issue price: £ 18.95
Series Closed

26-W90-1.1 "Windsor Castle"
1969 Wedgwood Christmas
26-W90-2.1 "Sportive Love" and
26-W90-2.11 "Mare and Foal"
1971 and 1981 Wedgwood Mothers

Three examples of the varied colours of Wedgwood's vitreous, unglazed stoneware, known as Jasperware. The white or coloured bas-relief decorations are applied by hand.

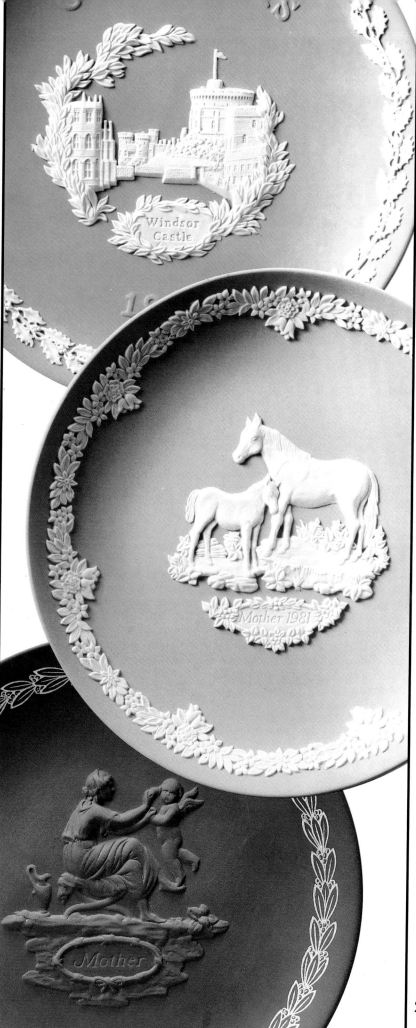

GREAT BRITAIN
WEDGWOOD

26-W90-0.0

WEDGWOOD
Barlaston, Stoke-on-Trent, Staffordshire

Josiah Wedgwood I, Fellow of the Royal Society is known as the "father of English potters". He founded the firm that bears his name in 1759 and built a new factory, which he called "Etruria", 10 years later.

Wedgwood himself developed many of the processes and materials used by the firm today. He is perhaps best known for his "Jasper ware", which he perfected in 1774. A vitreous, unglazed stoneware, Jasper is pure white in its original form but can be stained to produce a wide variety of coloured backgrounds — green, filac, yellow, primrose, black, and most popular of all, classic "Wedgwood blue" — onto which white or coloured basrelief decorations of the same material are applied by hand while in the "cheese hard" state. The object is then fired only once, fusing the decoration to the base object.

Although potters in England and abroad tried to duplicate Jasper ware, none was successful. To this day, the Wedgwood name is so firmly linked with Jasper that many people mistakenly think it is the only ware Wedgwood produces and that it is made only in blue.

In 1940, having outgrown the pottery at Etruria, the firm moved to what has been described as the most up-to-date pottery in the world, near the village of Barlaston, Stoke-on-Trent, Staffordshire, England. There, in 1969, the firm celebrated the 200th anniversary of the Etruria pottery by introducing a *Christmas* series of classic Wedgwood blue-and-white Jasper collector's plates commemorating famous English monuments. In 1971, Wedgwood began an annual series of *Mothers* plates made in Black Basalt ware and Jasper wares and bearing designs created in the late 18th century. The *Blossoming of Suzanne* series on Wedgwood bone china, with designs by Mary Vickers, started in 1977. The series ended in 1980. The *Mary Vickers My Memories* series began in 1981 and ended in 1986.

In 1986, the *Street Sellers of London* series was introduced with artwork by John Finnie, a tribute to 19th-century street life in Victorian London. *The Legend of King Arthur* series on Wedgwood bone china, with artwork by Richard Hook, and Mary Vickers' *Portraits of First Love* series on Queen's ware, were also introduced in 1986.

1987 was the year of introduction for *Colin Newman's Country Panorama* series, a unique collection that shows a 360-degree view of an English landscape.

Artists for Wedgwood over the past two centuries have included some of the most distinguished names in the world. William Hackwood was a modeller for Wedgwood from 1769 to 1832, and his 18th-century designs have been used on Wedgwood Jasper ware for generations. Lady Elizabeth Templetown was a designer for Wedgewood from 1783 to 1787. Most of her designs were modeled by William Hackwood. Among the renowned artists who have worked with Wedgwood over the past 40 years are Rex Whistler, Eric Ravilious, Edward Bawden, Arnold Machin, Richard Guyatt and Eduardo Paolozzi.

Christmas Series

Artist: Tom Harper until 1978; undisclosed thereafter

Jasper stoneware

Diameter: 20.3 centimetres (8 inches)

No hanger

Edition size undisclosed, limited by year of issue

Not numbered, with certificate

26-W90-1.1
1969 *Windsor Castle*
Issue price: £ 4.00

26-W90-1.2
1970 *Christmas in Trafalgar Square*
Issue price: £ 4.95

26-W90-1.3
1971 *Piccadilly Circus, London*
Issue price: £ 5.50

26-W90-1.4
1972 *St. Paul's Cathedral*
Issue price: £ 7.25

26-W90-1.5
1973 *The Tower of London*
Issue price: £ 7.50

26-W90-1.6
1974 *The Houses of Parliament*
Issue price: £ 8.25

26-W90-1.7
1975 *Tower Brigde*
Issue price: £ 9.75

26-W90-1.8
1976 *Hampton Court*
Issue price: £ 10.95

26-W90-1.9
1977 *Westminster Abbey*
Issue price: £ 11.95

26-W90-1.10
1978 *The Horse Guards*
Issue price: £ 13.95

26-W90-1.11
1979 *Buckingham Palace*
Issue price: £ 14.95

26-W90-1.12
1980 *St. James Palace*
Issue price: £ 17.50

26-W90-1.13
1981 *Marble Arch*
·Issue price: £ 19.00

26-W90-1.14
1982 *Lambeth Palace*
Issue price: £ 19.00

26-W90-1.15
1983 *All Souls, Langham Palace*
Issue price: £ 19.00

26-W90-1.16
1984 *Constitutional Hill*
Issue price: £ 19.00

26-W90-1.17
1985 *Tate Gallery*
Issue price: £ 19.75

26-W90-1.18
1986 Albert Memorial
Issue price: £ 21.00

26-W90-1.19
1987 The Guildhall
Issue price: £ 21.95

Mothers Series

Artist: as indicated

Jasper stoneware in varying colours

Diameter: 16.5 centimetres (6 ¹/₂ inches)

No hanger

Edition size undisclosed, limited by year of issue

Not numbered, without certificate

26-W90-2.1
1971 Sportive Love
Artist: Lady Elizabeth Templetown
Issue price: £ 3.80

26-W90-2.2
1972 The Sewing Lesson
Artist: Emma Crewe
Issue price: £ 3.80

26-W90-2.3
1973 The Baptism of Achilles
Artist: Lady Elizabeth Templetown
Issue price: £ 4.15

26-W90-2.4
1974 Domestic Employment
Artist: Lady Elizabeth Templetown
Issue price: £ 4.45

26-W90-2.5
1975 Mother and Child
Artist: Lady Elizabeth Templetown
Issue price: £ 5.85

26-W90-2.6
1976 *The Spinner*
Artist: Willam Hackwood
Issue price: £ 5.85

26-W90-2.7
1977 *Leisure Time*
Artist: William Hackwood
Issue price: £ 6.75

26-W90-2.8
1978 *Swan and Cugnets*
Artist: undisclosed
Issue price: £ 7.95

26-W90-2.9
1979 *Deer and Fawn*
Artist: undisclosed
Issue price: £ 9.50

26-W90-2.10
1980 *Birds*
Artist: undisclosed
Issue price: £ 9.95

26-W90-2.11
1981 *Mare and Foal*
Artist: undisclosed
Issue price: £ 11.50

26-W90-2.12
1982 *Cherubs with Swing*
Artist: undisclosed
Issue price: £ 12.50

26-W90-2.13
1983 *Cupid and Butterfly*
Artist: undisclosed
Issue price: £ 12.50

26-W90-2.14
1984 *Cupid and Music*
Artist: undisclosed
Issue price: £ 12.50

26-W90-2.15
1985 *Cupid and Doves*
Artist: undisclosed
Issue price: £ 12.50

26-W90-2.16
1986 *Cupids at Play*
Artist: undisclosed
Issue price: £ 12.50

26-W90-2.17
1987 *Anemones*
Artist: undisclosed
Issue price: unavailable at press time

Blossoming of Suzanne Series

Artist: Mary Vickers. Artist's signature appears on front

Bone china banded in gold

Diameter: 23.5 centimetres (9 $^1/_4$ inches)

No hanger

Edition size limited to 17,000 in 1977; 24,000 thereafter

Numbered, with certificate

26-W90-4.1
1977 *Innocence*
Issue price: £ 30.00

26-W90-4.2
1978 *Cherish*
Issue price: £ 30.00

26-W90-4.3
1979 *Daydream*
Issue price: £ 30.00

26-W90-4.4
1980 *Wistful*
Issue price: £ 32.00
Series Closed

GREAT BRITAIN
WEDGWOOD

26-W90-5.1

Mary Vickers My Memories Series

Artist: Mary Vickers. Artist's signature appears on front

Queensware banded in gold

Diameter: 20.3 centimetres (8 inches)

No hanger

Edition size undisclosed, limited by announced period of issue

Numbered, with certificate

26-W90-5.1
1981 *Be My Friend*
Issue price: £ 9.90

26-W90-5.2
1982 *Playtime*
Issue price: £ 11.50

26-W90-5.3
1983 *Our Garden*
Issue price: £ 12.65

26-W90-5.4
1984 *The Recital*
Issue price: £ 12.65

26-W90-5.5
1985 *Mother's Treasures*
Issue price: £ 13.95

26-W90-5.6
1986 *Riding High*
Issue price: £ 13.95
Series Closed

Calendar Series

Artist: Wedgwood Design Studio

Diameter: 25.4 centimetres (10 inches)

No hanger

Edition size undisclosed, limited by year of issue

Not numbered, without certificate

26-W90-6.1
1971 *Victorian Almanac*
Issue price: £ 2.10

26-W90-6.2
1972 *The Carousel*
Issue price: £ 2.30

26-W90-6.3
1973 *Beautiful Butterfly*
Issue price: £ 2.50

26-W90-6.4
1974 *Camelot*
Issue price: £ 2.60

26-W90-6.5
1975 *Children's Games*
Issue price: £ 2.85

26-W90-6.6
1976 *Robin*
Issue price: £ 4.95

26-W90-6.7
1977 *Tonatiuh*
Issue price: £ 5.95

26-W90-6.8
1978 *Samurai*
Issue price: £ 6.95

26-W90-6.9
1979 *Sacred Scarab*
Issue price: £ 8.75

26-W90-6.10
1980 *Safari*
Issue price: £ 9.50

26-W90-6.11
1981 *Horses*
Issue price: £ 10.95

26-W90-6.12
1982 *Wild West*
Issue price: £ 11.50

26-W90-6.13
1983 *The Age of Reptiles*
Issue price: £ 11.50

26-W90-6.14
1984 *Dogs*
Issue price: £ 11.50

26-W90-6.15
1985 *Cats*
Issue price: £ 11.50
Series Closed

A Child's Christmas Series

Artist: Wedgwood Design Studio

Queen's stoneware

Diameter: 20.3 centimetres (8 inches)

No hanger

Edition size undisclosed, limited by year of issue

Not numbered, without certificate

26-W90-7.1
1979 *Snowman*
Issue price: £ 6.75

26-W90-7.2
1980 *Bringing Home the Tree*
Issue price: £ 7.95

26-W90-7.3
1981 *Tobagganing*
Issue price: £ 7.95

26-W90-7.4
1982 *Skaters*
Issue price: £ 7.95

26-W90-7.4
1983 *Carol Singing*
Issue price: £ 7.95

26-W90-7.6
1984 *Mixing the Christmas Pudding*
Issue price: £ 8.50
Series Closed

GREAT BRITAIN
WEDGWOOD

26-W90-9.1

Queen's Ware Christmas

Artist: Wedgwood Design Studio

Queen's stoneware

Diameter: 21 centimetres (8 ¹/₂ inches)

No hanger

Edition size undisclosed, limited by year of issue

Not numbered, without certificate

26-W90-9.1
1980 *Windsor Castle*
Issue price: £ 6.95

26-W90-9.2
1981 *Trafalgar Square*
Issue price: £ 7.50

26-W90-9.3
1982 *Piccadilly Circus*
Issue price: £ 7.95

26-W90-9.4
1983 *St. Paul's*
Issue price: £ 7.95

26-W90-9.5
1984 *Tower of London*
Issue price: £ 8.50

26-W90-9.6
1985 *Palace of Westminster*
Issue price: £ 8.50

26-W90-9.7
1986 *Tower Brigde*
Issue price: £ 8.95
Series Closed

Street Sellers of London Series

Artist: John Finnie. Artist's signature appears on front

Bone china

Diameter: 21.3 centimetres (8 3/8 inches)

No hanger

Edition size undisclosed, limited by announced period of issue

Numbered, with certificate

26-W90-10.1
1986 *The Baked Potato Man*
Issue price: £ 11.95

26-W90-10.2
1986 *Street Seller of Hot Elder Wine*
Issue price: £ 11.95

26-W90-10.3
1986 *Ginger Beer Fountain*
Issue price: £ 13.25

26-W90-10.4
1986 *Street Seller of Green Peas*
Issue price: £ 13.25

26-W90-10.5
1986 *Water Carrier*
Issue price: £ 13.25

26-W90-10.6
1986 *Street Seller of Fried Fish*
Issue price: £ 14.85

26-W90-10.7
1986 *The Milk Man*
Issue price: £ 14.85

26-W90-10.8
1986 *The Bread Roundsman*
Issue price: £ 14.85

GREAT BRITAIN
WEGDWOOD

26-W90-17.1

The Legend of King Arthur Series

Artist: Richard Hook. Artist's signature appears on front

Bone china

Diameter: 23 centimetres (9 inches)

No hanger

Edition size undisclosed, limited by announced period of issue

Numbered, with certificate

26-W90-17.1
1986 *Arthur Draws the Sword*
Issue price: £ 17.95

26-W90-17.2
1986 *Arthur Is Crowned King*
Issue price: £ 17.95

26-W90-17.3
1987 *Excalibur*
Issue price: £ 21.95

26-W90-17.4
1987 *The Wedding of Arthur and Guinevere*
Issue price: £ 21.95

26-W90-17.5
1987 *The Knights of the Round Table*
Issue price: £ 21.95

26-W90-17.6
1988 *Lancelot and Guinevere*
Issue price: £ 19.95

Portrais of First Love Series

Artist: Mary Vickers. Artist's signature appears on front

Queensware

Diameter: 21.6 centimetres (8 ¹/₂ inches)

No hanger

Edition size undisclosed, limited by announced period of issue

Numbered, with certificate

26-W90-18.1
1986 *The Love Letter*
Issue price: £ 17.75

26-W90-18.2
1986 *The Ring*
Issue price: £ 17.75

26-W90-18.3
1986 *The Gift*
Issue price: £ 18.85

26-W90-18.4
1986 *The Pearls*
Issue price: £ 18.85

John Finnie's Viktorian Christmas Series

Artist: John Finnie. Artist's signature appears on front

Fine earthenware

Diameter: 22.5 centimetres (9 inches)

No hanger

Edition size undisclosed, limited by announced period of issue

Numbered, with certificate

26-W90-26.1
1986 *Carollers*
Issue price: £ 13.25

26-W90-26.2
1987 *The Christmas Pudding*
Issue price: £ 15.25

GREAT BRITAIN
WEDGWOOD
26-W90-27.1

Colin Newman's Country Panorama Series

Artist: Colin Newman. Artist's signature appears on front

Overglaze-decorated bone china

Diameter: 21 centimetres (8 ¹/₄ inches)

No hanger

Edition size undisclosed, limited by announced period of issue

Numbered, with certificate

26-W90-27.1
1986 *Meadows and Wheatfields*
Issue price: £ 15.55

26-W90-27.2
1987 *The Meandering Stream*
Issue price: £ 15.55

26-W90-27.3
1987 *Village in the Valley*
Issue price: £ 16.85

Jasper Christmas Cathedrals

Artist: undisclosed

Jasper stoneware

Diameter: 18 centimetres (7 inches)

No hanger

Edition size undisclosed, limited by year of issue

Not numbered, without certificate

26-W90-29.1
1986 *Canterbury*
Issue price: £ 10.50

26-W90-29.2
1987 *York Minster*
Issue price: £ 10.95

Calendar: British Birds

Artist: undisclosed

Queen's stoneware

Diameter: 25.4 centimetres
(10 inches)

No hanger

Edition size undisclosed,
limited by year of issue

Not numbered, without
certificate

26-W90-30.1
1986 *Garden Birds*
Issue price: £ 11.50

26-W90-30.2
1987 *Water Birds*
Issue price: £ 12.50

Mother's Day: Spring Hedgerow Flowers

Artist: undisclosed

Jasper stoneware

Diameter: 16.5 centimetres
(6 1/2 inches)

No hanger

Edition size undisclosed,
limited by year of issue

Not numbered, without
certificate

26-W90-31.1
1987 *Anemone*
Issue price: £ 12.95

26-W90-31.2
1988 *Tiger Lily*
Issue price: £ 13.50

Christmas Traditions

Artist: undisclosed

Oueen's stoneware

Diameter: 20 centimetres
(7 4/5 inches)

No hanger

Edition size undisclosed,
limited by year of issue

Not numbered, without
certificate

26-W90-32.1
1987 *Dressing the Tree*
Issue price: £ 8.95

ITALY
ANRI

38-A54-0.0

Exclusively through Schmid

ANRI
Santa Christina

The House of Anri, which claims to be the world's largest woodcarving manufactory, is a family firm that was established in 1916 by Anton Riffeser, Sr. It is now headed by his grandson, Ernst Riffeser. The factory is located in the Tyrolean Alps, an area with a long tradition of wood carving.

Anri's *Christmas* series began in 1971. Using a material known as "toriart", the plates are hand-crafted in wood material and handpainted to produce a three-dimensional effect. Each plate is mounted in a circular European maple frame.

A master woodcarver from Saint Ulrich, Italy, Josef Malfertheiner is the predominant artist who produces this series.

Christmas Series

Artist: Joseph Malfertheiner until 1978; undisclosed thereafter

Hand-painted moulded wood material

Diameter: 30.5 centimetres (12 inches)

Attached back hanger

Edition size limited to 10,000 until 1976; 6,000 thereafter

Numbered since 1972, without certificate

38-A54-1.1
1971 *St. Jakob in Groden*
Issue price: £ 22.75

38-A54-1.2
1972 *Pipers at Alberobello*
Issue price: £ 27.30

38-A54-1.3
1973 *Alpine Horn*
Issue price: £ 27.30

38-A54-1.4
1974 *Young Man and Girl*
Issue price: £ 30.30

38-A54-1.5
1975 *Christmas in Ireland*
Issue price: £ 36.35

38-A54-1.6
1976 *Alpine Christmas*
Issue price: £ 39.40

38-A54-1.7
1977 *Legend of Heiligenblut*
Issue price: £ 39.40

38-A54-1.8
1978 *The Klockler Singers*
Issue price: £ 48.50

ITALY
ANRI
38-A54-1.9

38-A54-1.9
1979 *The Moss Gatherers of Villnoess*
Issue price: £ 81.85

38-A54-1.10
1980 *Wintry Church-going in Santa Christina*
Issue price: £ 100.00

38-A54-1.11
1981 *Santa Claus in Tyrol*
Issue price: £ 100.00

38-A54-1.12
1982 *Star Singers*
Issue price: £ 100.00

38-A54-1.13
1983 *Unto Us a Child Is Born*
Issue price: £ 100.00

38-A54-1.14
1984 *Yuletide in the Valley*
Issue price: £ 100.00

38-A54-1.15
1985 *Good Morning, Good Cheer*
Issue price: £ 100.00

38-A54-1.16
1986 *A Groden Christmas*
Issue price: £ 100.00

38-A54-1.17
1987 *Down from the Alps*
Issue price: £ 118.20

38-K32-2.5 „Anemones"
1977 King's Flowers of America
These plates are among the few in the
market to have such high-relief
decoration.

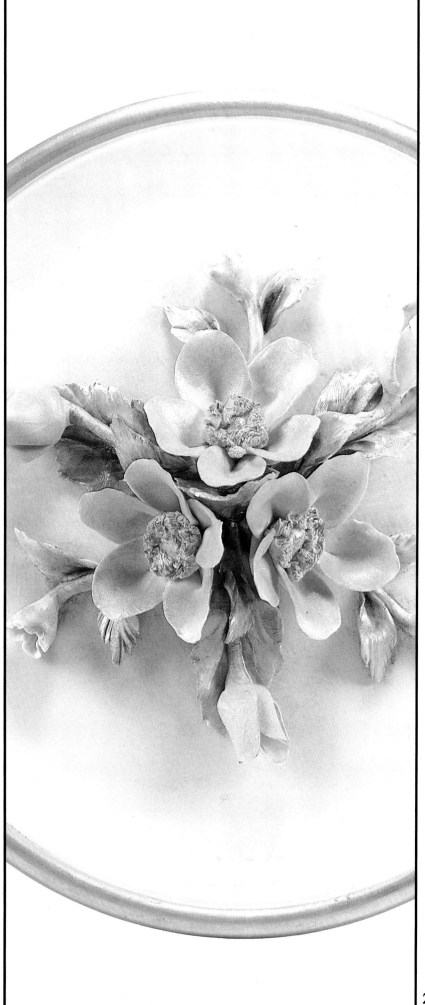

ITALY
KING'S

38-K32-0.0

KING'S
Usmate, Milan

King's Porcelain was established in the original Giuseppe Cappe factory in the 1960s. The factory had been known for its Cappe figurines of which King's has retained the original moulds.

King's *Flowers of America* series began in 1973 and ended in 1977.

Chief sculptor for King's Porcelain is the Italian artist Aldo Falchi, who studied sculpture in Milan and later collaborated with Bjørn Wiinblad on works for Rosenthal of Germany. Some of his pieces in terra cotta can be found in Verona, Mantova and Bozzolo, Italy.

Flowers of America Series

Artist: Aldo Falchi. Artist's signature appears on back since 1975

High-relief, hand-painted porcelain banded in gold

Diameter: 22.3 centimetres (8 ³/₄ inches)

Attached back hanger

Edition size limited to 1,000

Numbered, without certificate

38-K32-2.1
1973 *Pink Carnation*
Issue price: £ 51.55

38-K32-2.2
1974 *Red Roses*
Issue price: £ 60.65

38-K32-2.3
1975 *Yellow Dahlia*
Issue price: £ 66.65

38-K32-2.4
1976 *Bluebells*
Issue price: £ 78.80

38-K32-2.5
1977 *Anemones*
Issue price: £ 78.80
Series Closed

ITALY
LE PORCELLANE FONTANA DEI MEDICI
38-P63-0.0

LE PORCELLANE FONTANA DEI MEDICI
Verona

The artistic heritage of Le Porcellane Fontana dei Medici dates back four centuries, to 1575. In that year, the Florentines, Orazio Fontana and Bernardo Buontalenti, with the patronage of the powerful Francesco de Medici, succeeded in creating the first soft-paste porcelain ever made in Europe. The very few examples of this early porcelain known to exist today are in private collections or museums.

The Women of Puccini series by master painter Riccardo Benvenuti is the first offering of Le Porcellane Fontana dei Medici in the collector's plate medium. *The Women of Puccini* series was initiated in 1986. This historic series presents a full-colour gallery of six heroines from Puccini's immortal grand operas.

The Women of Puccini Series

Artist: Riccardo Benvenuti. Artist's signature appears on front

Porcelain banded in 24 k gold

Diameter: 21 centimetres (8 ¹/₄ inches)

No hanger

Edition size undisclosed, limited by announced period of issue

Numbered, with certificate

38-P63-1.1
1986 *Musetta*
Issue price: £ 18.95

38-P63-1.2
1986 *Mimi*
Issue price: £ 18.95

38-P63-1.3
1986 *Manon*
Issue price: £ 19.95

38-P63-1.4
1986 *Madame Butterfly*
Issue price: £ 19.95

38-P63-1.5
1987 *Tosca*
Issue price: £ 21.95

38-P63-1.6
1987 *Turandot*
Issue price: £ 21.95
Series Closed

ITALY
VENETO FLAIR
38-V22-0.0

VENETO FLAIR
Treviso

Veneto Flair was established in 1946 by a consortium of potters and painters. Creative World of White Plains, New York, acts as importer and distributor of Veneto Flair collector's plates.

A centuries-old technique is used to create Veneto Flair plates. The resulting decorated and glazed earthenware is known as majolica, or faience pottery. In this ancient process, terra cotta is hand-thrown on a potter's wheel and the design is incised with a scalpel on the baked clay. Co-lours are then handapplied and the plates undergo a series of paintings and firings before a final firing with a secret-formula glaze, which produces Veneto Flair's unique mosaic-effect finish.

In 1971, Veneto Flair entered the limited-edition plate market with a single issue, the Bellini "Madonna" plate. The *Last Supper* series, based on Leonardo da Vinci's painting, started in 1973. Their *St. Mark's of Venice* series began in 1984.

Born in Torgiano, Italy, Vincente Tiziano is credited with reviving ancient Etruscan techniques of ceramic production. His classical style was greatly influenced by the ceramic traditions of the 16th century. He is a recipient of the Amerigo Longhi Award from the International Ceramic Show of Deruta in the Italian province of Perugia. Many of his works are on display at the Deruta Ceramic Museum.

Last Supper Series

Artist: Vincente Tiziano (after Leonardo da Vinci's *Last Supper*) Artist's signature appears on front

Terra cotta banded in gold

Diameter: 21.6 centimetres (8 ¹/₂ inches)

Pierced foot rim

Edition size limited to 2,000

Numbered, with certificate

38-V22-6.1
1973 *Last Supper—Scene I*
Issue price: £ 60.65

38-V22-6.2
1973 *Last Supper—Scene II*
Issue price: £ 42.45

38-V22-6.3
1974 *Last Supper—Scene III*
Issue price: £ 42.45

38-V22-6.4
1975 *Last Supper—Scene IV*
Issue price: £ 42.45

38-V22-6.5
1976 *Last Supper—Scene V*
Issue price: £ 42.45
Series Closed

ITALY
VENETO FLAIR

38-V22-15.1

St. Mark's of Venice Series

Artist: Franco Lamincia. Artist's signature appears on front

Majolica-style earthenware, hand-painted and banded in gold

Diameter: 20.3 centimetres (8 inches)

Pierced foot rim

Edition size undisclosed, limited by announced period of issue

Numbered with certificate

38-V22-15.1
1984 *Noah and the Dove*
Issue price: £ 43.00

38-V22-15.2
1985 *Moses and the Burning Bush*
Issue price: £ 43.00

38-V22-15.3
1986 *Abraham and the Journey*
Issue price: £ 43.00

38-V22-15.4
1986 *Josef and the Coat*
Issue price: £ 43.00
Series Closed

38-V90-1.3 „Carmen"
1978 di Volteradici, Grand Opera
First series from Studio Dante di
Volteradici. All di Volteradici plates are
made of ivory alabaster.

ITALY
STUDIO DANTE DI VOLTERADICI

38-V90-0.0

STUDIO DANTE DI VOLTERADICI
Toscana

Located in Tuscany, world centre for the mining and carving of alabaster, the Studio Dante di Volteradici continues the Italian tradition of alabaster sculpturing.

Di Volteradici's *Grand Opera* series, commissioned by the Museo Teatrale alla Scala to commemorate the 200th anniversary of La Scala Opera House, began in 1976 and ended in 1982. *Madonne Viventi (Living Madonnas)*, its first proprietary series, began in 1978 and ended in 1984. Their *Ghiberti Doors* series began in 1983. In 1985, they introduced a series by contemporary sculptor Sergio Benvenuti, entitled *Benvenuti's Muses*.

Gino Ruggeri, a sculptor in the neo-classic tradition, is best known for his work "The Crucifix", sculpted from the Casa Serena Institute of Cecina Mare, and his two sculptures, "Memorials to the Fallen", which pay tribute to World War I victims. Now in his late 70s, Ruggeri's last completed work was the "Aida" plate. His successor as designer of the *Grand Opera* series was Franco Ingargiola, whom Ruggeri personally tutored and who worked in onyx and ceramics as well as alabaster. Alberto Santangela, current sculptor of the *Madonne Viventi* and *Ghiberti Doors* series, sculpts in the style of the Italian High Renaissance.

In 1986, Alberto Santangela created the *Renaissance Madonnas: Gifts of Maternal Love* series, the first ivory alabaster collector's plate series ever to be hand-painted. Also in 1986, *The Christmas Crèche* series was started, with designs by Ennio Furiesi in the tradition of 18th- and 19th-century Neapolitan Christmas crèche figures.

Grand Opera Series

Artist: Gino Ruggeri throught 1979; Franco Ingargiola thereafter. Artist's signature appears on front

Ivory alabaster

Diameter: 21.6 centimetres (8 ½ inches)

Attached back hanger

Edition size undisclosed, limited by announced period of issue

Numbered, with certificate

38-V90-1.1
1976 *Rigoletto*
Issue price: £ 15.95

38-V90-1.2
1977 *Madame Butterfly*
Issue price: £ 15.95

38-V90-1.3
1978 *Carmen*
Issue price: £ 17.95

38-V90-1.4
1979 *Aida*
Issue price: £ 17.95

38-V90-1.5
1980 *The Barber of Seville*
Issue price: £ 17.95

38-V90-1.6
1981 *Tosca*
Issue price: £ 19.95

38-V90-1.7
1982 *I Pagliacci*
Issue price: £ 19.95
Series Closed

ITALY
STUDIO DANTE DI VOLTERADICI

38-V90-2.1

Madonne Viventi

(Living Madonnas)

Artist: Ado Santini in 1978;
Alberto Santangela thereafter.
Artist's signature appears on
front

Ivory alabaster

Diameter: 21.6 centimetres
(8 $\frac{1}{2}$ inches)

Attached back hanger

Edition size undisclosed,
limited by announced period of
issue

Numbered, with certificate

38-V90-2.1
1978 *Madonna Pensosa*
(The Pensive Madonna)
Issue price: £ 19.95

38-V90-2.2
1979 *Madonna Serena*
(The Serene Madonna)
Issue price: £ 19.95

38-V90-2.3
1980 *Madonna Beata*
(The Beatific Madonna)
Issue price: £ 19.95

38-V90-2.4
1981 *Madonna Profetica*
(The Prophetic Madonna)
Issue price: £ 19.95

38-V90-2.5
1982 *Madonna Modesta*
(The Demure Madonna)
Issue price: £ 19.95

38-V90-2.6
1983 *Madonna Saggio*
(The Wise Madonna)
Issue price: £ 19.95

38-V90-2.7
1984 *Madonna Tenera*
(The Tender Madonna)
Issue price: £ 19.95
Series Closed

Ghiberti Doors Series

Artist: Alberto Santangela.
Artist's signature appears on front

Ivory alabaster

Diameter: 21.6 centimetres (8 ¹/₂ inches)

Attached back hanger

Edition size undisclosed, limited by announced period of issue

Numbered, with certificate

38-V90-3.1
1983 *Adoration of the Magi*
Issue price: £ 32.35

38-V90-3.2
1984 *The Nativity*
Issue price: £ 32.35

38-V90-3.3
1985 *The Annunciation*
Issue price: £ 32.35

38-V90-3.4
1986 *Christ Among the Doctors*
Issue price: £ 35.65

38-V90-3.5
1986 *Christ Walks on the Water*
Issue price: £ 35.65

38-V90-3.6
1986 *Christ and the Expulsion of the Moneychangers*
Issue price: £ 35.65

38-V90-3.7
1987 *Entry into Jerusalem*
Issue price: £ 35.65

38-V90-3.8
1987 *The Raising of Lazarus*
Issue price: £ 35.65

ITALY
STUDIO DANTE DI VOLTERADICI

38-V90-4.1

*Benvenuti's Muses
Series*

Artist: Sergio Benvenuti.
Artist's signature appears on
front

Ivory alabaster

Diameter: 21.6 centimetres
(8 ¹/₂ inches)

Attached back hanger

Edition size undisclosed,
limited by announced period of
issue

Numbered, with certificate

38-V90-4.1
1985 *Erato*
Issue price: £ 34.85

38-V90-4.2
1985 *Clio*
Issue price: £ 34.85

38-V90-4.3
1986 *Terpsichore*
Issue price: £ 34.85

38-V90-4.4
1986 *Euterpe*
Issue price: £ 34.85
Series Closed

*Renaissance
Madonnas: Gifts of
Maternal Love Series*

Artist: Alberto Santangela.
Artist's signature appears on
front

Hand-painted ivory alabaster

Diameter: 21.6 centimetres
(8 ¹/₂ inches)

Edition size undisclosed,
limited by announced period of
issue

Numbered, with certificate

38-V90-5.1
1986 *The Gift of Wisdom*
Issue price: £ 43.45

38-V90-5.2
1987 *The Gift of Faith*
Issue price: £ 43.45

38-V90-5.3
1987 *The Gift of Comfort*
Issue price: unavailable at press time

38-V90-5.4
1987 *The Gift of Patience*
Issue price: unavailable at press time

38-V90-5.5
1988 *The Gift of Devotion*
Issue price: unavailable at press time

The Christmas Crèche Series

Artist: Ennio Furiesi. Artist's signature appears on front

Ivory alabaster

Diameter: 20.3 centimetres (8 inches)

Attached back hanger

Edition size undisclosed, limited by year of issue

Numbered, with certificate

38-V90-7.1
1986 *Joy of the World*
Issue price: £ 36.95

38-V90-7.2
1987 *Hark the Herald Angels Sing*
Issue price: £ 36.95

JAPAN
FUKAGAWA

42-F78-0.0

FUKAGAWA
Arita

Although the present Fukagawa Porcelain factory was organized in Arita in the 1880s by the Fukagawa family, the heritage of its Izumistone porcelain goes back some four centuries to the discoverty of kaolin deposits on the island of Kyushu, Japan. It was there, on the slopes of Mount Izumi, that the Korean master potter Yi Samp'yŏng ended his 20-year search for a pure white clay base to be used in the manufacture of fine porcelain. As the direct result of his discovery, a number of small porcelain workshops — the first in all Japan — sprang up in the nearby town of Arita. Delicate plates and saucers were being shipped to the West from the harbour city of Imari decades before porcelain manufacture began in Europe.

The establishment of Fukagawa Porcelain was actually a merger of a number of small workshops whose standards and techniques dated back to the time of Yi Samp'yŏng. In 1913, Fukagawa was granted the title "Purveyor to the Imperial Household", which indicates patronage from the royal family of Japan. In recognition of this honour, all Fukagawa ceramics bear the imprint "Imperial". The factory, which is still in the hands of the Fukagawa family, continues to employ the original Izumiyama day from Mount Izumi to give its porcelain a uniquely white body.

In 1977, Fukagawa began its first series of collector's plates — the *Warabe No Haiku (Haiku about Children)* series. The series ended in 1980.

Master of the traditional "Sea of Whiteness" style, Suetomi is the principal artist for Fukagawa and is the recipient of the Gold Prize from Japan's Ministry of International Trade and Industry.

Warabe No Haiku
(Haiku about Children)

Artist: Suetomi. Artist's signature appears on front

Overglaze-decorated porcelain

Diameter: 26 centimetres (10 ¼ inches)

No hanger

Edition size undisclosed, limited by year of issue

Numbered, with certificate

Original Haiku poem appears on front

42-F78-1.1
1977 *Beneath the Plum Branch*
Issue price: £ 23.00

42-F78-1.2
1978 *Children of Straw*
Issue price: £ 25.45

42-F78-1.3
1979 *Dragon Dance*
Issue price: £ 25.45

42-F78-1.4
1980 *Mask Dancing*
Issue price: £ 25.45
Series Closed

JAPAN
NORITAKE
42-N60-0.0

NORITAKE
Nagoya

Founded by Baron Itschisaemon Morimura in 1904, the Noritake Porcelain Factory is one of the largest in the world and produces both high-class tableware and collectors' plates for the world market. Its German subsidiary, Deutsche Noritake GmbH, was established in 1971.

The *Christmas Series* by Noritake was begun in 1975. 1977 saw the beginning of a *Year Plate Series* which depicts the traditional Japanese symbols for long life, happiness and contentment. Both series were continued until 1981.

Christmas Series

Artist: as indicated
Porcelain
Pierced foot rim
Edition size limited to 3,000
Numbered, with certificate

42-N60-1.1
1975
Artist: Osamu Tsutsui
Issue price: £ 250.00

42-N60-1.2
1976
Artist: Kiyomi Akagi
Issue price: £ 250.00

42-N60-1.3
1977
Artist: Kiyomi Akagi
Issue price: £ 250.00

42-N60-1.4
1978
Artist: Kiyomi Akagi
Issue price: £ 250.00

42-N60-1.5
1979
Artist: Akio Kato
Issue price: £ 250.00

42-N60-1.6
1980
Artist: Akio Kato
Issue price: £ 250.00

42-N60-1.7
1981
Artist: Fujio Kojima
Issue price: £ 250.00
Series Closed

JAPAN
NORITAKE
42-N60-2.1

Artist: 1977 and 1978 Akio Kato, Toorn Jamamoto thereafter.

Porcelain

Diameter: 35.9 centimetres (14 $\frac{1}{8}$ inches)

Pierced foot rim

Edition size limited to 3,000

Numbered, with certificate

42-N60-2.1
1977
Issue price: £ 440.00

42-N60-2.2
1978
Issue price: £ 440.00

42-N60-2.3
1979
Issue price: £ 440.00

42-N60-2.4
1980
Issue price: £ 440.00

42-N60-2.5
1981
Issue price: £ 440.00
Series Closed

54-P62-5.1
Guests are Coming for
Christmas Eve
1978 Porsgrund Traditional
Norwegian Christmas

PORSGRUND
Porsgrunn, Telemark County

Johan Jeremiason established Porsgrund, Norway's only porcelain factory, in 1885. Jeremiason began his business by importing English clay which was modelled by ceramist Carl Bauer. Porcelain tableware and decorative wares have been produced since then. Porsgrund's first collector's plate was a 1909 Christmas issue entitled "Christmas Flowers" (OTC). The series was abandoned after a single issue.

A *Christmas* series based on religious themes was introduced in 1968 and ended with the 1977 issue. The *Mother's Day* series began in 1970. In 1978 Porsgrund began a nostalgic Christmas series entitled the *Traditional Norwegian Christmas* series. The series closed in 1982.

Born in Fredrikstad, Norway, Gunnar Bratlie is a master of the traditional Norwegian folk art known as "rosemaling". He is the principal artist for Porsgrund.

Christmas Series

Artist: Gunnar Bratlie

Porcelain decorated in cobalt blue underglaze

Diameter: 17.8 centimetres (7 inches)

Pierced foot rim

Edition size undisclosed, limited by year of issue

Not numbered, without certificate

54-P62-1.1
1968 *Church Scene*
Issue price: £ 7.25

54-P62-1.2
1969 *Three Kings*
Issue price: £ 7.25

54-P62-1.3
1970 *Road to Bethlehem*
Issue price: £ 7.25

54-P62-1.4
1971 *A Child is Born in Bethlehem*
Issue price: £ 7.25

54-P62-1.5
1972 *Hark, the Herald Angels Sing*
Issue price: £ 7.25

54-P62-1.6
1973 *Promise of the Savior*
Issue price: £ 9.10

54-P62-1.7
1974 *The Shepherds*
Issue price: £ 9.10

54-P62-1.8
1975 *Jesus on the Road to the Temple*
Issue price: £ 11.85

NORWAY
PORSGRUND
54-P62-1.9

54-P62-1.9
1976 *Jesus and the Elders*
Issue price: £ 13.35

54-P62-1.10
1977 *The Draught of Fish*
Issue price: £ 14.55
Series Closed

Mother's Day Series

Artist: Gunnar Bratlie through 1982; Thorstein Rittun thereafter

Porcelain decorated in cobalt blue underglaze

Diameter: 12.7 centimetres (5 inches)

Pierced foot rim

Edition size undisclosed, limited by year of issue

Not numbered, without certificate

54-P62-2.1
1970 *Mare and Foal*
Issue price: £4.55

54-P62-2.2
1971 *Boy and Geese*
Issue price: £4.55

54-P62-2.3
1972 *Doe and Fawn*
Issue price: £6.10

54-P62-2.4
1973 *Cat and Kittens*
Issue price: £6.10

54-P62-2.5
1974 *Boy and Goats*
Issue price: £6.10

54-P62-2.6
1975 *Dog and Puppies*
Issue price: £7.60

54-P62-2.7
1976 *Girl and Calf*
Issue price: £ 9.10

54-P62-2.8
1977 *Boy and Chickens*
Issue price: £ 10.00

54-P62-2.9
1978 *Girl and Pigs*
Issue price: £ 10.60

54-P62-2.10
1979 *Boy and Reindeer*
Issue price: £ 11.85

54-P62-2.11
1980 *Girl and Lambs*
Issue price: £ 13.00

54-P62-2.12
1981 *Boy and Birds*
Issue price: £ 14.55

54-P62-2.13
1982 *Girl and Rabbits*
Issue price: £ 15.75

54-P62-2.14
1983 *Mother and Kittens*
Issue price: £ 15.75

NORWAY
PORSGRUND
54-P62-2.15

54-P62-2.15
1984 *By the Pond*
Issue price: £ 15.15

54-P62-2.16
1985 *Mother's Day*
Issue price: £ 15.50

54-P62-2.17
1986 *First Feeding*
Issue price: £ 16.45
Series Closed

Traditional Norwegian Christmas Series

Artist: Gunnar Bratlie through 1982, Thorstein Rittun thereafter. Artist's signature appears on front

Porcelain decorated in cobalt blue underglaze

Diameter: 17.8 centimetres (7 inches)

Pierced foot rim

Edition size undisclosed, limited by year of issue

Not numbered, without certificate

54-P62-5.1
1978 *Guests Are Coming for Christmas Eve*
Issue price: £ 11.95

54-P62-5.2
1979 *Home for Christmas*
Issue price: £ 11.95

54-P62-5.3
1980 *Preparing for Christmas*
Issue price: £ 13.50

54-P62-5.4
1981 *Christmas Skating*
Issue price: £ 14.50

54-P62-5.5
1982 *White Christmas*
Issue price: £ 15.50
Series Closed

54-P62-5.6
1983 *Christmas Quartet*
Issue price: £ 15.15

54-P62-5.7
1984 *Christmas Gifts*
Issue price: £ 23.00

54-P62-5.8
1985 *Farmer's Wedding*
Issue price: £ 23.00

54-P62-5.9
1986 *Christmas Singing*
Issue price: £ 23.00

54-P62-5.10
1987 *Dressing the Tree*
Issue price: £ 23.00

LLADRÓ

LLADRÓ
Tabernes Blanques, Valencia

The Lladró porcelain factory was established in the 1950s by three Lladró brothers – Juan, Jose and Vicente, sons of a preasant. At night, they studied porcelain designing, modelling and firing and built their first kiln while in their teens. By 1970, their factory was one of the best-equipped in Europe and had become known for its vases and figurines.

Lladró initiated its limited-edition *Mother's Day* series in 1971. The series closed in 1979.

Artists for Lladró plates were not disclosed.

Mother's Day Series

Artist: undisclosed

White bisque centre in bas relief with underglaze-decorated porcelain border and banded in gold

Diameter: 20.3 centimetres (8 inches)

No hanger

Edition size undisclosed, limited by year of issue

Not numbered, without certificate

72-L41-2.1
1971 *Kiss of the Child*
Issue price: £16.65

72-L41-2.2
1972 *Bird and Chicks*
Issue price: £16.65

72-L41-2.3
1973 *Mother and Children*
Issue price: £ 21.25

72-L41-2.4
1974 *Mother Nursing*
Issue price: £ 27.25

72-L41-2.5
1975 *Mother and Child*
Issue price: £ 36.35

72-L41-2.6
1976 *Tender Vigil*
Issue price: £ 36.35

72-L41-2.7
1977 *Mother and Daughter*
Issue price: £ 40.95

72-L41-2.8
1978 *The New Arrival*
Issue price: £ 48.50

72-L41-2.9
1979 *Off to School*
Issue price: £ 54.55
Series Closed

SWEDEN
ORREFORS

76-O74-1.1

ORREFORS
Orrefors, Smaland

Orrefors was originally established in 1726 as an ironworks. In 1898 they began manufacturing glass ink bottles and window glass. Although the ironworks was no longer profitable, Johan Ekman purchased the property in 1913. He was interested in improving the facilities for glassmaking and recognized the importance of the valuable forest land of the area as fuel for glass furnaces. He eventually built an entire community around the glassworks.

Orrefors crystal is made from a mixture of seashore sand and potash, plus a heavy lead content. The ornamentation is created by master blowers who apply liquid molten glass in desired shapes.

In 1970, Orrefors began its *Annual Cathedral* series made in untinted crystal and depicting famous places of worship. This series ended in 1978. These plates are handmade with the designs engraved in the crystal and filled with 24-karat gold.

John Selbing is regarded as one of the world's leading photographers of glass. He is credited with developing the technique which enabled production of inlaid-gold crystal plates. At the age of 19 he joined Orrefors and for 46 years handled their design, photography and advertising projects. During the last several years, he has been working independently in fine art.

Annual Cathedral Series

Artist: John Selbing

Leaded crystal with engraved designs inlaid in 24k gold

Diameter: 25.4 centimetres (10 inches)

No hanger

Edition size limited to 5,000 throught 1975; 3,000 thereafter

Numbered since 1975, without certificate

76-O74-1.1
1970 *Notre Dame Cathedral*
Issue price: £ 30.30

76-O74-1.2
1971 *Westminster Abbey*
Issue price: £ 30.30

76-O74-1.3
1972 *Basilica di San Marco*
Issue price: £ 30.30

76-O74-1.4
1973 *Cologne Cathedral*
Issue price: £ 30.30

76-O74-1.5
1974 *Tempel Rue de la Victoire, Paris*
Issue price: £ 36.35

76-O74-1.6
1975 *Basilica di San Pietro, Rome*
Issue price: £ 51.50

76-O74-1.7
1976 *Christ Church, Philadelphia*
Issue price: £ 51.50

76-O74-1.8
1977 *Masiid-E-Shah*
Issue price: £ 54.55

76-O74-1.9
1978 *Santiago de Compostela*
Issue price: £ 57.60
Series Closed

SWEDEN
RÖRSTRAND
76-R54-1.1

RÖRSTRAND
Lidkoping

The Rörstrand porcelain factory is Sweden's oldest pottery and the second oldest in Europe. Originally founded in Stockholm in 1726 under government patronage, the plant was later moved inland to Lidkoping for safety reasons during World War II.

Rörstrand is one of the few factories in the world that produces all three ceramic bodies — porcelain, stoneware and high-fired earthenware. The output of the factory includes both dinner-ware and decorative art, including collector's plates. Rörstrand's first collector's plate series was a *Christmas* series started in 1904 and ended in 1926. In 1968 Roerstrand began its series of square *Christmas* plates with designs derived from Swedish folk tales and traditions.

Rörstrand artist Gunnar Nylund has exhibited his work at the Swedish National Museum and is widely known for his monumental ceramic reliefs.

Christmas Series

Artist: Gunnar Nylund

Porcelain decorated in Scandia blue underglaze

Diameter: 19 centimetres (7 1/2 inches)

Pierced foot rim

Edition size undisclosed, limited by year of issue

Not numbered, without certificate

76-R54-1.1
1968 *Bringing Home the Tree*
Issue price: £ 5.95

76-R54-1.2
1969 *Fisherman Sailing Home*
Issue price: £ 6.50

76-R54-1.3
1970 *Nils with His Geese*
Issue price: £ 6.50

76-R54-1.4
1971 *Nils in Lapland*
Issue price: £ 7.50

76-R54-1.5
1972 *Dalecarlian Fiddler*
Issue price: £ 7.95

76-R54-1.6
1973 *Farm in Smaland*
Issue price: £ 8.50

76-R54-1.7
1974 *Vadstena*
Issue price: £ 8.50

76-R54-1.8
1975 *Nils in Vastmanland*
Issue price: £ 9.95

76-R54-1.9
1976 *Nils in Uppland*
Issue price: £ 14.50

76-R54-1.10
1977 *Nils in Varmland*
Issue price: £ 14.50

76-R54-1.11
1978 *Nils in Fjallbacka*
Issue price: £ 14.95

SWEDEN
RÖRSTRAND
76-R54-1.12

76-R54-1.12
1979 *Nils in Vaestergoetland*
Issue price: £ 14.95

76-R54-1.13
1980 *Nils in Halland*
Issue price: £ 33.30

76-R54-1.14
1981 *Nils in Gotland*
Issue price: £ 33.35

76-R54-1.15
1982 *Nils at Skansen in Stockholm*
Issue price: £ 28.80

76-R54-1.16
1983 *Nils in Oland*
Issue price: £ 25.75

76-R54-1.17
1984 *Nils in Angermanland*
Issue price: £ 25.75

76-R54-1.18
1985 *Nils in Jamtland*
Issue price: £ 25.75

76-R54-1.19
1986 *Nils in Karlskrona*
Issue price: £ 31.25

76-R54-1.20
1987 *Nils in Dalsland*
Issue price: £ 32.25

78-L5-1.1 Grandfather Tells a Story
1986 Langenthal, Anker's Heritage
Series
This plate was introduced in 1986 as
the first from Switzerland, which has a
small but highly-regarded porcelain
industry.

78-L5-0.0

LANGENTHAL
Langenthal

The Langenthal Swiss China Works was founded 80 years ago when a group of Swiss investors decided to apply their business skills to the manufacture of hard-paste porcelain. The decision was not an easy one because everything, from raw materials to skilled craftsmen, had to be imported.

Today, Langenthal is respected all over the world as a superior manufacturer of fine porcelain. Although materials must still be imported, Langenthal craftsmen are locally trained through the company's rigorous apprenticeship program. Known as a pioneer in applying modern technology to the ancient traditions of porcelain making, the company is an excellent example of Swiss efficiency. Scientists and craftsmen work together to insure that every piece of porcelain is unsurpassed in delicacy, translucency and strength.

The *Anker's Heritage* series introduces the first collector's plate series based on artwork by the beloved Swiss painter Albert Anker. Initiated in 1986, the series is endorsed by the Neuchatel Museum of Fine Árts, home of one of the largest and finest Anker collections in the world.

Albert Anker, one of the best-known of Swiss artists, is also perhaps the most accomplished of native Swiss painters. The *Anker's Heritage* series, depicting scenes of everyday Swiss village life from the 19th century, reflects the strong values of hardy self-reliance, industry, order and respect for the individual that define the Swiss character.

Anker's Heritage Series

Artist: Albert Anker. Artist's signature appears on front

Porcelain banded in 14k gold

Diameter: 22.9 centimetres (9 inches)

Pierced foot rim

Edition size undisclosed, limited by announced period of issue

Numbered, with certificate

78-L5-1.1
1986 *Grandfather Tells a Story*
Issue price: £ 19.95

78-L5-1.2
1987 *The First Smile*
Issue price: £ 19.95

78-L5-1.3
1987 *Girl Feeding Chickens*
Issue price: £ 21.95

78-L5-1.4
1987 *The School Promenade*
Issue price: £ 21.95

78-L5-1.5
1987 *The Day-Nursery*
Issue price: £ 21.95

SWITZERLAND
LANGENTHAL

78-L5-2.1

Appenzeller Traditions Series

Artist: Dölf Mettler. Artist's signature appears on front

Fine china

Diameter: 22.5 centimetres (8.9 inches)

Pierced foot rim

Edition size undisclosed, limited by announced period of issue

Numbered, with certificate

78-L5-2.1
1987 *Summer Trip to the Alp*
Issue price: £ 23.95

78-L5-2.2
1987 *Autumn Dance*
Issue price: £ 23.95

78-L5-2.3
1988 *Winter Carnival*
Issue price: unavailable at press time

78-L5-2.4
1988 *Farmer's Wedding*
Issue price: unavailable at press time

Alpine Wildlife Series

Artist: Sonja Meyer. Artist's signature appears on front

Fine china, banded in gold

Diameter: 19 centimetres (7 ¹/₂ inches)

No hanger

Edition size undisclosed, limited by announced period of issue

Numbered, with certificate

78-L5-3.1
1987 *Marmots on the Watch*
Issue price unavailable at press time

78-L5-3.2
1988 *Golden Eagle*
Issue price: unavailable at press time

78-L5-3.3
1988 *Ibex*
Issue price: unavailable at press time

Artists of the World

ARTISTS OF THE WORLD
Scottsdale, Arizona

Initially organized as DeGrazia of Scottsdale, the company was founded by James LaFond to represent Arizona artist Ted De Grazia. The present name, Artists of the World, was adopted in 1977 when the company's scope was enlarged to include additional artists.

Most DeGrazia plate issues produced by the company are today listed under the dual heading Fairmont/Artists of the World; they are found in this book under the Fairmont name, which was the company that originally manufactured them.

Children of Aberdeen, a proprietary series with artwork by Kee Fung Ng, began in 1979 and depicts the children who live on boats anchored at the fishing village of Aberdeen near Hong Kong. The series closed in 1984. (For another Ng series, see China, Republic of, PAVILION OF T'SANG YING HSÜAN.)

In 1987, Artist's of the World introduced the *Children of the Sun* series by Ted DeGrazia; it was made on Knowles china.

Children of Aberdeen Series

Artist: Kee Fung Ng. Artist's signature appears on front

China banded in gold

Diameter: 25.4 centimetres (10 inches)

No hanger

Edition size undisclosed, limited by year of issue

Numbered, with certificate

84-A72-1.1
1979 *Girl with Little Brother*
Issue price: £ 25.00

84-A72-1.2
1980 *Sampan Girl*
Issue price: £ 25.00

84-A72-1.3
1981 *Girl with Little Sister*
Issue price: £ 27.50

84-A72-1.4
1982 *Girl with Seashells*
Issue price: £ 30.00

84-A72-1.5
1983 *Girl with Seabirds*
Issue price: £ 30.00

84-A72-1.6
1984 *Brother and Sister*
Issue price: £ 30.00
Series Closed

DeGrazia's Children of the Sun Series

Artist: Ted DeGrazia. Artist's signature appears on front

Overglaze-decorated china

Diameter: 21.6 centimetres (8 ¹/₂ inches)

No hanger

Edition size undisclosed, limited by announced period of issue

Numbered, with certificate

84-A72-13.1
1987 *Spring Blossoms*
Issue price: £ 21.95

84-A72-13.2
1987 *My Little Pink Bird*
Issue price: £ 21.95

84-A72-13.3
1988 *Bright Flowers of the Desert*
Issue price: unavailable at press time

UNITED STATES
FAIRMONT

84-F4-1.1

Fairmont

Perfect Porcelain

FAIRMONT
Pasadena, Californien

Fairmont China was established in 1976 to produce limited-edition plates. Two series began that year: the *Holiday* series with artwork by Ted DeGrazia and the *Famous Clowns* series by comedian Red Skelton. The *Famous Clowns* series ended in 1979 and the *Holiday* series closed in 1985. In 1978, Fairmont issued the third plate in the *DeGrazia Children* series, originally started by Gorham (see United States, GORHAM). This series ended in 1985. In 1979, Fairmont started the *Classical American Beauties* series by artist Vincent, which closed in 1981, and, in 1981, began the *Playful Memories* series with artwork by Sue Etém. This series ended in 1983.

In 1985, Fairmont introduced the *DeGrazia's Children at Play* series. In 1986, the *DeGrazia's Western* series began. All these DeGrazia series are produced under the auspices of Artists of the World (see United States, ARTISTS OF THE WORLD).

DeGrazia Holiday Series

Artist: Ted DeGrazia. Artist's signature appears on front

China banded in gold

Diameter: 26 centimetres (10 ¹/₄ inches)

No hanger

Edition size limited to 10,000

Numbered since 1977, without certificate

84-F4-1.1
1976 *The Festival of Lights*
Issue price: £ 27.50

84-F4-1.2
1977 *The Bell of Hope*
Issue price: £ 27.50

84-F4-1.3
1978 *Little Madonna*
Issue price: £ 27.50

84-F4-1.4
1979 *The Nativitu*
Issue price: £ 30.50

84-F4-1.5
1980 *Little Pima Indian Drummer Boy*
Issue price: £ 30.50

84-F4-1.6
1981 *Little Prayer — the Christmas Angel*
Issue price: £ 33.50

84-F4-1.7
1982 *The Blue Boy*
Issue price: £ 36.50

84-F4-1.8
1983 *Heavenly Blessings*
Issue price: £ 39.50

84-F4-1.9
1984 *Navajo Madonna*
Issue price: £ 39.50

84-F4-1.10
1985 *Saguaro Dance*
Issue price: £ 39.50

UNITED STATES
FRANKLIN MINT

84-F64-0.0

FRANKLIN MINT
Franklin Center, Pennsylvania

The Franklin Mint, the world's largest private mint, was established in 1965 in the Philadelphia area by Joseph Segel. The firm specializes in porcelain collectibles, sculptures, fine art prints, jewellery and has several international subsidiaries and branches.

The Franklin Mint entered the limited-edition plate field in 1970 with the six-plate *Rockwell Christmas* series, crafted in sterling silver.

The *Rockwell Christmas* series is the only one to be designed especially for the collector's plate market by the artist, Norman Rockwell.

Rockwell Christmas Series

Artist: Norman Rockwell.
Artist's signature appears on front

Etched sterling silver

Diameter: 20.3 centimetres (8 inches)

Edition size: as indicated

Numbered, with certificate since 1972

84-F64-1.1
1970 *Bringing Home the Tree*
Edition size: 18.321
Issue price: £ 61.00

84-F64-1.2
1971 *Under the Mistletoe*
Edition size: 24.792
Issue price: £ 61.00

84-F64-1.3
1972 *The Carollers*
Edition size: 29.074
Issue price: £ 76.00

84-F64-1.4
1973 *Trimming the Tree*
Edition size: 18.010
Issue price: £ 76.00

84-F64-1.5
1974 *Hanging the Wreath*
Edition size: 12.822
Issue price: £ 106.00

84-F64-1.6
1975 *Home for Christmas*
Edition size: 11.059
Issue price: £ 109.00
Series Closed

GORHAM
Providence, Rhode Island

In 1831, silversmith Jabez Gorham, established the Gorham Corporation. Today a division of Textron, the firm is one of the world's largest producers of sterling and hollowware, figurines and ornaments.

Gorham Corporation acquired crystal and china manufacturing companies in 1970, enabling it to produce limited-edition plates in china as well as silver.

Gorham's *Rockwell Four Seasons* series, which began in 1971 and ended in 1980, was comprised of four plates each year (spring, summer, autumn, and winter). A *Christmas* series, also with artwork by Norman Rockwell, was started in 1974. The *DeGrazia Children* series and the *Sugar and Spice* series, with artwork by Leo Jansen, began in 1976 with the former ending in 1977 and the latter ending in 1979.

Since 1978, Fairmont China has made the *DeGrazia Chidren* plates (see United States, FAIRMONT). The *Sugar and Spice* series is produced for Kern Collectibles by Gorham (see United States, KERN COLLECTIBLES).

Rockwell Four Seasons Series

Artist: Norman Rockwell. Artist's signature appears on front

China banded in 24k gold

Diameter: 26.7 centimetres (10 ½ inches)

No hanger

Edition size undisclosed, limited by year of issue

Not numbered, without certificate

Issued in sets of four

84-G58-1.1-1
1971 *A Boy and His Dog*
A Boy Meets His Dog
Issue price: £ 30.50

84-G58-1.1-2
1971 *Adventurers Between Adventurers*

84-G58-1.1-3
1971 *A Mysterious Malady*

84-G58-1.1-4
1971 *Pride of a Parenthood*

84-G58-1.2-1
1972 *Young Love Flying Colers*
Issue price: £ 36.50

84-G58-1.2-2
1972 *Beguiling Buttercup*

84-G58-1.2-3
1972 *A Scholarly Pace*

84-G58-1.2-4
1972 *Downhill Daring*

UNITED STATES
GORHAM
84-G58-1.3-1

84-G58-1.3-1
1973 *The Ages of Love*
Sweet Song So Young
Issue price: £ 36.50

84-G58-1.3-2
1973 *Flowers in Tender Bloom*

84-G58-1.3-3
1973 *Fondly Do We Remember*

84-G58-1.3-4
1973 *Gaily Sharing Vintage*

84-G58-1.4-1
1974 *Grandpa and Me; Day*
Dreamers
Issue price: £ 36.50

84-G58-1.4-2
1974 *Goin' Fishin'*

84-G58-1.4-3
1974 *Pensive Pals*

84-G58-1.4-4
1974 *Gay Blades*

84-G58-1.5-1
1975 *Me and My Pal;*
Young Man's Fancy
Issue price: £ 42.50

84-G58-1.5-2
1975 *Fisherman's Paradise*

84-G58-1.5-3
1975 *Disatrous Daring*

84-G58-1.5-4
1975 *A Little Good Bath*

84-G58-1.6-1
1976 *Grand Pals; Soaring Spirits*
Issue price: £ 42.50

84-G58-1.6-2
1976 *Fish Finders*

84-G58-1.6-3
1976 *Ghostly Geurds*

84-G58-1.6-4
1976 *Snow Sculpture*

84-G58-1.7-1
1977 *Going on Sixteen, Sweet Serenade*
Issue price: £ 45.50

84-G58-1.7-2
1977 *Shear Agena*

UNITED STATES
GORHAM
84-G58-1.7-3

84-G58-1.7-3
1977 *Pilgrimage*

84-G58-1.7-4
1977 *Chilling Chore*

84-G58-1.8-1
1978 *The Tender Years; Spring Tonic*
Issue price: £ 61.00

84-G58-1.8-2
1978 *Cool Aid*

84-G58-1.8-3
1978 *Chilly Reception*

84-G58-1.8-4
1978 *New Year Look*

84-G58-1.9-1
1979 *A Helping Hand;*
Closed for Business
Issue price: £ 61.00

84-G58-1.9-2
1979 *Swatter's Rights*

84-G58-1.9-3
1979 *The Coal Season's Coming*

84-G58-1.9-4
1979 *Year End Count*

84-G58-1.10-1
1980 *Dad's Boy; In His Spirit*
Issue price: £ 82.00

84-G58-1.10-2
1980 *Trout Dinner*

84-G58-1.10-3
1980 *Careful Aim*

84-G58-1.10-4
1980 *Ski Skills*
Series Closed

UNITED STATES
INCOLAY

84-I31-1.1

Incolay Studios of California

INCOLAY
San Fernando, Californien

Incolay Studios has been creating cameo *objets d'art* in Incolay stone since 1965. The manufacturing process by which Incolay stone is created is a closely guarded secret, but it is acknowledged that the process includes the addition of a range of quartz-based minerals to replicate the colouring and weight of semi-precious stone cameos of the past.

Incolay Studios began its first series of collector's plates, the *Romantic Poets Collection,* in 1977. The series is inspired by the poetry of early 19th-century poets and it closed in 1985. In 1979, a second series of cameo plates, the *Great Romances of*

History Collection, began. This series ended in 1982. The *Voyage of Ulysses* series began in 1984.

Gayle Bright Appleby was the designer of the first four issues in the *Romantic Poets Collection.* Roger Akers completed the collection. Carl Romanelli was the sculptor for the *Great Romances of History* series and Alan Brunettin is the creator of *Voyage of Ulysses.* In 1987, Roger Akers created his first independent series for Incolay, the *Love Sonnets of Shakespeare* series. Alan Brunettin began his *The Fall of Troy* series, a sequel to the *Ulysses* series, in the same year.

Romantic Poets Collection

Artist: as indicated. Artist's signature appears on front

Incolay stone with high relief cameos

Diameter: 26 centimetres
(10 ¼ inches)

Attached back hanger

Edition size undisclosed, limited by announced period of issue

Numbered, with certificate

84-I31-1.1
1977 She Walks in Beauty
Artist: Gayle Bright Appleby
Issue price: £ 30.00

84-I31-1.2
1978 A Thing of Beauty Is a Joy Forever
Artist: Gayle Bright Appleby
Issue price: £ 30.00

84-I31-1.3
1979 *To a Skylark*
Artist: Gayle Bright Appleby
Issue price: £ 32.50

84-I31-1.4
1980 *She Was a Phantom of Delight*
Artist: Gayle Bright Appleby
Issue price: £ 32.50

84-I31-1.5
1981 *The Kiss*
Artist: Roger Akers
Issue price: £ 32.50

84-I31-1.6
1982 *My Heart Leaps Up, When I Behold*
Artist: Roger Akers
Issue price: £ 32.50

84-I31-1.7
1983 *I Stood Tiptoe*
Artist: Roger Akers
Issue price: £ 35.75

84-I31-1.8
1984 *A Dream*
Artist: Roger Akers
Issue price: £ 35.75

84-I31-1.9
1985 *The Recollection*
Artist: Roger Akers
Issue price: £ 35.75
Series Closed

UNITED STATES
INCOLAY

84-I31-3.1

Great Romances of History Collection

Artist: Carl Romanelli. Artist's signature appears on front

Incolay stone with high relief cameos

Diameter: 26 centimetres (10 1/4 inches)

Attached back hanger

Edition size undisclosed, limited by announced period of issue

Numbered, with certificate

84-I31-3.1
1979 *Antony and Cleopatra*
Issue price: £ 39.50

84-I31-3.2
1980 *The Taj Mahal Lovers*
Issue price: £ 39.50

84-I31-3.3
1981 *Lancelot and Guinevere*
Issue price: £ 39.50

84-I31-3.4
1982 *Lord Nelson and Lady Hamilton*
Issue price: £ 42.50
Series Closed

Voyage of Ulysses Series

Artist: Alan Brunettin. Artist's signature appears on front

Incolay stone with high-relief cameos

Diameter: 21.6 centimetres (8 1/2 inches)

Pierced foot riem

Edition size undisclosed, limited by year of issue

Numbered, with certificate

84-I31-4.1
1984 *The Isle of Circe*
Issue price: £ 38.85

84-I31-4.2
1985 *The Sirens*
Issue price: £ 38.85

84-I31-4.3
1985 *The Isle of Calypso*
Issue price: £ 38.85

84-I31-4.4
1986 *The Land of the Phaeacians*
Issue price: £ 38.85

84-I31-4.5
1986 *The Return of Ulysses*
Issue price: £ 41.15

84-I31-4.6
1986 *Penelope and Ulysses: The Reunion*
Issue price: £ 41.15
Series Closed

Love Sonnets of Shakespeare Series

Artist: Roger Akers. Artist's signature appears on front

Incolay stone with high-relief cameos

Diameter: 27 centimetres (9 ¹/₄ inches)

Pierced foot riem

Edition size undisclosed, limited by announced period of issue

Numbered, with certificate

84-I31-6.1
1987 *Shall I Compare Thee to a Summer's Day*
Issue price: £ 38.25

84-I31-6.2
1987 *Thou Art Too Dear for My Possessing*
Issue price: £ 38.25

UNITED STATES

INCOLAY

84-I31-7.1

The Fall of Troy Series

Artist: Alan Brunettin. Artist's signature appears on front

Incolay stone with high-relief cameos

Diameter: 21.6 centimetres (8 1/2 inches)

Pierced foot riem

Edition size undisclosed, limited by announced period of issue

Numbered, with certificate

84-I31-7.1
1987 *The Judgment of Paris*
Issue price: £ 35.45

84-I31-7.2
1987 *Helen and Paris*
Issue price: £ 35.45

84-K20-7.4 Future Teacher
1983 Kern Collectibles Leaders of Tomorrow
Artist Leo Jansen earned a position of respect among collectors before his untimely death at the age of 50.

KERN COLLECTIBLES
Stillwater, Minnesota

The story of Kern Collectibles dates to 1969 when Oscar L., Kern founded Commemorative Imports, a distributor of limited-edition collectibles. Kern expanded his business one step further in 1972 with the establishment of Kern Collectibles. In 1984, Kern Collectibles was purchased by the Consumer Products Division of 3M Company. After Kern's death in 1986, the company was transferred back to the ownership of Commemorative Editions, which is now continuing several of the firm's existing series.

Kern Collectibles issues limited-edition plates produced especially for the company by several of the world's fine china manufacturers. *Leaders of Tomorrow* began in 1980 and comprised four issues by the late Leo Jansen.

Leaders of Tomorrow Series

Artist: Leo Jansen. Artist's signature appears on front

China banded in gold

Diameter: 21.6 centimetres (8 ¹/₂ inches)

No hanger

Edition size limited to 9,800

Numbered, with certificate

84-K20-7.1
1980 *Future Physician*
Issue price: £ 31.00

84-K20-7.2
1981 *Future Farmer*
Issue price: £ 31.00

84-K20-7.3
1982 *Future Florist*
Issue price: £ 31.00

84-K20-7.4
1983 *Future Teacher*
Issue price: £ 31.00
Series Closed

EDWIN M. KNOWLES
Newell, West Virginia

The Edwin M. Knowles heritage of fine china can be traced to the early 19th century when Isaac Knowles, father of Edwin, established the family firm – Knowles, Taylor and Knowles – in East Liverpool, Ohio. The site was chosen for its proximity to deposits of high-quality kaolin clay. The firm became well known for its delicate Lotus ware.

After apprenticing with his father's firm, Edwin established his own company in Newell, West Virginia, and became a pre-eminent force in American china, honoured by election to the presidency of the United States Potters Association.

After his death, the company ceased operations for a time until entering into an affiliation with The Bradford Exchange to preserve its time-honoured name.

The Edwin M. Knowles name has appeared on both the firm's own series, beginning with the *Wizard of Oz* in 1977 (which closed in 1980) and also on issues certified by the Rockwell Society of America since 1975 (See United States, ROCKWELL SOCIETY).

The *Americana Holidays* series, by Don Spaulding, and the landmark *Gone With the Wind* series, by Raymond Kursár, both began in 1978. The former closed in 1984 and the latter in 1986. Knowles introduced the *Csatari Grandparents* series in 1980.

The *Annie Collector's Plate* series, by William Chambers, began in 1983 and closed in 1987. The *Biblical Mothers* series, with art by Eve Licea, also began in 1983 but ended in 1986, as did the Jeanne Down's *Friends I Remember* series.

The year 1984 saw into introduction of the *Four Ancient Elements* series, *A Father's Love* and *Hibel Mother's Day*. Both the *Ancient Elements* series and *Father's Love* closed in 1985.

Also appearing in 1984 was the first of the new series based on the musical masterworks of Rodgers and Hammerstein: *The King and I*, by William Chambers. This was followed in 1985 by a second series, *Oklahoma!*, by Mort Künstler and in 1986 by *The Sound of Music* by Tony Crnkovich.

The first series ever sponsored by the *Encyclopaedia Britannica*, entitled *Birds of Your Garden*, was introduced in 1985 with art by Kevin Daniel. That year also saw the creation of the first Knowles series by the last Frances Hook, the *Legacy* series.

In 1986, besides *The Sound of Music* series, Knowles introduced two new wildlife series: *Living with Nature: Jerner's Ducks* by Bart Jerner, and the *Upland Birds of North America* by Wayne Anderson. The *American Innocents* series, designed by Barbara Marsten and Valentin Mandrajji, also appeared in 1986 and closed in 1987. Knowles also introduced the *Jessie Willcox Smith Childhood Holiday Memories* series in 1986.

In 1987, Knowles began two new series by William Chambers, *Portraits of Motherhood* and *Tom Sawyer*. Also new this year in the Rodgers and Hammerstein cycle was *South Pacific*, by Elaine Gignilliat.

Two other popular Knowles artists debuted second series: Eve Licea, with her *Licea's Christmas* series, and Mort Künstler, with *Lincoln, Man of America*. New also was *A Swan is Born*, by Lu Ann Roberts. Finally, two new animal series, *Friends in the Forest* by Kevin Daniel and *Amy Brackenbury's Cat Tales*, were also introduced.

Wizard of Oz Series

Artist: James Auckland. Artist's signature appears on front

China

Diameter: 21.6 centimetres (8 ½ inches) throught 1979; 25.4 centimetres (10 inches) for 1980 plate

No hanger

Edition size undisclosed, limited by announced period of issue

Numbered, without certificate

84-K41-1.1
1977 *Over the Rainbow*
Issue price: £ 11.95

84-K41-1.2
1978 *If I Only Had a Brain*
Issue price: £ 11.95

84-K41-1.3
1978 *If I Only Had a Heart*
Issue price: £ 11.95

84-K41-1.4
1978 *If I Were King of the Forest*
Issue price: £ 11.95

84-K41-1.5
1979 *The Wicked Witch of the West*
Issue price: £ 11.95

84-K41-1.6
1979 *Follow the Yellow Brick Road*
Issue price: £ 11.95

84-K41-1.7
1979 *Wonderful Wizard of Oz*
Issue price: £ 11.95

84-K41-1.8
1980 *The Grand Finale (We're Off to See the Wizard)*
Issue price: £ 13.50
Series Closed

UNITED STATES
EDWIN M. KNOWLES

84-K41-3.1

Gone With the Wind Series

Artist: Raymond Kursár.
Artist's signature appears on front

China

Diameter: 21.6 centimetres
(8 ½ inches) throught 1985;
25.7 centimetres (10 ⅛ inches)
for 1986 plate

No hanger

Edition size undisclosed,
limited by announced period of
issue

Numbered, with certificate

84-K41-3.1
1978 *Scarlett*
Issue price: £ 12.40

84-K41-3.2
1979 *Ashley*
Issue price: £ 12.40

84-K41-3.3
1980 *Melanie*
Issue price: £ 12.40

84-K41-3.4
1981 *Rhett*
Issue price: £ 13.40

84-K41-3.5
1982 *Mammy Lacing Scarlett*
Issue price: £ 13.40

84-K41-3.6
1983 *Melanie Gives Birth*
Issue price: £ 14.75

84-K41-3.7
1984 *Scarlett's Green Dress*
Issue price: £ 14.75

84-K41-3.8
1985 *Rhett and Bonnie*
Issue price: £ 16.25

84-K41-3.9
1986 *Scarlett and Rhett: The Finale*
Issue price: £ 16.25
Series Closed

Csatari Grandparent Plate Series

Artist: Joseph Csatari. Artist's signature appears on front

China

Diameter: 21.6 centimetres (8 ¹/₂ inches)

No hanger

Edition size undisclosed, limited by announced period of issue

Numbered, with certificate

84-K41-4.1
1980 *Bedtime Story*
Issue price: £ 11.40

84-K41-4.2
1981 *The Skating Lesson*
Issue price: £ 11.40

84-K41-4.3
1982 *The Cookie Tasting*
Issue price: £ 11.40

84-K41-4.4
1983 *The Swinger*
Issue price: £ 12.50

84-K41-4.5
1984 *The Skating Queen*
Issue price: £ 12.50

UNITED STATES
EDWIN M. KNOWLES

84-K41-4.6

84-K41-4.6
1985 *The Patriot's Parade*
Issue price: £ 15.50

84-K41-4.7
1986 *The Home Run*
Issue price: £ 15.50

84-K41-4.8
1987 *The Sneak Preview*
Issue price: £ 15.50

Annie Collector's Plate Series

Artist: William Chambers. Artist's signature appears on front

China

Diameter: 21.6 centimetres (8 ½ inches)

No hanger

Edition size undisclosed, limited by announced period of issue

Numbered, with certificate

84-K41-5.1
1983 *Annie and Sandy*
Issue price: £ 16.15

84-K41-5.2
1983 *Daddy Warbucks*
Issue price: £ 16.15

84-K41-5.3
1983 *Annie and Grace*
Issue price: £ 17.15

84-K41-5.4
1984 *Annie and the Orphans*
Issue price: £ 17.15

84-K41-5.5
1985 *Tomorrow*
Issue price: £ 18.85

84-K41-5.6
1986 *Annie and Miss Hannigan*
Issue price: £ 18.85

84-K41-5.7
1986 *Annie, Lily and Rooster*
Issue price: £ 18.85

84-K41-5.8
1986 *Grande Finale*
Issue price: £ 18.85
Series Closed

Biblical Mothers Series

Artist: Eve Licea. Artist's signature appears on front

China banded in 24k gold

Diameter: 26 centimetres (10 ¹/₄ inches)

No hanger

Edition size undisclosed, limited by announced period of issue

Numbered, with certificate

84-K41-6.1
1983 *Bathsheba and Salomon*
Issue price: £ 27.65

84-K41-6.2
1984 *The Judgment of Salomon*
Issue price: £ 27.65

84-K41-6.3
1984 *Pharaoh's Daughter and Moses*
Issue price: £ 29.95

84-K41-6.4
1984 *Mary and Jesus*
Issue price: £ 29.95

84-K41-6.5
1985 *Sarah and Isaac*
Issue price: £ 29.95

UNITED STATES
EDWIN M. KNOWLES

84-K41-6.6

84-K41-6.6
1986 *Rebekka, Jakob and Esau*
Issue price: £ 29.95
Series Closed

Jeanne Down's Friends I Remember Series

Artist: Jeanne Down. Artist's signature appears on front

China

Diameter: 21.6 centimetres (8 ¹/₂ inches)

No hanger

Edition size undisclosed, limited by announced period of issue

Numbered, with certificate

84-K41-7.1
1983 *Fish Story*
Issue price: £ 17.90

84-K41-7.2
1984 *Office Hours*
Issue price: £ 17.90

84-K41-7.3
1984 *A Coat of Paint*
Issue price: £ 17.90

84-K41-7.4
1985 *Here Comes the Bride*
Issue price: £ 17.90

84-K41-7.5
1985 *Fringe Benefits*
Issue price: £ 19.25

84-K41-7.6
1985 *High Society*
Issue price: £ 19.25

84-K41-7.7
1986 *The Flower Arrangement*
Issue price: £ 19.65

84-K41-7.8
1986 *The Taste Test*
Issue price: £ 19.65
Series Closed

Four Ancient Elements Series

Artistin: Georgia Lambert.
Artist's signature appears on front

China

Diameter: 23.5 centimetres
(9 ¹/₄ inches)

No hanger

Edition size undisclosed, limited by announced period of issue

Numbered, with certificate

84-K41-8.1
1984 *Earth*
Issue price: £ 19.45

84-K41-8.2
1984 *Water*
Issue price: £ 19.45

84-K41-8.3
1985 *Air*
Issue price: £ 21.45

84-K41-8.4
1985 *Fire*
Issue price: £ 21.45
Series Closed

323

UNITED STATES
EDWIN M. KNOWLES

84-K41-9.1

Hibel Mother's Day Series

Artist: Edna Hibel. Artist's signature appears on front

China banded in burnished gold

Diameter: 21.6 centimetres (8 ¹/₂ inches)

No hanger

Edition size undisclosed, limited by announced period of issue

Numbered, with certificate

84-K41-9.1
1984 *Abby and Lisa*
Issue price: £ 28.90

84-K41-9.2
1985 *Erica and Jamie*
Issue price: £ 28.90

84-K41-9.3
1986 *Emily and Jennifer*
Issue price: £ 31.75

84-K41-9.4
1987 *Catherine and Heather*
Issue price: £ 32.25

A Father's Love Series

Artist: Betsey Bradley. Artist's signature appears on front

China

Diameter: 21.6 centimetres (8 ¹/₂ inches)

No hanger

Edition size undisclosed, limited by announced period of issue

Numbered, with certificate

84-K41-10.1
1984 *Open Wide*
Issue price: £ 18.15

84-K41-10.2
1984 *Batter Up*
Issue price: £ 18.15

84-K41-10.3
1985 *Little Shaver*
Issue price: £ 19.95

84-K41-10.4
1985 *Swing Time*
Issue price: £ 19.95
Series Closed

The King and I Series

Artist: William Chambers.
Artist's signature appears on front

China

Diameter: 21.6 centimetres
(8 ¹/₂ inches)

No hanger

Edition size undisclosed, limited by announced period of issue

Numbered, with certificate

84-K41-11.1
1984 *A Puzzlement*
Issue price: £ 13.55

84-K41-11.2
1985 *Shall We Dance?*
Issue price: £ 13.55

84-K41-11.3
1985 *Getting to Know You*
Issue price: £ 15.55

84-K41-11.4
1985 *We Kiss in a Shadow*
Issue price: £ 15.55
Series Closed

UNITED STATES

EDWIN M. KNOWLES

84-K41-12.1

Birds of Your Garden Series

Artist: Kevin Daniel. Artist's signature appears on front

China

Diameter: 21.6 centimetres (8 ¹/₂ inches)

No hanger

Edition size undisclosed, limited by announced period of issue

Numbered, with certificate

84-K41-12.1
1985 *The Cardinal*
Issue price: £ 13.75

84-K41-12.2
1985 *The Blue Jay*
Issue price: £ 13.75

84-K41-12.3
1985 *The Baltimore Oriole*
Issue price: £ 13.75

84-K41-12.4
1986 *Die Chickadee*
Issue price: £ 15.85

84-K41-12.5
1986 *The Bluebird*
Issue price: £ 15.85

84-K41-12.6
1986 *The Robin*
Issue price: £ 15.85

84-K41-12.7
1987 *The Hummingbird*
Issue price: £ 17.25

84-K41-12.8
1987 *The Goldfinch*
Issue price: £ 17.25

Edna Hibel Christmas Series

Artist: Edna Hibel. Artist's signature appears on front

China banded in 24k gold

Diameter: 26 centimetres (10 $^1/4$ inches)

No hanger

Edition size undisclosed, limited by announced period of issue

Numbered, with certificate

84-K41-15.1
1985 *The Angels' Message*
Issue price: £ 32.25

84-K41-15.2
1986 *The Gifts of the Magi*
Issue price: £ 32.35

84-K41-15.3
1987 *The Flight Into Egypt*
Issue price: £ 34.25

A Swan is Born Series

Artist: Lu Ann Roberts. Artist's signature appears on front

Overglaze-decorated china

Diameter: 21.6 centimetres (8 $^1/2$ inches)

No hanger

Edition size undisclosed, limited by announced period of issue

Numbered, with certificate

84-K41-16.1
1986 *Hopes and Dreams*
Issue price: £ 19.95

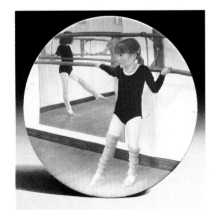

84-K41-16.2
1987 *At the Barre*
Issue price: £ 20.55

327

UNITED STATES
EDWIN M. KNOWLES

84-K41-17.1

Oklahoma! Series

Artist: Mort Künstler. Artist's signature appears on front

China

Diameter: 21.6 centimetres (8 ½ inches)

No hanger

Edition size undisclosed, limited by announced period of issue

Numbered, with certificate

84-K41-17.1
1985 *Oh, What a Beautiful Mornin'*
Issue price: £ 19.95

84-K41-17.2
1986 *The Surrey With the Fringe on Top*
Issue price: £ 19.95

84-K41-17.3
1986 *I Cain't Say No*
Issue price: £ 19.95

84-K41-17.4
1986 *Oklahoma!*
Issue price: £ 19.95
Series Closed

The Sound of Music Series

Artist: Tony Crnkovich. Artist's signature appears on front

China

Diameter: 21.6 centimetres (8 ½ inches)

No hanger

Edition size undisclosed, limited by announced period of issue

Numbered, with certificate

84-K41-18.1
1986 *The Sound of Music*
Issue price: £ 17.25

84-K41-18.2
1986 *Do-Re-Mi*
Issue price: £ 17.25

84-K41-18.3
1986 *My Favorite Things*
Issue price: £ 17.25

84-K41-18.4
1986 *Laendler*
Issue price: £ 18.95

84-K41-18.5
1987 *Edelweiss*
Issue price: £ 18.95

Upland Birds of North America Series

Artist: Wayne Anderson.
Artist's signature appears on front

China

Diameter: 21.6 centimetres
(8 ¹/₂ inches)

No hanger

Edition size undisclosed,
limited by announced period of
issue

Numbered, with certificate

84-K41-20.1
1986 *The Pheasant*
Issue price: £ 14.95

84-K41-20.2
1986 *The Grouse*
Issue price: £ 14.95

84-K41-20.3
1987 *The Quail*
Issue price: £ 16.95

84-K41-20.4
1988 *Wild Turkey*
Issue price: unavailable

84-K41-20.5
1988 *The Grey Partridge*
Issue price: unavailable

UNITED STATES
EDWIN M. KNOWLES

84-K41-23.1

Living with Nature:
Jerner's Ducks Series

Artist: Bart Jerner. Artist's
signature appears on front

China banded in gold

Diameter: 21.6 centimetres
(8¹/₂ inches)

No hanger

Edition size undisclosed,
limited by announced period of
issue

Numbered, with certificate

84-K41-23.1
1986 *The Pintal*
Issue price: £ 21.95

84-K41-23.2
1986 *The Mallard*
Issue price: £ 21.95

84-K41-23.3
1987 *The Wood Duck*
Issue price: £ 23.45

84-K41-23.4
1987 *The Green-Winged Teal*
Issue price: £ 23.45

84-K41-23.5
1987 *The Northern Shoveler*
Issue price: £ 23.45

Eve Licea Christmas
Series

Artist: Eve Licea. Artist's
signature appears on front

Overglaze-decorated china

Diameter: 26 centimetres
(10 ¹/₄ inches)

No hanger

Edition size undisclosed,
limited by announced period of
issue

Numbered, with certificate

84-K41-32.1
1987 *The Annunciation*
Issue price: £ 28.45

Friends of the Forest Series

Artist: Kevin Daniel. Artist's signature appears on front

China

Diameter: 21.6 centimetres (8 ¹/₂ inches)

No hanger

Edition size undisclosed, limited by announced period of issue

Numbered, with certificate

84-K41-45.1
1987 *The Rabbit*
Issue price: £ 18.95

84-K41-45.2
1987 *The Raccoon*
Issue price: £ 18.95

84-K41-45.3
1987 *The Squirrel*
Issue price: unavailable at press time

Amy Brackenbury's Cat Tales Series

Artist: Amy Brackenbury. Artist's signature appears on front

China

Diameter: 21.6 centimetres (8 ¹/₂ inches)

No hanger

Edition size undisclosed, limited by announced period of issue

Numbered, with certificate

84-K41-47.1
1987 *A Chance Meeting: American White Shorthairs*
Issue price: £ 16.95

84-K41-47.2
1987 *Gone Fishing: Main Coons*
Issue price: £ 16.95

LENOX

LENOX
Lawrenceville, New Jersey

Walter Scott Lenox and his partner, Jonathan Coxon, Sr., established the Ceramic Art Company in 1889 in Trenton, New Jersey. Their goal was to produce an American china surpassing the finest in Europe. In 1895, Lenox bought out Coxon and operated the business alone until it was reorganized in 1906 as Lenox, Inc. The plant later moved to Pomona. The firm's early products were bowls, vases, figurines, and later, tableware. All were made in "American Belleek", named for the town in Ireland this creamy, ivory-tinted ware was first produced.

In 1918, Lenox was commissioned to supply President Wilson with a complete 1,700-piece dinner service, the first wholly American china ever used in the White House. Later, both Presidents Franklin Roosevelt and Harry Truman commissioned Lenox to make sets of dinnerware. In 1981, the Reagan administration commissioned Lenox to create a 4,372-piece dinnerware set for the White House.

Today, in its facilities in Pomona, New Jersey, and Oxford, North Carolina, Lenox still handcrafts dinnerware, china gifts and collectibles with the same meticulous care as the early thimbles, inkstands and parasol handles.

In 1970, Lenox introduced its *Boehm Bird* series using paintings by artist Edward Marshall Boehm. The series ended in 1981.

Boehm Bird Series

Artist: Edward Marshall Boehm. Artist's name appears on back

China with 24 k gold design on border

Diameter: 26.7 centimetres (10 ½ inches)

No hanger

Edition size undisclosed

Not numbered, without certificate

84-L18-1.1
1970 *Wood Thrush*
Issue price: £ 21.25

84-L18-1.2
1971 *Goldfinch*
Issue price: £ 21.25

84-L18-1.3
1972 *Mountain Bluebird*
Issue price: £ 22.75

84-L18-1.4
1973 *Meadowlark*
Issue price: £ 24.75

84-L18-1.5
1974 *Rufous Hummingbird*
Issue price: £ 27.25

84-L18-1.6
1975 *American Redstart*
Issue price: £ 30.25

84-L18-1.7
1976 *Cardinal*
Issue price: £ 32.25

84-L18-1.8
1977 *Robins*
Issue price: £ 33.25

UNITED STATES
LENOX

84-L18-1.9

84-L18-1.9
1978 *Mockingbirds*
Issue price: £ 35.15

84-L18-1.10
1979 *Golden-Crowned Kinglets*
Issue price: £ 39.45

84-L18-1.11
1980 *Black-Throated Blue Warblers*
Issue price: £ 48.50

84-L18-1.12
1981 *Eastern Phoebes*
Issue price: £ 54.55
Series Closed

84-M58-1.3 Heather
1983 Morgantown Crystal, Country
Ladies

double-engraved crystal plate

MORGANTOWN CRYSTAL
Morgantown, West Virginia

Floyd Jones and his father founded the Monongahela Valley Cut Glass Company in 1912 in Morgantown, West Virginia. Their most famous design was an elegant pattern known as "Morgantown Rose". The company flourished under the direction of the Jones family for four generations. In 1977, John Heiner purchased the firm and renamed it Morgantown Crystal, which recently expanded operations to include glass etching and engraving as well as cutting.

The first limited-edition collector's plate series to bear the Morgantown Crystal hallmark, *Yates' Country Ladies,* began in 1981 and closed in 1984.

Designs for issues in the series were by Michael Yates.

Michael Yates'
Country Ladies Series

Artist: Michael Yates. signature appears on front

Full-lead crystal

Diameter: 22.6 centimetres (8 7/8 inches)

No hanger

Edition size limited to 30,000

Numbered, with certificate

84-M58-1.1
1981 *Angelica*
Issue price: £ 26.90

84-M58-1.2
1982 *Violet*
Issue price: £ 28.70

84-M58-1.3
1983 *Heather*
Issue price: £ 31.60

84-M58-1.4
1984 *Laurel*
Issue price: £ 31.60
Series Closed

NEWELL POTTERY
Newell, West Virgina

The Newell Pottery Company is a division of the Edwin M. Knowles China Company. The firm is best known for its Newellware, a variety of earthenware.

After having first produced the *Rockwell on Tour* series for the Rockwell Society of America in 1984, the Newell Pottery Company entered the limited-edition plate market under its own name with its *Sarah Stilwell Weber Calendar* series.

Sarah Stilwell Weber Calendar Series

Artist: Sarah Stilwell Weber

Newellware

Diameter: 18.4 centimetres
(7 ¹/₄ inches)

No hanger

Edition size undisclosed, limited by announced period of issue

Numbered, with certificate

84-N18-1.1
1984 *June*
Issue price: £ 19.95

84-N18-1.2
1985 *July*
Issue price: £ 19.95

84-N18-1.3
1985 *August*
Issue price: £ 19.95

84-N18-1.4
1985 *September*
Issue price: £ 21.55

84-N18-1.5
1985 *October*
Issue price: £ 21.55

84-N18-1.6
1985 *November*
Issue price: £ 21.55

84-N18-1.7
1986 *December*
Issue price: £ 21.55

84-N18-1.8
1986 *January*
Issue price: £ 21.55

84-N18-1.9
1986 *February*
Issue price: £ 21.55

84-N18-1.10
1986 *March*
Issue price: £ 23.55

84-N18-1.11
1987 *April*
Issue price: £ 23.55

UNITED STATES
PEMBERTON & OAKES

84-P19-0.0

PEMBERTON & OAKES
Santa Barbara, California

Pemberton & Oakes was founded in 1977. Originally located in Evanston, Illinois, the firm moved to Santa Barbara, California, in 1979 and opened a gallery for the display of original art works from its proprietary plate series.

The first two U.S. Bradex-listed series produced by the company, *Zolan's Children* and the *Nutcracker Ballet Plate Collection,* were introduced in 1978. They are listed under the maker's name, Viletta China Co. (see United States, VILETTA). The three most recent U.S. Bradex-listed series from the company are listed under the Pemberton & Oakes name. The *Children at Christmas Collection,* introduced in 1981, *Wonder of Childhood Collection,* introduced in 1982 and *Children and Pets* series, introduced in 1984, all feature the work of Donald Zolan, already well known to collectors for his earlier *Zolan's Children* series.

Wonder of Childhood Collection

Artist: Donald Zolan. Artist's signature appears on front

China

Diameter: 21.6 centimetres (8 1/2 inches)

No hanger

Edition size undisclosed, limited by announced period of issue

Numbered, with certificate

84-P19-1.1
1982 *Touching the Sky*
Issue price: £ 15.95

84-P19-1.2
1983 *Spring Innocence*
Issue price: £ 17.55

84-P19-1.3
1984 *Winter Angel*
Issue price: £ 17.55

84-P19-1.4
1985 *Small Wonder*
Issue price: £ 19.35

84-P19-1.5
1986 *Grandma's Garden*
Issue price: £ 19.35

84-P19-1.6
1987 *Daydreamer*
Issue price: £ 19.35

UNITED STATES
PEMBERTON & OAKES

84-P19-2.1

Children at Christmas Collection

Artist: Donald Zolan. Artist's signature appears on front

China banded in gold

Diameter: 26 centimetres (10 ¹/₄ inches)

No hanger

Edition size limited to 15,000

Numbered, with certificate

84-P19-2.1
1981 *Gift of Laurie*
Issue price: £ 29.10

84-P19-2.2
1982 *Christmas Prayer*
Issue price: £ 29.10

84-P19-2.3
1983 *Erik's Delight*
Issue price: £ 29.10

84-P19-2.4
1984 *Christmas Secret*
Issue price: £ 29.10

84-P19-2.5
1985 *Christmas Kitten*
Issue price: £ 29.10

84-P19.2.6
1986 *Laurie and the Creche*
Issue price: £ 29.10
Series Closed

Children and Pets Series

Artist: Donald Zolan. Artist's signature appears on front

China

Diameter: 19 centimetres (7 ¹/₂ inches)

No hanger

Edition size undisclosed, limited by announced period of issue

Numbered, with certificate

84-P19-3.1
1984 *Tender Moment*
Issue price: £ 19.70

84-P19-3.2
1984 *Golden Moments*
Issue price: £ 19.70

84-P19-3.3
1985 *Making Friends*
Issue price: £ 19.70

84-P19-3.4
1985 *Tender Beginning*
Issue price: £ 21.55

84-P19-3.5
1986 *Backyard Discovery*
Issue price: £ 21.55

84-P19-3.6
1986 *Waiting to Play*
Issue price: £ 21.55

PICKARD
Antioch, Illinois

Pickard was established in Edgerton, Wisconsin, in 1894 by Wilder Austin Pickard, then moved to Chicago in 1897. For some 40 years the Pickard China Studio, as the firm was then known, was a decorating company employing artists to hand-paint white blanks of bowls, pitchers, and other items obtained from factories in Europe.

In 1920, Pickard was incorporated and in 1938 moved to Antioch, Illinois, the site of the present pottery. Here the firm began making its own fine china. Today Pickard, Inc. is headed by Henry A. Pickard, a third generation descendant of the founder, making it the only American china company in the hands of the founding family.

In 1970, Pickard introduced its *Lockhart Wildlife* series, with artwork by James Lockhardt. These plates were issued in pairs during the first four years of the series, but from 1974 individual plates were issued. The series ended in 1980. The *Christmas* series began in 1976 and closed in 1981, and in 1978 Pickard began the *Children of Renoir* series, which ended in 1980. Pickard began its *Mother's Love* series in 1980 with artwork by Irene Spencer. This series ended in 1983. In 1981, Pickard introduced *Oleg Cassini's Most Beautiful Women of All Time Collection*. This series closed in 1984. In 1982, the *Symphony of Roses* series began with artwork by Irene Spencer. This series ended in 1985.

Lockhart Wildlife Series

Artist: James Lockhart. Artist's signature appears on front
China banded in 24 k gold
Diameter: as indicated
No hanger
Edition size: as indicated
Numbered, with certificate
Issued in sets of two

84-P29-1.1-1
1970 *Woodcock*
Edition: 2,000
Diameter: 26.7 centimetres
(10 ¹/₂ inches)
Issue price: £ 91.00

84-P29-1.1-2
1970 *Ruffed Grouse*

84-P29-1.2-1
1971 *Green-Winged Teal*
Edition: 2,000
Diameter: 26.7 centimetres
(10 ¹/₂ inches)
Issue price: £ 91.00

84-P29-1.2-2
1971 *Mallard*

84-P29-1.3-1
1972 *Mockingbird*
Edition: 2,000
Diameter: 26.7 centimetres
(10 ¹/₂ inches)
Issue price: £ 99.00

84-P29-1.3-2
1972 *Cardinal*

84-P29-1.4-1
1973 *Wild Turkey*
Edition: 2,000
Diameter: 26.7 centimetres
(10 ¹/₂ inches)
Issue price: £ 99.00

84-P29-1.4-2
1973 *Ring-Necked Pheasant*

84-P29-1.5
1974 *American Bald Eagle*
Edition size: 2,000
Diameter: 33 centimetres
(13 inches)
Issue price: £ 90.25

84-P29-1.6
1975 *White-Tailed Deer*
Edition size: 2,500
Diameter: 28 centimetres
(11 inches)
Issue price: £ 60.65

84-P29-1.7
1976 *American Buffalo*
Edition size: 2,500
Diameter: 33 centimetres
(13 inches)
Issue price: £ 100.00

84-P29-1.8
1977 *Great Horned Owl*
Edition size: 2,500
Diameter: 28 centimetres
(11 inches)
Issue price: £ 60.65

84-P29-1.9
1978 *American Panther*
Edition size: 2,000
Diameter: 33 centimetres
(13 inches)
Issue price: £ 106.10

84-P29-1.10
1979 *Red Foxes*
Edition size: 2,500
Diameter: 27,9 centimetres
(11 inches)
Issue price: £ 72.75

84-P29-1.11
1980 *Trumpeter Swan*
Edition size: 2,000
Diameter: 33 centimetres
(13 inches)
Issue price: £ 121.25
Series Closed

Oleg Cassini's Most Beautiful Women of All Time Collection

Artist: Oleg Cassini. Artist's signature appears on front

China banded in 24 k gold

Diameter: 26.7 centimetres (10 ¹/₂ inches)

No hanger

Edition size undisclosed, limited by year of issue

Numbered, with certificate

84-P29-5.1
1981 *Helen of Troy*
Issue price: £ 28.30

84-P29-5.2
1982 *Marie Antoinette*
Issue price: £ 35.00

84-P29-5.3
1983 *Lillie Langtry*
Issue price: £ 35.00

84-P29-5.4
1984 *Salomé*
Issue price: £ 38.45
Series Closed

Mother's Love Series

Artist: Irene Spencer. Artist's signature appears on front

China banded in 24k gold

Diameter: 23.8 centimetres (9 ³/₈ inches)

No hanger

Edition size limited to 7,500

Numbered, without certificate

84-P29-6.1
1980 *Miracle*
Issue price: £ 29.00

84-P29-6.2
1981 *Story Time*
Issue price: £ 29.00

RECO INTERNATIONAL
Port Washington, New York

Reco International was founded in 1967 by Heio W. Reich who continues as its president. From the beginning the firm has been an importer and maker of limited-edition plates. The firm has won numerous awards from the National Association of Limited Edition Dealers, and in 1986, Mr. Reich received the coveted Lee Benson Award from this organization for his service to the collectibles industry.

World of Children, Reco International's first U.S. proprietary series, was introduced in 1977, with designs by John McClelland. The series ended in 1980. A second series with designs by the same artist, *McClelland's Mother Goose* series, was introduced in 1979. In 1981, Reco International began a third series, the *McClelland Children's Circus Collection* which ended in 1983. The *Days Gone By* series, with award-winning artwork by Sandra Kuck, began in 1983 and closed in 1985. The *Becky's Day* series, with artwork by John McClelland, began in 1985 and ended in 1987.

World of Children Series

Artist: John McClelland. Artist's signature appears on front

China banded in 24 k gold

Diameter: 26.7 centimetres (10 ¹/₂ inches)

No hanger

Edition size limited to 10,000 in 1977; 15,000 thereafter

Numbered, with certificate since 1978

84-R60-1.1
1977 *Rainy Day Fun*
Issue price: £ 30.50

84-R60-1.2
1978 *When I Grow Up*
Issue price: £ 30.50

84-R60-1.3
1979 *You're Invited*
Issue price: £ 30.50

84-R60-1.4
1980 *Kittens for Sale*
Issue price: £ 30.50
Series Closed

McClellands Mother Goose Series

Artist: John McClelland. Artist's signature appears on front

China

Diameter: 21.6 centimetres (8 ¹/₂ inches)

No hanger

Edition size undisclosed, limited by year of issue

Numbered, with certificate

84-R60-2.1
1979 *Mary, Mary*
Issue price: £ 13.50

84-R60-2.2
1980 *Little Boy Blue*
Issue price: £ 13.50

84-R60-2.3
1981 *Little Miss Muffet*
Issue price: £ 13.50

84-R60-2.4
1982 *Little Jack Horner*
Issue price: £ 14.50

84-R60-2.5
1983 *Little Bo Peep*
Issue price: £ 14.50

84-R60-2.6
1984 *Diddle, Diddle Dumpling*
Issue price: £ 15.50

84-R60-2.7
1985 *Mary Had a Little Lamb*
Issue price: £ 15.50

84-R60-2.8
1986 *Jack and Jill*
Issue price: £ 15.50

McClellands Children's Circus Collection

Artist: John McClelland. Artist's signature appears on front

China

Diameter: 23.5 centimetres
(9 ¹/₄ inches)

No hanger

Edition size undisclosed, limited by announced period of issue

Numbered, with certificate

84-R60-3.1
1981 *Tommy, the Clown*
Issue price: £ 15.50

84-R60-3.2
1982 *Katie the Tightrope Walker*
Issue price: £ 15.50

84-R60-3.3
1983 *Johnny, the Strong Man*
Issue price: £ 15.50

84-R60-3.4
1984 *Maggie, the Animal Trainer*
Issue price: £ 16.95
Series Closed

Days Gone By Series

Artist: Sandra Kuck. Artist's
signature appears on front

China banded in 23 k gold

Diameter: 23.5 centimetres
(9 ¹/4 inches)

No hanger

Edition size undisclosed,
limited by announced period of
issue

Numbered, with certificate

84-R60-8.1
1983 *Sunday Best*
Issue price: £ 29.50

84-R60-8.2
1983 *Amy's Magic Horse*
Issue price: £ 29.50

84-R60-8.3
1984 *Little Anglers*
Issue price: £ 29.50

84-R60-8.4
1984 *Afternoon Recital*
Issue price: £ 29.50

84-R60-8.5
1984 *Little Tutors*
Issue price: £ 29.50

UNITED STATES
RECO INTERNATIONAL
84-R60-8.6

84-R60-8.6
1985 *Easter at Grandmother's*
Issue price: £ 32.50

84-R60-8.7
1986 *Morning Sun*
Issue price: £ 32.50

84-R60-8.8
1986 *Surrey Ride*
Issue price: £ 32.50
Series Closed

Becky's Day Series

Artist: John McClelland. Artist's
signature appears on front

China

Diameter: 21.6 centimetres
(8 ¹/₂ inches)

No hanger

Edition size undisclosed,
limited by announced period of
issue

Numbered, with certificate

84-R60-10.1
1985 *Awakening*
Issue price: £ 15.35

84-R60-10.2
1985 *Getting Dressed*
Issue price: £ 15.35

84-R60-10.3
1986 *Breakfast*
Issue price: £ 15.35

84-R60-10.4
1986 *Learning is Fun*
Issue price: £ 15.35

84-R60-10.5
1987 *Muffin Makin*
Issue price: £ 15.35

84-R60-10.6
1987 *Tub Time*
Issue price: £ 15.35

84-R60-10.7
1987 *Evening Prayer*
Issue price: £ 15.35
Series Closed

REED & BARTON
Taunton, Massachusetts

Reed & Barton Silversmiths traces its origin to a factory established by Isaac Babbitt in the early nineteenth century. In 1824 Babbitt developed an alloy, harder and more lustrous than pewter, which he named Britannia metal. Henry G. Reed and Charles E. Barton, artists working for Babbitt, acquired the firm in the 1830s and continued to manufacture Brittania ware. In the late 1840s, the factory began to produce plated silverware. Reed & Barton was incorporated in 1888 and started producing solid silver services. Sterling flatware and hollowware soon replaced plated ware as their largest line. In 1903 the firm began reproducing colonial pewter ware.

In 1970 Reed & Barton began their *Christmas* series which changes theme every three years. The first three plates are based on Christmas carols; the second three are based on fifteenth-century altar art; the next are based on American Christmas scenes; and the next depict nineteenth-century American illustrations.

Artist Robert Johnson, whose works are in private collections throughout the United States, Europe, and the Far East, developed the patented electroplating process used in the creation of the Reed & Barton *Christmas* series. The medium, known as Damascene silver, combines silver, gold, copper, and bronze, and the electroplating process is derived from a hand-craft method perfected at Damascus in the middle ages.

Christmas Series

Artist: as indicated

Damascene silver

Diameter: 27.9 centimetres
(11 inches) through 1978;
20.3 centimetres (8 inches)
thereafter

No hanger

Edition size: as indicated

Numbered without certificate
through 1978; numbered with
certificate thereafter

84-R18-2.1
1970 *A Partridge in a Pear Tree*
Artist: Robert Johnson
Edition: 2,500
Issue price: £ 33.50

84-R18-2.2
1971 *We Three Kings of Orient Are*
Artist: Robert Johnson
Edition: 7,500
Issue price: £ 36.50

84-R18-2.3
1972 *Hark! The Herald Angels Sing*
Artist: Robert Johnson
Edition: 7,500
Issue price: £ 36.50

84-R18-2.4
1973 *Adoration of the Kings*
Artist: Rogier van der Weyden
Edition: 7,500
Issue price: £ 36.50

84-R18-2.5
1974 *The Adoration of the Magi*
Artist: Fra Angelico and Fra Lippi
Edition: 7,500
Issue price: £ 39.50

84-R18-2.6
1975 *Adoration of the Kings*
Artist: Steven Lochner
Edition: 7,500
Issue price: £ 39.50

84-R18-2.7
1976 *Morning Train*
Artist: Maxwell Mays
Edition: 7,500
Issue price: £ 39.50

84-R18-2.8
1977 *Decorating the Church*
Artist: Maxwell Mays
Edition: 7,500
Issue price: £ 39.50

UNITED STATES
REED & BARTON

84-R18-2.9

84-R18-2.9
1978 *The General Store at Christmas Time*
Artist: Maxwell Mays
Edition: 7,500
Issue price: £ 39.50

84-R18-2.10
1979 *Merry Old Santa Claus*
Artist: Thomas Nast
Edition: 2,500
Issue price: £ 39.50

84-R18-2.11
1980 *Gathering Christmas Greens*
Artist: unknown
Edition: 2,500
Issue price: £ 39.50

84-R18-2.12
1981 *The Shopkeeper at Christmas*
Artist: W.L. Sheppard
Edition: 2,500
Issue price: £ 45.50
Series Closed

84-R30-1.1 Moses and the Ten
Commandments
1986 Rhodes Studio
Treasures of the Doré Bible

UNITED STATES
RHODES STUDIOS

84-R30-0.0

RHODES STUDIOS
Chicago, Illinois

Rhodes Studios searches the world to bring under its aegis the perfect union of artist and maker, to create limited editions of unusual and distinctive appeal. The firm's hallmark — the sign of the griffin — represents a mythical beast with the body of a lion and the head and wings of an eagle, which in medieval heraldry was a guardian of treasure. Today, this hallmark serves as a symbol of Rhodes Studios' dedication to the creation of "art that endures".

After first commissioning artist and sculptor Merri Roderick's work for the *Treasures of the Doré Bible* series, Rhodes located an American maker who was capable of producing her sculpture in the unique medium of hand-cast hand-finished fused bronze. This series was introduced in 1986.

The Treasures of the Doré Bible Series

Artist: Merri Roderick, Artist's signature incised on front

Hand-cast tused bronze

Diameter: 21 centimetres (8 ¹/₄ inches)

No hanger

Edition size undisclosed, limited by announced period of issue

Numbered, with certificate

84-R30-1.1
1986 *Moses and the Ten Commandments*
Issue price: £ 38.95

84-R30-1.2
1987 *Jacob and the Angel*
Issue price: £ 38.95

84-R69-0.0

RIVER SHORE
Caledonia, Michigan

River Shore, Ltd. was established in 1975 to market limited-edition collectibles.

In 1976, River Shore began its *Famous Americans* series, the first collector's plates crafted in copper. This series, based on artwork by Norman Rockwell and sculpted by Roger Brown, ended in 1979. River Shore introduced its *Signs of Love* series in 1981 with artwork by Yin-Rei Hicks.

The company ceased production of collector's plates upon the completion of the *Signs of Love* series in 1985.

Famous Americans Series

Artist: Roger Brown (after works by Norman Rockwell). Artist's signature appears on front along with name of Norman Rockwell

Copper

Diameter: 20.3 centimetres (8 inches)

No hanger

Edition size limited to 9,500

Numbered, with certificate

84-R69-1.1
1976 *Lincoln*
Issue price: £ 24.25

84-R69-1.2
1977 *Rockwell*
Issue price: £ 27.25

84-R69-1.3
1978 *Peace Corps*
Issue price: £ 27.25

84-R69-1.4
1979 *Spirit of Lindbergh*
Issue price: £ 30.25
Series Closed

Signs of Love Series

Artist: Yin-Rei Hicks. Artist's signature appears on front

China

Diameter: 21.6 centimetres (8 ¹/₂ inches)

No hanger

Edition size undisclosed, limited by announced period of issue

Numbered, with certificate

84-R69-2.1
1981 *A Kiss for Mother*
Issue price: £ 12.95

84-R69-2.2
1981 *A Watchful Eye*
Issue price: £ 12.95

UNITED STATES
RIVER SHORE
84-R69-2.3

84-R69-2.3
1982 *A Gentle Persuasion*
Issue price: £ 13.95

84-R69-2.4
1983 *A Protective Embrace*
Issue price: £ 13.95

84-R69-2.5
1983 *A Tender Coaxing*
Issue price: £ 15.35

84-R69-2.6
1984 *A Reassuring Touch*
Issue price: £ 15.35

84-R69-2.7
1985 *A Trusting Hug*
Issue price: £ 15.35

84-R69-2.8
1985 *A Loving Guidance*
Issue price: £ 15.35
Series Closed

84-R70-1.8 Wrapped Up in
Christmas
1981 Rockwell Society
Christmas series

ROCKWELL SOCIETY
Ardsley, New York

The Rockwell Society of America is a chartered non-profit organization devoted to the study and appreciation of the works of Norman Rockwell. The Society's *Christmas* series began in 1974, with the first issue manufactured by Ridgewood. Subsequent issues have been made by the Edwin M. Knowles China Company (see United States, KNOWLES). The *Mother's Day* series started in 1976 and the *Rockwell Heritage* series began in 1977. The *Rockwell's Rediscovered Women* series was introduced in 1981. It ended in 1984. The *Rockwell on Tour Collection* and *Rockwell's Light Campaign* series both started in 1983 and closed in 1984.

In 1985, the Rockwell Society introduced the first Rockwell series to earn recognition and endorsement by the Norman Rockwell Family Trust, comprised of Norman Rockwell's heirs. The first series to bear the seals of the Rockwell Society, Knowles and the Rockwell Family Trust is entitled *Rockwell's American Dream.*

Rockwell's Colonials: The Rarest Rockwells series, a tribute to the Colonial era of American history and a personal favourite of Norman Rockwell, followed in 1986. *A Mind of Her Own: Rockwell's Studies of Girlhood* series was also begun in 1986.

In 1987, the Rockwell Society introduced a series showing Norman Rockwell's insight into the "golden years" of adult life, titled *Rockwell's Golden Moments.*

Christmas Series

Artist: Norman Rockwell.
Artist's signature appears on front

China

Diameter: 21 centimetres
(8 ¹/₄ inches)

No hanger

Edition size undisclosed, limited by announced period of issue

Numbered, with certificate

84-R70-1.1
1974 *Scotty Gets His Tree*
Issue price: £ 12.50

84-R70-1.2
1975 *Angel with a Black Eye*
Issue price: £ 12.50

84-R70-1.3
1976 *Golden Christmas*
Issue price: £ 12.50

84-R70-1.4
1977 *Toy Shop Window*
Issue price: £ 12.50

84-R70-1.5
1978 *Christmas Dream*
Issue price: £ 13.40

84-R70-1.6
1979 *Somebody's Up There*
Issue price: £ 14.90

84-R70-1.7
1980 *Scotty Plays Santa*
Issue price: £ 14.90

84-R70-1.8
1981 *Wrapped Up in Christmas*
Issue price: £ 14.90

UNITED STATES
ROCKWELL SOCIETY

84-R70-1.9

84-R70-1.9
1982 *Christmas Courtship*
Issue price: £ 14.90

84-R70-1.10
1983 *Santa in the Subway*
Issue price: £ 15.35

84-R70-1.11
1984 *Santa in His Workshop*
Issue price: £ 16.35

84-R70-1.12
1985 *Grandpa Plays Santa*
Issue price: £ 16.35

84-R70-1.13
1986 *Dear Santa Claus*
Issue price: £ 17.35

84-R70-1.14
1987 *Santa's Golden Gift*
Issue price: £ 17.35

Mother's Day Series

Artist: Norman Rockwell.
Artist's signature appears on
front

China

Diameter: 21.6 centimetres
(8 ½ inches)

No hanger

Edition size undisclosed,
limited by announced period of
issue

Numbered, with certificate

84-R70-2.1
1976 *A Mother's Love*
Issue price: £ 13.30

84-70-2.2
1977 *Faith*
Issue price: £ 13.30

84-R70-2.3
1978 *Bedtime*
Issue price: £ 13.30

84-R70-2.4
1979 *Reflections*
Issue price: £ 13.30

84-R70-2.5
1980 *A Mother's Pride*
Issue price: £ 13.30

84-R70-2.6
1981 *After the Party*
Issue price: £ 13.30

84-R70-2.7
1982 *The Cooking Lesson*
Issue price: £ 13.30

84-R70-2.8
1983 *Add Two Cups and a Measure of Love*
Issue price: £ 14.65

84-R70-2.9
1984 *Grandma's Courting Dress*
Issue price: £ 15.95

84-R70-2.10
1985 *Mending Time*
Issue price: £ 15.95

84-R70-2.11
1986 *Pantry Raid*
Issue price: £ 15.95

UNITED STATES
ROCKWELL SOCIETY

84-R70-3.1

Rockwell Heritage Series

Artist: Norman Rockwell.
Artist's signature appears on front

China

Diameter: 21.6 centimetres (8 ¹/₂ inches)

No hanger

Edition size undisclosed, limited by announced period of issue

Numbered, with certificate

84-R70-3.1
1977 *The Toy Maker*
Issue price: £ 9.95

84-R70-3.2
1978 *The Cobbler*
Issue price: £ 12.40

84-R70-3.3
1979 *The Lighthouse Keeper's Daughter*
Issue price: £ 12.40

84-R70-3.4
1980 *The Ship Builder*
Issue price: £ 12.40

84-R70-3.5
1981 *The Music Maker*
Issue price: £ 12.40

84-R70-3.6
1982 *The Tycoon*
Issue price: £ 13.40

84-R70-3.7
1983 *The Painter*
Issue price: £ 13.40

84-R70-3.8
1984 *The Storyteller*
Issue price: £ 14.75

84-R70-3.9
1985 *The Gourmet*
Issue price: £ 14.75

84-R70-3.10
1986 *The Professor*
Issue price: £ 16.05

84-R70-3.11
1987 *The Shadow Artist*
Issue price: £ 16.05

Rockwell's Rediscovered Women Series

Artist: Norman Rockwell. Artist's signature appears on front

China

Diameter: 21.6 centimetres (8 ¹/₂ inches)

No hanger

Edition size undisclosed, limited by announced period of issue

Numbered, with certificate

84-R70-4.1
1981 *Dreaming in the Attic*
Issue price: £ 13.50

84-R70-4.2
1982 *Waiting on the Shore*
Issue price: £ 13.50

84-R70-4.3
1983 *Pondering on the Porch*
Issue price: £ 14.50

84-R70-4.4
1983 *Making Believe at the Mirror*
Issue price: £ 14.50

84-R70-4.5
1983 *Waiting at the Dance*
Issue price: £ 14.50

84-R70-4.6
1983 *Gossiping in the Alcove*
Issue price: £ 15.95

84-R70-4.7
1983 *Standing in the Doorway*
Issue price: £ 15.95

84-R70-4.8
1983 *Flirting in the Parlor*
Issue price: £ 15.95

84-R70-4.9
1984 *Working in the Kitchen*
Issue price: £ 15.95

84-R70-4.10
1984 *Meeting on the Path*
Issue price: £ 16.95

84-R70-4.11
1984 *Confiding in the Den*
Issue price: £ 16.95

84-R70-4.12
1984 *Reminiscing in the Quiet*
Issue price: £ 16.95
Series Closed

Rockwell on Tour Collection

Artist: Norman Rockwell.
Artist's signature appears on front

Newellware with raised border

Diameter: 19.7 centimetres (7 ³/₄ inches)

No hanger

Edition size undisclosed, limited by announced period of issue

Numbered, with certificate

84-R70-5.1
1983 *Walking through Merrie England*
Issue price: £ 10.90

84-R70-5.2
1983 *Promenade à Paris*
Issue price: £ 10.90

84-R70-5.3
1983 *When in Rome . . .*
Issue price: £ 10.90

84-R70-5.4
1984 *Die Walk am Rhein*
Issue price: £ 11.95
Series Closed

Rockwell's Light Campaign Series

Artist: Norman Rockwell.
Artist's signature appears on front

China banded in 14 k gold

Diameter: 21.6 centimetres (8 ¹/₂ inches)

No hanger

Edition size undisclosed, limited by announced period of issue

Numbered, with certificate

84-R70-6.1
1983 *This Is the Room That Light Made*
Issue price: £ 16.30

84-R70-6.2
1984 *Grandpa's Treasure Chest*
Issue price: £ 16.30

UNITED STATES
ROCKWELL SOCIETY

84-R70-6.3

84-R70-6.3
1984 *Father's Help*
Issue price: £ 17.30

84-R70-6.4
1984 *Evening's Ease*
Issue price: £ 17.30

84-R70-6.5
1984 *Close Harmony*
Issue price: £ 18.30

84-R70-6.6
1984 *The Birthday Wish*
Issue price: £ 18.30
Series Closed

Rockwell's American Dream Series

Artist: Norman Rockwell.
Artist's signature appears on front

China banded in 14 k gold

Diameter: 21.6 centimetres
(8 ½ inches)

No hanger

Edition size undisclosed, limited by announced period of issue

Numbered, with certificate

84-R70-7.1
1985 *A Young Girl's Dream*
Issue price: £ 12.45

84-R70-7.2
1985 *A Couple's Commitment*
Issue price: £ 12.45

84-R70-7.3
1985 *A Family's Full Measure*
Issue price: £ 12.45

84-R70-7.4
1986 *A Mother's Welcome*
Issue price: £ 15.45

84-R70-7.5
1986 *A Young Man's Dream*
Issue price: £ 15.45

84-R70-7.6
1986 *The Musician's Magic*
Issue price: £ 15.45

84-R70-7.7
1986 *An Orphan's Hope*
Issue price: £ 16.95

84-R70-7.8
1986 *Love's Reward*
Issue price: £ 16.95
Series Closed

Rockwell's Colonials: The Rarest Rockwells Series

Artist: Norman Rockwell. Artist's signature appears on front

China banded in gold

Diameter: 23.5 centimetres (9 ¹/₄ inches)

No hanger

Edition size undisclosed, limited by announced period of issue

Numbered, with certificate

84-R70-8.1
1986 *The Unexpected Proposal*
Issue price: £ 19.95

84-R70-8.2
1986 *Words of Comfort*
Issue price: £ 19.95

84-R70-8.3

84-R70-8.3
1986 *Light for the Winter*
Issue price: £ 21.95

84-R70-8.4
1987 *Portrait for a Bridgegroom*
Issue price: £ 21.95

A Mind of Her Own Series

Artist: Norman Rockwell. Artist's signature appears on front

China banded in gold

Diameter: 21.6 centimetres (8 ¹/₂ inches)

No hanger

Edition size undisclosed, limited by announced period of issue

Numbered, with certificate

84-R70-9.1
1986 *Sitting Pretty*
Issue price: £ 19.95

84-R70-9.2
1987 *Serious Business*
Issue price: £ 19.95

Rockwell's Golden Moments Series

Artist: Norman Rockwell. Artist's signature appears on front

China banded in 22 k gold

Diameter: 21.6 centimetres (8 ¹/₂ inches)

No hanger

Edition size undisclosed, limited by announced period of issue

Numbered, with certificate

84-R70-10.1
1987 *Grandpa's Gift*
Issue price: £ 16.95

84-R70-10.2
1987 *Keeping Company*
Issue price: £ 16.95

84-R70-10.3
1987 *Best Friends*
Issue price: unavailable at press time

UNITED STATES
ROMAN

84-R53-0.0

ROMAN
Roselle, Illinois

Founded in 1963 by Ronald T. Jedlinski, Roman concentrated its initial efforts on religious articles and giftware. Its first venture into the collectors' market was the Ceramica Excelsis line of limited-edition porcelains, which focussed on Biblical and inspirational subjects. Later, the company entered into association with the well-known illustrator Frances Hook, who worked closely with the firm to translate her illustrations of children into three-dimensional sculptures and plat-es. Mrs. Hook created Roman's first Bradex-listed series, *A Child's Play*, in 1982.

In 1986, Roman introduced the first collector's plate series created in the same indestructible polymer material as the famous Fontanini creche figures, for which it is the exclusive North American importer. The series, titled Fontanini Christmas Story, is deeply undersculpted, hand-painted and patinaed to a warm amber tone to give it the appearance of hand-carved wood.

A Child's Play Series

Artist: Frances Hook. Artist's signature appears on front

China banded in 24 k gold

Diameter: 21.6 centimetres (8 ½ inches)

No hanger

Edition size undisclosed, limited by announced period of issue

Numbered, with certificate

84-R53-1.1
1982 *Kite Flying*
Issue price: £ 18.25

84-R53-1.2
1982 *Breezy Day*
Issue price: £ 18.25

84-R53-1.3
1984 *First Snow*
Issue price: £ 18.25

84-R53-1.4
1984 *Bathtub Sailor*
Issue price: £ 18.25
Series Closed

Fontanini Christmas Story Series

Artist: Elio Simonetti. Artist's signature incised on front

moulded polymer material, handpaitned and patinaed

Diameter: 22 centimetres (9 inches)

No hanger

Edition size undisclosed, limited by announced period of issue

Numbered, with certificate

84-R53-12.1
1986 *A King is Born*
Issue price: £ 36.50

84-R53-12.2
1987 *Oh Come, Let Us Adore Him*
Issue price: £ 36.50

UNITED STATES
VILETTA

84-V36-0.0

VILETTA
Houston, Texas

Viletta China Company was started in 1959 in Roseberg, Oregon by Viletta West, who hand-painted china and sold it through stores in the Pacific Northwest. The firm is involved many areas of the giftware and fine china field, including commemorative china items and limited-edition collector's plates.

In 1979, Viletta China moved from Roseberg to Houston, Texas.

The *Zolan's Children* series, by Donald Zolan, began in 1978 and was completed in 1981. The *Nutcracker Ballet Plate Collection* began in 1978 and ended in 1980. The artist for the series was Shell Fisher.

Zolan's Children Series

Artist: Donald Zolan. Artist's signature appears on front

China

Diameter: 21.6 centimetres (8 ¹/₂ inches)

No hanger

Edition size undisclosed, limited by announced period of issue

Numbered, with certificate

84-V36-1.1
1978 *Erik and Dandelion*
Issue price: £ 11.50

84-V36-1.2
1979 *Sabina in the Grass*
Issue price: £ 13.50

84-V36-1.3
1980 *By Myself*
Issue price: £ 14.50

84-V36-1.4
1981 *For You*
Issue price: £ 14.50
Series Closed

Nutcracker Ballet Plate Collection

Artist: Shell Fisher. Artist's signature appears on front

China

Diameter: 21.6 centimetres (8 ¹/₂ inches)

No hanger

Edition size undisclosed, limited by announced period of issue

Numbered, with certificate

84-V36-2.1
1978 *Clara and Nutcracker*
Issue price: £ 11.95

84-V36-2.2
1979 *A Gift from Godfather*
Issue price: £ 11.95

UNITED STATES
VILETTA
84-V36-2.3

84-V36-2.3
1979 *The Sugarplum Fairy*
Issue price: £ 11.95

84-V36-2.4
1979 *The Snow King and Queen*
Issue price: £ 11.95

84-V36-2.5
1980 *The Waltz of the Flowers*
Issue price: £ 11.95

84-V36-2.6
1980 *Clara and the Prince*
Issue price: £ 11.95
Series Closed

PLATE ARTIST INFORMATION

AKERS, Roger (1940–   ) Roger Aker's artwork ranges from massive wooden sculpture to the delicately rendered cameos of Incolay's *Romantic Poets Collection.* Akers was educated at the Cooper School of Art in Cleveland, the Art Institute of Chicago and the American Academy of Art in Chicago. Akers' awards include Best of Show at the Excellence in Woodcarving Show in 1981. The American Numismatic Association commissioned him for "Coin of the Year" in 1974. He is a freelance artist in Chicago and his works hang in midwestern galleries and have been selected for permanent museum display by the Illinois Arts Council. He was born and raised in Cleveland.

ALLINGHAM, Helen
(1848 – 1926)   Helen Allingham was born in Barton, Trent in the Victorian era. Rejecting the confines of Victorian life, she was determined to support herself, and won admission to the Royal Academy of Art in London through sheer stubborness of effort. After working in oils her first year as a student, she decided she could express herself better in watercolors, but brought some of the techniques and disciplines of oil painting to the new medium. As a result, she managed to create watercolors of such unique and original quality that her name ranked with the major male artists of the period. She began her commercial career as a free-lance illustrator for the *London Graphic,* and also illustrated a number of books and magazines, with her first work done mostly in black ink on wood. She also did portraits, mostly at the request of friends.

A highly prolific painter, Mrs. Allingham turned our nearly a thousand completed works in her lifetime, many inspired by the rolling hills and trees of southeast England where she and her husband lived. In 1987, her artwork was the basis of the *Happy England* plate series from Royal Worcester.

ANDERSON, Wayne (1951–   ) Wayne Anderson, a native of Wisconsin, earned a degree in fine art from the University of Wisconsin at Stevens Point. Since then, he has had extensive commissions and has been represented in numerous shows. His oil paintings are in many private collections across the United States and Canada, and he has participated in the prestigious National Exhibition of Alaskan Wildlife at Anchorage. Anderson, who grew up with a love of nature, is best-known for his wildlife art, which he says is influenced by the work of realist painter Richard Estes and wildlife artists John James Audobon and J. Fenwick Lansdowne. In 1986, Anderson created his first collector's plate series for the Knowles China Company, titled *The Upland Birds of North America.*

PLATE ARTIST INFORMATION

ANKER, Albert (1831–1910) Albert Anker was born and raised in the small French town of Ins, near Bern, midway between French- and German-speaking Switzerland. He was ordained a minister before turning to painting as his life's work. Anker studied in Paris and became a student of classic French realism while attending the famous studio of Charles Gleyre and the prestigious Ecole des Beaux Arts. He is said to belong to the school of Realist "genre" painters, whose art depicted everyday people and scenes. Anker was a much-honoured artist in his lifetime and a civic leader widely known for his successful effort to persuade the Swiss government to encourage the arts. He also participated in the planning of a museum which would later house the largest collection of his work—the Neuchâtel Museum of Fine Arts. In 1986, the Langenthal Swiss China Works introduced the *Anker's Heritage* series, which features scenes from Swiss village life in the nineteenth century. It is the first series based on this artist's work.

APPLEBY, Gayle Bright
(1949–   ) Gayle Bright Appleby is designer of the first four issues in Incolay's *Romantic Poets Collection*. She studied at San Fernando Valley State College in California and at Otis Art School. Her works have appeared in exhibits at Mari's of Hawaii in Lahaina and Alchemists Garden, Kihei, Hawaii. She is widely known for the intricate detail of her sculptures in bronze, silver and gold.

ARD, Kurt (1925–   ) Kurt Ard's career got off to an inauspicious start when a bomb in wartime Denmark destroyed both his artwork and the publisher for his first major commission. But Ard has enjoyed international success in the four decades since. His illustrations have appeared in virtually every printed form, including magazines, posters, greeting cards and calendars. His credits include cover and story illustrations in such magazines as *The Saturday Evening Post, Redbook, McCalls, Modern Maturity* and equally prestigious publications in Germany, France and Scandinavia. He shares with Norman Rockwell an uncanny ability to capture the trauma and adventure of growing up, as shown in his *Moments of Truth* series for Bing & Grøndahl. Ard is a self-taught artist.

AUCKLAND, James (1946–   ) James Auckland, creator of the *Wizard of Oz* series produced by Edwin M. Knowles, was copying Van Gogh prints at the age of six, using his mother's palette and brushes. He studied at the Art Centre College of Design in Los Angeles and privately with Richard Huebnes, Lorser Feitelson, Joe Hehnigar and Harry Carmen.

BAHNSEN, Frode (1923–1983) Frode Bahnsen's training in sculpture, ceramics and drawing is evident in the plates he designed for Grande Copenhagen's *Christmas* series, with bas-relief scenes from the fairy tales of Hans Christian Andersen. He studied at the Copenhagen Royal Academy of Art and subsequently worked for the Royal Mint in Copenhagen, rising to the position of head sculptor in 1968. His works hang in the Denmark National Museum and have been exhibited in many places, including the Charlottenborg Art Exhibition in Copenhagen and F.I.D.M.E. (Federal International

Danish Medal Exhibitions). The Queen of Denmark titled him knight of Dannebrog in 1978.

BAND, Ursula (1937–   ) Born in Meissen, Germany, Alt Tirschenreuth artist Ursula Band displayed talent for painting and drawing in her early childhood. As a young woman she attended the Painting and Drawing School of the Meissen State Porcelain Manufactury. After her rigorous training she was selected to be among the handful of people who hand-paint Meissen china. In 1964, she established her own atelier. SHe portrayed the songbirds of the woodlands surrounding her home in Germany in her first collector's plate series, *Songbirds of Europe*.

BARKER, Cicely Mary (1895–1973) Heinrich/Villeroy & Boch artist Cicely Mary Barker published the first of her numerous Flower Fairy books in 1923. A largely self-taught artist, she also had formal training at the Croyden School of Art. A stained glass window of her design hangs in St. Andrew's Church in Croyden. Her works have been exhibited at the Royal Institute and are in the collection of the British royal family.

BARRER, Gertrude (1921–   ) With her husband Frank Russell, Gertrude Barrer has produced art displayed in some of the United States' most prestigious museums, including the Whitney Museum of American Art and the Art Institute of Chicago, and in the private collections of Cyrus Vance and Helmut Schmidt and the United Nations Interfaith Chapel in New York. Together they created the *Triptych* and *Romantic Love* series for Anna-Perenna. Barrer and Russell first met at the Art Student's League in New York. Five years later, they reunited in New York's art centre, Greenwich Village, to work jointly on photographs, lithographs, frescoes, serigraphs and sculpture.

BEDAL, Karl (1914–   ) The man whose illustrations of West Germany's classic half-timbered farmhouses appear on *Deutsches Fachwerk* plates is well-known throughout Bavaria for his architecture research and literature on German folk history. His artistic creations range from wall-size paintings to delicate water colours and linocut book illustrations. Bedal has been a freelance artist since 1958. He travels throughout Germany in search of his country's finest regional architecture, making his sketches on the spot to capture the patterns of wooden beams and braces on houses built centuries ago.

BENVENUTI, Riccardo (1939–   ) Riccardo Benvenuti was born in Lucca, the same town that produced one of Italy's greatest operatic composers, Giacomo Puccini. (He is the brother of Sergio Benvenuti, the sculptor of the *Benvenuti's Muses* series.) Raised in Puccini's shadow, Riccardo Benvenuti eventually developed an artistic style that reflects the great romantic themes of that composer. Benvenuti's paintings speak of the immortal power of passionate women and the joys and sorrows of unrequited love. The artist has explored these themes in three major exhibitions honouring the 50th anniversary of Puccini's death. In 1985, Le Porcellane Fontana Dei Medici commissioned Benvenuti to create *The Women of Puccini*, a series of haunting portraits of Puccini's great heroines.

PLATE ARTIST INFORMATION

BENVENUTI, Sergio (1940–)
The designer of the *Muses* plate series for Studio Dante di Volteradici is an Italian master who gained international prominence in 1984 with two important commissions for bronze sculptures. He created his Beato Angelico statue at the request of the Dominican monks for the Church of San Marco in Florence. Italian National Television covered the statue's unveiling, which was attended by His Eminence, the Archbishop of Florence. Americans were introduced to Benvenuti with the critically acclaimed fountain he executed for the First International Bank Plaza in San Diego, California. Benvenuti has won numerous awards in his thirty-year career.

BESSER, Ilse (1941 –)
Ilse Besser was born in the German city of Aachen. In a family of artists her talents began to develop early. She started her professional career as scriptgirl and cutter in various filmstudios. There she received a thorough education in design and production of cultural films, advertisement spots and trickfilms. Since 1961 she participated in TV-productions, and designed storyboards and layouts for various contributions. She was also busy as interviewer of famous persons from the art and culture scene, economy and gastronomy for "Besser's Gourmet Journal". During all these years she was painting and drawing in her free time. In the early 1970's her work was presented to the public for the first time. This première in Cologne became a tremendous success, nearly all exhibits were sold. Further exhibitions with irregular intervals testified to her continuous artistic achievement. In 1987 Höchst-Decor presented her first collectors' plate series: *Lifecycle*.

BLANDFORD, W.A. (1915–)
W.A. Blandford's career in the British ceramics industry began in the 1930s, when he was apprenticed to Wood & Sons, the Staffordshire ceramics house that produced many of the earliest Toby jugs. Since then he has modelled thousands of intricate ceramic pieces. In order to create the "Toby Fillpot" collector's plate for Davenport Pottery, Blandford spent hours examining antique Toby pieces before sketching his own design, true to the eighteenth century ceramics that inspired it.

BOEHM, Edward Marshall (1914–1969) From a background as farmer and veterinarian, the artist for Lenox's *Boehm Bird* series became a full-time sculptor in 1949. The self-taught Boehm was recognized as one of America's greatest wildlife artists. His faithful replication of nature scenes won a substantial following and his work has appeared in the collections of Dwight D. Eisenhower, John F. Kennedy, Lyndon B. Johnson, Queen Elizabeth II and Pope John XXIII. Boehm won numerous awards and his art is displayed in the Smithsonian Institution, the Metropolitan Museum of Art and other museums.

BORNHOLT, Karen (1957–)
Although she is an American artist and illustrator, Karen Bornholt drew on her Scandinavian heritage to create *The Ugly Duckling* series, the first full-colour plate series from

Grande Copenhagen Porcelain. The series, introduced in 1985, is based on one of the most famous tales of Denmark's greatest story-teller, Hans Christian Andersen. The whisper-soft pastel colours of Bornholt's palette capture both the natural beauty and the subtle moral lesson of this beloved children's story.

BOULMÉ, Claude (1930–) When Gerard Boyer of D'Arceau-Limoges approached the great porcelain artist Claude Boulmé about a plate series capturing the porcelain style of the Sèvres Empire, Boulmé knew the subject of the plates must be the Emperor Napoléon, whose patronage permitted the Sèvres art to flower. In the *Joséphine et Napoléon* series, he portrays, in neo-Classical style, the passion of Napoléon for his Empress Joséphine.

BOYER, Gene (1948–) Crown Parian artist Gene Boyer is best known for more than 45 illustrations that appeared in the *Saturday Evening Post* between 1975 and 1978. Boyer got his first big break when Norman Rockwell awarded him second place in a cover contest for the new magazine. Although his portrait assignments for the Post included such contemporary celebrities as Elizabeth Taylor and Jimmy Carter, Boyer was attracted to the history and integrity offered by the past. In his portraits of such legends as Johnny Appleseed and Davy Crockett in the *American Folk Heroes* plate series, Boyer strives to capture with almost photographic realism the courage and qualities of heroes. Self-taught Boyer has done numerous portrait commissions and exhibited primarily in the Denver, Colorado and Washington, D.C. areas.

BRACKENBURY, Amy (1953–) Amy Brackenbury's work has been included for three years in the exclusive and prestigious Leigh Yawkey Woodson Birds in Art Museum in Wisconsin, in a show for new and unusual bird art, and has twice been selected to participate in the museum's world tour. Her inspiration for her animal art comes from the family ranch, located in the foothills of northern Colorado where she lives with her husband and two children.

Ms. Brackenbury first studied art and painting at Colorado State University. She admires Oriental art, but chooses realism to depict the animals she portrays, preferring to paint them as close to life-size as possible. She keeps many pets on her ranch—including geckos and tree frogs. In her free time she likes to cross-country ski and run sled dogs; she also teaches dog obedience classes.

PLATE ARTIST INFORMATION

BRADLEY, Betsey (1949–   )
Edwin M. Knowles artist Betsey Bradley first realized she had talent when her fifth grade profiles of classmates showed a striking likeness to their subjects. She has been doing portraits ever since in pastels, pencil, acrylic and oils, and more recently began doing landscapes and still lifes. Bradley studied art at Smith College for Women in Massachusetts, the Minneapolis School of Art and the Rocky Mountain School of Art. Her paintings have been shown in several exhibitions. To her collector's plate series *A Father's Love* Bradley brings a softer version of her strikingly realistic artwork, inspiration from her own happy family, and support for the increasingly active role today's fathers take with their children.

BRAITHWAITE, Derek
(1929–   ) After an art college education at Harrogate in England, Derek Braithwaite spent a great portion of his career as the art director of a large advertising studio (he is a member of the Society of Illustrators). But while pursuing his profession in the commercial world, he always retained an avid interest in his personal artistic passion—landscape painting and wildlife art. Far from the hectic pace of the advertising world, the wilderness landscape teeming with life presented a compelling artistic challenge as well as a place of solace and refuge. Braithwaites's refined artistic sensibility, combined with his rare command of technique and patient study, brings a unique quality to his work. This is evident in the *Braithwaite Game Birds Collection*, his first series by Royal Grafton.

Braithwaite was born in Folifoot near Knaresborough, North Yorkshire, England. He and his wife live in England. They have two children; his daughter Ann is also an illustrator. For relaxation he enjoys walking and photography.

BRATLIE, Gunnar (1918–   )
Born in Fredrikstad, Norway, Gunnar Bratlie is a master of the traditional Norwegian folk art known as "rosemaling." He has worked in such diverse styles as oil, tempera, aquarelle and etching. Among his many awards are the Scandinavian book prize for illustration, a contest-winning design for Fredrikstad's 400th-year jubilee and a special stipend from the Norwegian Design Organization. His work is represented in many museums around the world, most notably at the Commune of Oslo, the Art Society of Fredrikstad and the Museo del Arte in Pisoia, Italy. Sole artist since 1967 for Porsgrund Pottery, his plates in the *Christmas, Mother's Day* and *Traditional Norwegian Christmas* series primarily depict Norwegian country scenes.

BRENOT, Pierre- Laurent
(1913–   ) A Parisian by birth, Pierre-Laurent Brenot studied at the Ecole Estienne in Paris and finished in first place at the end of his schooling. As one of France's leading interpreters of women, he uses a technique called *une réalité poetique*. Brenot has worked on fashion illustrations for such magazines as *Elle* and *Vogue*. He was a medalist at the *Salon des Artistes Français* in 1965 and 1966, and received the *Prix Henner* in Paris in 1971. He also won the *Grand Prix de Tour* in 1975. Brenot is a permanent exhibitor at the prestigious *Galleria d'Arte Firenze* in Florence, Italy. He is also a member of the *Jury des Artistes Française*, and exhibits in galleries throughout the world. In 1985, D'Arceau-Limoges introduced his first plate series, *The Women of the Belle Epoque*, a historic tribute to the glamorous women of Paris at the turn of the century.

BROWN, Roger (1933–   ) Roger Brown studied under Dorothea Denslow at the New York Sculpture Centre and is a member of the New York Sculpture Centre and the National Sculpture Centre. Brown's works are in the collections of the Whitney Museum of American Art and the Remington Museum in New York, the Studebaker Museum in South Bend, Indiana, the Lyndon Baines Johnson Memorial Library and the Teterboro Aviation Museum, among others. He is sculptor of the *Famous Americans* series for River Shore, Ltd.

BRUNETTIN, Alan (1954–   )
Incolay artist Alan Brunettin mastered the art of traditional sculpture in a nine-year apprenticeship to his father, internationally celebrated sculptor Alfred Brunettin. Today his art in several media ranges from striking photorealism to cartoon-like surrealism. In *Voyage of Ulysses*, his first collector's plate series, Brunettin uses traditional sculptural techniques to render scenes from the Greek epic in cameo-carved high relief. Brunettin earned a Bachelor of Fine Arts degree with an emphasis in painting at Northern Illinois University and also studied at the American Academy of Art in Chicago. He has exhibited at Chicago-area art fairs and won prizes two consecutive years at the National Exhibit of Italian-American Art in Chicago.

CAMBIER, Guy (1923–   ) Self-taught artist Guy Cambier had his first one-man show at age 19 and has been exhibiting ever since in Belgium, France and at the Zantman Art Galleries in Carmel, California. He has won numerous awards and honours through the years, from the *Prix de la Jeune Peinture Méditerranée* in 1955 to the *Laureate de la Médaille International des Artes* in 1977. He designed the *Girls of the Seasons* and *Cambier Mother's Day* series in a neo-Classical style for D'Arceau-Limoges.

CASSINI, Oleg (1913–   ) Oleg Cassini is one of the best-known names in contemporary fashion—his name has appeared on everything from sunglasses to perfume—as well as an accomplished artist. Born to Countess Loiewski Cassini in Paris, Cassini renounced his right to the title of Count to become an American citizen after immigrating to the United States in the late 1930s. He designed film costumes in Hollywood for such celebrities as Gene Tierney and Grace Kelly before going to New York to put his name on a par with Dior and Cardin. Jacqueline Kennedy named Cassini her official couturier during her White House years. He received a law degree from the University of Florence and graduated from Florence's prestigious Academia delle Belle Artes. For *Oleg Cassini's Most Beautiful Women of All Time Collection* for Pickard, Cassini explored the historical and cultural aspects of the lives of women such as Helen of Troy.

CHAMBERS, William (1940–   ) William Chambers came to the plate world almost by accident and became an overnight success in the midst of his career as a well-known illustrator and prize-winning portraitist. He had never heard of collector's plates when he got a letter from an Edwin M. Knowles art representative inviting him to discuss the *Annie Collector's Plate* series. Soon afterwards his debut plate, "Annie and Sandy," made history when it walked off with two of the most coveted awards, Plate of the Year and New Edition of the Year for 1983—the first time a single plate has won both honours. Chambers paid his dues as an illustrator and photographer before he came to the realization that he could both make a living and satisfy his artistic needs painting portraits. He has exhibited in the American Society of Illustrators' annual show, The American Show at Marshall Field's and the Mongerson Galleries (both in Chicago), and won first prize in the John Howard Sanden portrait competition. His works hang in various homes and businesses and at Ron De Bouver Fine Arts in Chicago. Chambers studied at Northeastern Illinois University and the American Academy of Art in Chicago.

PLATE ARTIST INFORMATION

CRNKOVICH, Tony (1962–)
While other youngsters played baseball after school, Tony Crnkovich taught himself to draw. He watched old films on TV, and then recreated what he saw on the screen—including portraits of many famous film characters. Born in Chicago, Illinois, Crnkovich eventually enrolled at the American Academy of Art in that city, where he received his professional art training. From there, he developed his two loves—art and classic movies—into a respected body of work that captures not only the details of great films, but also the mood of a film and its important characters. His first series is *The Sound of Music* for the Knowles China Company, in which he recreates the musical highlights of the film.

CSATARI, Joseph (1929–) Joseph Csatari, long-time friend and protégé of the late master of realism Norman Rockwell, is one of the most highly regarded realist painters of today. He and Rockwell collaborated on the annual calendars published by the Boy Scouts of America for a decade until 1975, when Rockwell turned the calendar commission over to Csatari, who has continued it. Edwin M. Knowles commissioned him for the *Csatari Grandparent Plate* series. His other important recent commissions include cover illustrations for numerous books and a commemorative stamp for the U.S. Postal Service. Csatari studied at the Academy of Art in Newark, New Jersey and the Pratt Institute in New York City. His awards include a Gold Medal from the Society of Illustrators.

DALI, Louis (1906–) A noted Impressionist, Louis Dali is a Fellow of the *Salon de l'Ecole Française* and of the *Salon des Indépendants*, and winner of the *Prix Dessin de Briton*. Dali is a self-taught artist whose works hang in many private collections and salons, including the *Salon de la Marine, Salon de la Nationale des Beaux-Artes*, and the *Salon de l'Ecole Française des Indépendants*. Dali designed his *Twelve Parisian Places of Louis Dali* for D'Arceau-Limoges.

DANIEL, Kevin (1951–) For Edwin M. Knowles artist Kevin Daniel, painting is a way of preserving wildlife. He used to hunt with a gun; now he combs the wilds with his camera, collecting photographs from which to paint highly accurate, detailed portrayals of animals from pheasants to fishes. For his *Birds of Your Garden* series, Daniel erected a camera on the birdfeeder in the backyard of his house near Minneapolis. Daniel, who learned to paint by studying the work of other artists, was named Artist of the Year by the Indiana Chapter of Ducks Unlimited, a waterfowl conservation group, in 1984, and won second place in the Minnesota Duck Stamp art competition the same year. Proceeds from the sale of his prints have helped save the endangered blue heron in Minnesota.

DEFREGGER, Franz von (1835– 1921) Even as a child, Franz von Defregger displayed the immense but raw talent he would later refine into his unique mature style. He was born in Austria in 1835 into a farmer's family, the second of seven children. Circumstances forced von Defregger to run his father's farm, although he wanted desperately to become an artist.
Eventually his wish was fulfilled. War and crop failures forced him to abandon farming, and he became an art student in Munich. In 1862 he went to Paris, where the international art community flourished, to study at the world-famous Académie des Beaux-Arts. After two years he returned to Munich for further study. Soon he would begin his long career as a painter, moving through Austria and Germany, recording with the exquisite

talent and sensibility that made him famous, the daily life of his era. Ultimately he was appointed by King Ludwig II of Bavaria to the honoured position of Professor at the Academy of Fine Arts in Munich. But he always remained a rural, traditional artist. *Masterpieces of Franz von Defregger* from Lilien Porzellan is the first collector's plate series that pays tribute to his artistic work.

DEGRAZIA, Ted (1909–1982) Ted DeGrazia, one of America's most popular and instantly-recognizable artists, was a man of contrasts and paradoxes. Born in Morenci, Arizona, the son of an Italian copper miner, he didn't attend school for the first 11 years of his life but later earned three degrees in art and music from the University of Arizona. He studied with great Mexican muralists Diego Rivera and Jose Clemente Orozco and spent long hours of research and hard work on his paintings, yet he acquired the image of a drunken carouser. A millionaire in the last years of his life, his art was always of the people and for the people, and he strove to keep it affordable. His stylized paintings of Southwestern themes first came to international attention in 1960 when UNICEF sold 100 million Christmas cards bearing the image of his painting "Los Niños." Since then, they have appeared on everything from stained glass to figurines and in collector's plates series for Fairmont/Artists of the World and Gorham, including *DeGrazia Holiday* series and *DeGrazia Children* series.

DOWN, Jeanne (1928–   ) Artist Jeanne Down uses her palette and brushes to tell stories—especially of her childhood days in Altoona, Pennsylvania. Though she grew up during the Great Depression, her memories are happy ones. Among other things, she learned to paint at the knee of her grandfather, Pennsylvania realist E.E. Wilt. After graduating high school she temporarily abandoned her avocation to spend 16 years raising a family. But after studying oil painting, watercolour and etching techniques under private teachers she began to offer instruction herself throughout California's San Fernando Valley. In 1975 she opened her own gallery and studio. In her *Friends I Remember* series, Down uses an "impressionistic realist" style to impart feelings as well as images.

DURAND, Paul (1925–1977) Paul Durand achieved an international reputation for his illustrations of such children's classics as *The Three Musketeers* and *Treasure Island*. General Charles De Gaulle chose Durand's art to illustrate his 1969 Christmas message to French children. Durand was influenced in Paris by Christian Berard, Jacques DeMachy, René Gruau and André Dignimont. He exhibited at the *Festival Cannes* in 1965, was presented as a candidate for the Hans Christian Andersen Prize in 1970, and did illustrations for numerous French and U.S. publications, including Hachette, Delagrave and Flammarion editions, *Reader's Digest*, *Le Figaro* and *Paris Presse*. He was the artist for the Limoges-Turgot plate series *Durand's Children Collection*.

DUTHEIL, Jean (1927–   ) D'Arceau-Limoges artist Jean Dutheil experimented with pigments for more than a year and a half to try to duplicate the rich colours of the medieval French manuscript on which *The Very Rich Hours* plate series is based. Dutheil studied at *L'Ecole de Beaublance* in Limoges, France. His many awards and honours include the *Prix de la Ville de Limoges*, *Prix du Ministre*, *Grand Prix de Porcelaine de Limoges* and the *Meilleur Ouvrier de France*.

PLATE ARTIST INFORMATION

ETÉM, Sue (1941?–) Self-taught painter Sue Etém's first plate, "Renee," which launched the *Playful Memories* series by Fairmont, sold out in two hours at a gallery open house when it was first introduced. It also won NALED's Plate of the Year and Collectible of the Year for 1981. Etém herself was named NALED's Artist of the Year for 1981 and 1982. Like many of Etém's paintings, "Renee" began as a snapshot—in this case, of a little neighbour girl who came to the house for chewing gum and ended up playing with a drinking hose. Etém, who now designs for Derby Collection, began drawing at age 3. After a year of formal art training at Arlington State College, she joined an advertising agency as a commercial artist. In the early 1950s she moved to Huntington Beach, California, where she taught art to neighbourhood children. She has exhibited throughout the United States and Canada.

FAURE, Renée (1939?–) Granddaughter of the great American Impressionist Edmund Greacen and daughter of prominent painter Nan Greacon, Renée Faure has demonstrated talent and versatility as an artist in her own right. In the *Once Upon a Rhyme* collector's plate series she created for Heinrich/Villeroy & Boch, Faure captures the charm and appeal of age-old nursery rhymes. Scenes from such favourites as "A Tisket, a Tasket" come alive in Faure's subtle pastels and earth tones. Faure renders the fine detail with superb drafting skill.

a one-man show in Leicester in 1963, and another one in Brunei in 1983. His private commissions have included engraved and sculpted glass works for major corporations, for British nobility and even for her Majesty Queen Elizabeth the Queen Mother, for whom he designed, sculpted and engraved a large crystal presentation bowl. In 1984, he created his first plate series, *Street Sellers of London*, for Wedgwood.

FISHER, Shell (1931–) Shell Fisher's work, as seen on the plates he has created for Viletta, represents some of the finest examples of contemporary realism. But Fisher is a versatile artist whose credits include interpretive canvasses, portraits commissioned by Queen Elizabeth II and Sammy Davis, Jr., and cartoons for several men's magazines. In his *Nutcracker Ballet Plate Collection*, he depicts the favourite Christmas ballet in vivid colours. Fisher studied at the Art Institute of Chicago, where his work is on display, other places, and has exhibited widely.

FINNIE, John (1934–) British artist John Finnie works in a variety of artistic media, from pen, ink and wash to glass engraving and sculpting. Finnie received the National Diploma from the Leicester College of Art in 1956. His work has been exhibited throughout the United Kingdom and has appeared in numerous publications. He had

FURIESI, Ennio (1937–) Sculptural artist Ennio Furiesi is a native of Tuscany, Italy, which has been a source of fine alabaster marble for hundreds of years. Furiesi is an award-winning portraitist and professor of sculpture at the Art Institute of Volterra. He is known throughout Italy for his sculptural renderings of the Nativity, which led to his commission to create his first collector's plate series, *Christmas Crèche*, for Studio Dante di Volteradici. It is Sr. Furiesi's interpretation of the classic masterpieces of Neapolitan crèche figures. The series was started in 1986.

GANEAU, François (1912–1983) François Ganeau was one of Europe's leading costume and set designers and resident consultant to the *Theatre Comedie Français*. He was widely acclaimed in 1937 for the *Pavillon de l'Elegance*, a mural he created for the Paris World's Fair. As a sculptor and painter he decorated many public buildings and private homes throughout France. He was commissioned by D'Arceau-Limoges to create the *Women of the Century* series bearing the United Nations' emblem for the International Women's Year. The twelve plates in the series picture the progression of 19th and 20th century Paris fashion. Ganeau studied at L'École Boulle, Paris. His works hang in the *Comédie Français*, Paris Opera House and the Louvre.

GEHM, Charles (1944–   ) Charles Gehm is a prominent member of the Society of Illustrators and has gained a wide audience through his cover designs for Saul Bellow books. Gehm created the *Grimm's Fairy Tales* collector's plate series for Königszelt Bayern in 1981 to commemorate the two-hundredth anniversary of the Grimm brothers' birth. The plates bear vivid illustrations of such Grimm classics as *Rapunzel* and *Rumplestilzchen*. Gehm is a graduate of the Columbus Art School. He has exhibited at the James Marks Gallery in California and has works hanging in private collections in the United States.

GUIDOU, Jean-Claude (1946–   ) This young French painter won an international reputation with his sensitive pastel portraits and his studies of ballet dancers and race horses. Important personalities who have commis-

sioned Guidou to execute their portraits include the late General Charles De Gaulle. In "Gigi," the first issue in Guidou's first collector's plate series, he captured his subject's *joie de vivre* on D'Arceau-Limoges porcelain with the pastel soft-focus technique an Impressionist master might have used. Guidou studied at the Louvre and the Royal Museum of Belgium and has exhibited widely.

HALLETT, Charlotte (1943–   ) **and William** (1940–   ) In their unique art Charlotte and William Hallett draw upon a rich tradition of myth and ornament to create a world of unicorns, dragons and maidens in love. This husband-and-wife team has collaborated on everything from Greek-inspired sterling flatware to crystal and paintings. Like the *Love For All Seasons* series they designed for Hutschenreuther, all their plates are joint creations. They met as staff designers for a silver company and began to explore the world of colour together, having already studied Egyptian, Baroque and Rococo ornamentation, history, fine art and symbolism. Charlotte studied at the University of Connecticut in Bridgeport; William, at Vesper George School of Art in Boston. They have exhibited in local, regional and national shows and their art is in the collections of the Archdiocese of New York and the royal families of Saudi Arabia and Spain, among others.

HÉTREAU, Remy (1925–   ) Adept in a variety of styles, French painter Remy Hétreau is the principal artist for Haviland's collector's plates, with two distinctively different series to his credit—from historical chronicle to delightful yuletide fancy in *The Twelve Days of Christmas* series.

PLATE ARTIST INFORMATION

HIBEL, Edna (1917–) Edna Hibel is one of the most respected American painters of her time, and a pioneer in porcelain as a fine-art medium. The plates in her series—which include the *Nobility of Children* and *Oriental Gold* series for Rosenthal, *Hibel's Mother's Day* series for Edwin M. Knowles, and the *Mother and Child* series for Royal Doulton—demonstrate her ability to capture the beauty she sees in life and her love for human beings. Hibel at 22 became the youngest artist to have a painting in a major American museum when the Boston Museum purchased one of her canvasses. She is one of the few living female artists with a U.S. museum—the Hibel Museum of Art in Florida—devoted to her works. She is an elected member of the Royal Society of Arts in London. She has held numerous one-woman shows since 1962 in the United States, England, Monaco, Germany and Argentina and recently became the first American woman to exhibit in Jerusalem. Her works hang in museums across the country. Hibel studied at the Boston Museum of Fine Arts with Carl Zerbe and Jacovleff from 1934 to 1939, and privately with Gregory Michaels in Boston.

HICKS, Yin-Rei (1933–) Yin-Rei Hicks, a native of mainland China, was born during the Maoist takeover. Her family later fled to Taiwan, where her artistic ability first gained recognition. She won two scholarships from the University of Louisville in Kentucky and graduated with a Master's Degree in Creative Art. She has since become a prominent illustrator and designer of limited-edition collectibles. In 1981 River Shore introduced her *Signs of Love* series, in which Hick's paintings convey the tenderness between wild animals and their young. She has exhibited at the J.B. Speed Museum in Kentucky, the Floyd County Museum, the University of Louisville, and other galleries in Kentucky and southern Indiana. Her works hang in private collections in the United States.

HOOK, Frances (1913–1983) Her exquisite understanding of both children and art distinguishes the work of Frances Hook, one of America's premier child portraitists. Her soft pastel style captures dreamy-eyed children in commercial illustrations, prints, lithographs and figurines as well as collector's plates. The public discovered her with her illustrations of the Northern Bath Tissue children—so popular they were sold on 30 million prints. With her late husband Richard, she illustrated *The Children's Living Bible* for Tyndale House Publishers. Her first collector's plate issue was in 1980 for Roman, and her first Bradex-listed series, *A Child's Play*, also for Roman, began in 1982. She also designed the *Frances Hook Legacy* series for Edwin M. Knowles. Hook studied at the Pennsylvania Museum School of Art.

HOOK, Richard (1938–) Richard Hook is a well-known British illustrator who received his original schooling from the Reigate College of Art in England. In his work, Hook pursues meticulous historical accuracy and does lengthy research to re-create scenes from the past. Throughout his career, he has been in demand for book illustrations from publishers in the United Kingdom, continental Europe, the United States and Japan. In 1986, his first work in the collector's plate medium was introduced by Wedgwood: *The Legend of King Arthur*. It comprises famous incidents from the heroic king's life, and is fired on fine bone china.

HOOVER, G.A. (1943–) In *The Canterbury Tales Collection*, Longton Crown Pottery artist G.A. Hoover carries on a family tradition of artists which began with his grandfather. Hoover holds a Master of Fine Arts degree and is considered a master of the style known as Romantic Realism. He studied at Tulane University in New Orleans and at the John Herron School of Art in Indianapolis. He has executed designs and drawings for Little Brown & Company, McGraw-Hill, Playboy Press, MacMillan and Co., *Reader's Digest*, Harper & Row and Harcourt, Brace and Jovanovich. He has had three one-man shows at Bienville Gallery in New Orleans, participated in an invitational show in Colombia, and has works hanging in several museums and in private collections.

INGARGIOLA, Franco (1944–) Franco Ingargiola studied privately with sculptor Gino Ruggeri, from whom he took over design of the *Grand Opera* series for Studio Dante di Volteradici. Ingargiola worked in onyx and ceramics as well as in the ivory alabaster from which he sculpted the plates in this collection. Ingargiola also studied at Boy's Town in Rome and won first prize at the Craftsmen Arts Show in Cicena, Italy.

JANSEN, Leo (1930–1980) Leo Jansen was born in The Hague, The Netherlands. He spent his youth in Indonesia, where he developed his skills as a portrait painter by sketching the bronze-skinned Malay children. He returned to The Netherlands to study at the Academy of Fine Arts and later refined his work in the famous "Pigalle" section of Paris. Jansen designed plates for Kern Collectibles, including the *Leaders of Tomorrow* series, and Royal Bayreuth. In 1970 he won CALED's Plate of the Year award, in Canada. His art has been exhibited at the Avron Brothers Corporation in Los Angeles, California, and hangs in private collections in the United States.

JERNER, Bart (1925–) Bart Jerner received his artistic training at the Chicago Academy of Art, the Art Institute of Chicago, and the American Academy of Art. He has always combined his career with a great love of the outdoors. For the past 40 years, he has spent nearly every summer hiking in northern Michigan, the wetlands of central Canada and the mountainous frontier of the Canadian Yukon. Jerner is an active member of the Izaak Walton League of America, one of the first groups to support the conservation of natural resources. His work is exhibited by the National Wildlife Collectors Society, and several of his sculptures are displayed at the Wild Gallery in Dallas and at Taylor's Gallery of Western Art in Santa Fe. In 1986, the Knowles China Company issued Jerner's first collector's plate series, titled *Living with Nature: Jerner's Ducks*.

JOHNSON, Robert (1915–) Artist Robert Johnson, whose works are in private collections throughout the United States, Europe and the Far East, developed the patented electroplating process used in the creation of the Reed & Barton *Christmas* series. The medium, known as Damascene silver, combines silver, gold, copper and bronze. The process is derived from a hand-crafted method perfected at Damascus in the middle ages. Johnson designed the 1970, 1971 and 1972 plates in the series.

JULIEN, Michel (1947–) Born in Lille, France, child prodigy Michel Julien quickly gained international renown. Despite his parents poverty, they did everything they could to encourage him, and

PLATE ARTIST INFORMATION

by the age of eight he had exhibited in Rheims, Munich, and Tokyo. At fifteen, he was awarded the prestigious Medaile de Vermail of the Academy des Beaux Arts. Although he has a BA from the University of Paris, Julien considers himself to be basically self-taught. His work is on display in museums in Belgium, Germany, Canada, Brazil, Argentina, and the United States.

Julien uses the *lavis* technique, which involves working with a combination of black and colored inks to quickly create finely-detailed drawings. His style is a unique blend of Impressionism and Realism.

He lives with his wife and two daughters in a small village near Lille in Northern France; his artwork is exclusively represented by the Gallery Schesmes of Lille. His first plate series, *French Country Landscapes*, is by D'Arceau-Limoges.

KELLER, Hedi (1916–   ) Hedi Keller was born in Tuttlingen, West Germany, a village near the Black Forest. She studied for three years at the Kunstakademie in Stuttgart, learning about the great masters—Titian, Rembrandt and Breughel—but later was influenced by Van Gogh and the French Impressionists, who discarded conventional ideas to seek a more personal style. Keller shows her own colourful style in the *Hedi Keller Christmas* series produced by Königszelt Bayern.

Keller's work has been exhibited in galleries in Berlin, Munich and Dusseldorf.

KRØYER, Peter Severin (1851–1909) Peter Severin Krøyer grew up in Copenhagen and became interested in art in his teens. After years of painting landscapes and portraits in his native Denmark, Krøyer moved to Paris, where he became part of the Scandinavian artists' colony, and also part of the revolutionary movement that was redefining the criteria for art. It was here that Krøyer met his wife, Marie, in 1889. Although he travelled extensively, Krøyer spent most of his artistic life from 1882 to 1909 at Skagen, a small fishing village on the northern-most tip of Denmark's Jutland peninsula. From 1870 until 1920, Skagen was a unique gathering place for artists and intellectuals from all over the world, and it was there that Krøyer did his finest work. From this work Bing & Grøndahl has created a series titled *A Summer at Skagen*; it was introduced in 1986.

KRUMEICH, Thaddeus (1930–   ) Thaddeus Krumeich is a master of the style known as *trompe l'oeil*, which he calls "magic realism." His magical, clear-eyed cats seem ready to leap off the plates in Anna-Perenna's *Uncle Tad's Cats* series. Krumeich, who studied at New York University and Columbia University, has created illustrations for publications such as *Reader's Digest*, *Time-Life Books* and *Family Circle*. His work was selected for UNICEF greeting cards in 1981 and 1982. Krumeich has had shows throughout the United States and is represented in collections such as those of Mrs. Paul Mellon, "Doc" Severinson and His Excellency Seydou Traori, Mali Ambassador to the United States.

KUCK, Sandra (1946–   ) To capture the spontaneous moments in children's lives, Reco artist Sandra Kuck often rounds up a group of neighbourhood kids and takes them off to play in the setting she wants to paint. Her "Sunday Best," first issue in Reco's *Days Gone By* series, captured the Plate of the Show award at the 1983 South Bend Convention and was one of the most popular plates that year. Kuck, whose plate career began in 1979, studied art for one year at the University of California at Los Angeles before moving to Manhattan to be close to the great museums. She attended the Art Students' League in Manhattan and studied portraiture and anatomy with established artists. She has shown her work in galleries in New York City, Brooklyn and Long Island. Ms. Kuck has won numerous awards for her work, including *Plate World's* and *NALED's* Artist of the Year award for several years in a row.

KÜNSTLER, Mort (1931–   )
Mort Künstler's paintings chronicle American history from the time of the Indians to the present space age. He paints with both high realism and imagination. His passion for detail—and respect for history—is showcased in his first collector's plate series, *Oklahoma!*, produced by Edwin M. Knowles, featuring scenes from the classic Rodgers and Hammerstein musical that tells the story of the last frontier land rush. Künstler attended the Pratt Institute in New York City. In his career as an illustrator he has published more than 2,000 illustrations for books, advertisements and magazines, including *Newsweek*, *National Geographic*, *The Sat-*

urday Evening Post, *True*, *Sports Afield* and *Outdoor Life*. His paintings hang in the permanent collections of museums across the country.

KURSÁR, Raymond (1944–   )
Until 1978, when "Scarlett," the first plate in Edwin M. Knowles' *Gone With the Wind* series was issued, Raymond Kursár had earned his reputation primarily in the field of commercial illustration. His original paintings for covers for Random House and Ballantine Books have been widely exhibited. He has won awards for his New York theatre posters and published illustrations in such magazines as *Ladies Home Journal*, *Better Homes and Gardens* and *Good Housekeeping*. His corporate clients include RCA Records, McDonald's and Coca-Cola. Kursár was educated at the School of Advertising Art, the University of Oregon and the Museum of Modern Art in Portland, Oregon. He came to New York with his portfolio in hand, and, remarkably, has never had to work for a company as an employee.

LALIQUE, Marie-Claude
(1921–   ) Chief designer and president of the firm founded by her grandfather René Lalique, Marie-Claude Lalique created the *Annual* series of Lalique crystal collector's plates which began in 1965 and ended in 1976. The third generation in a family of artists, Lalique is know for her versatility. She is an accomplished painter, sculp-

tor, glass-blower and jewellry designer. She is a graduate of the *Grand Chaumiere* and *L'École Normale Superiore des Arts Decoratifs de Paris* where she concentrated on painting until her teacher, Andre Arbus, developed her appreciation of the decorative arts.

LAMBERT, Georgia (1948–   )
As the child of an Air Force colonel, Georgia Lambert lived for much of her youth in Europe, where she spent countless hours in the great art museums, learning about the techniques of the Old Masters. She most admired the depth of colour and sense of glowing light they achieved with numerous layers of paint and varnish. Today she uses the techniques she admired in the medium of china painting, raising a craft to an art form. Instead of simply tracing designs onto china or porcelain and filling them in, she paints originals directly onto porcelain "canvasses." For her first collector's plate series, *The Four Ancient Elements*, produced by Edwin M. Knowles, she applied 20 or more layers of paint to master plates to show the mythological figures of Earth, Air, Fire and Water.

PLATE ARTIST INFORMATION

LAMINCIA, Franco (1930–   ) Born into a family whose artistic heritage spans generations, Franco Lamincia grew up in Deruta, Italy, an ancient village on the Tiber River near Perugia, renowned since the 16th century for its fine majolica, also known as faience. He studied drawing at the local professional school under the great Alpinolo Maguini, who revived the production of true Deruta majolica in the early 1900s. Lamincia reproduced the majolica style when he designed "Noah and the Dove," first issue in Veneto Flair's *St. Mark's of Venice* series. Each plate is a hand-painted recreation of the great mosaics of St. Mark's Cathedral, which chronicle the Old Testament.

LANGE, Kai (1905–   ) Artist Kai Lange has been with Royal Copenhagen since the age of 17, and after more than half a century with the firm is regarded as one of the most knowledgable artists working in the porcelain medium. The first Lange design selected for the annual *Christmas* plate was for the 1940 issue, and since 1963 every plate except the 1976 issue has been a Lange creation. Lange studied drawing under Carl Schwenn. He is the recipient of several grants and an illustrator for several Danish newspapers. He has created wall hangings for many official institutions. His works hang in the Folkets Hus, Copenhagen.

LICEA, Eve (1928–   ) Eve Licea's art and life are a study in contrasts. She was born to a poor working-class family in New York's Bronx area, and her family could not afford art lessons. Yet today she lives and works in a fashionable loft in Greenwich Village, and her artworks are exhibited in such prestigious galleries as Lever House, Pindar Gallery and Les Mouches in New York City. A painter, sculptor and lithographer, she is best known for her embossed lithographs and large cast-paper sculptures. Her style is a unique blend of contrasting elements: geometric patterns and rounded natural forms, colour and white, matt and gloss surfaces, raised and flat areas. To her two collector's plate series, *Biblical Mothers* and *Licea Christmas*, produced by Edwin M. Knowles, she brings a sculptor's feel for light and shadow along with a painter's feel for line. A creator rather than a recorder, her treatment of subjects the Old Masters painted in a traditional way is very contemporary, and yet realistic. Licea studied at Parson's School of Design in New York. She has done illustrations for numerous publications, including *Good Housekeeping* and *Women's Day*.

LOCKHART, James (1912–   ) James Lockhart, an ardent naturalist and conservationist, is widely known for his realistic portrayals of wild animals in their natural habitats. His *Lockhart Wildlife* series for Pickard commemorates vanishing forms of American fauna. His paintings and drawings also have appeared in limited edition prints, books, calendars, gift items and magazines, including *Collier's*, *The Saturday Evening Post* and *Sports Afield*. He is a member of the Board of Governors of Brookfield Zoo and of Chicago's Shedd Aquarium and a trustee of Duck's Unlimited, a waterfowl conservation group.

LÜCKEL, Christian (1945–   ) Christian Lückel lives and works in Bavaria, surrounded by the rich beauty of the mountains, forests and the Danube River, all of which are reflected in his work. Lückel has been influenced by the Dutch masters, notably Rembrandt and Vermeer, as well as by such artists of the nineteenth century Munich School as Schleich, Schürer and Hänger, who themselves were followers of the Flemish tradition. Lückel paints mainly in the style known as "genre," preferring subjects such as landscapes, seascapes and farmyard scenes which reflect everyday life in the Germany of the nineteenth century. Recently, Lückel has concentrated on painting miniatures, small paintings of fine detail that are especially suited to the collector's plate medium. In 1986, Christian Seltmann issued the *Lückel's Idyllic Village Life* series, the first series for both artist and maker.

MALFERTHEINER, Josef
(1931–   ) A master woodcarver from Saint Ulrich, Italy, Josef Malfertheiner studied at the Ortesi Academy of Art and in 1966 became Master Carver for Anri, for whom he designed the *Christmas* series. He is best known for his portrayals of Tyrolean history and three-dimensional replication of Renoir, Van Eyck and Rembrandt. He has works in private collections in Italy, Austria, Germany and Australia.

MANDRAJJI, Valentin
(1929–   )
MARSTEN, Barbara (1935–   )
Barbara Marsten and Valentin Mandrajji are unique as an artistic team in that they work together on the same canvas. They have been working this way and exhibiting together since 1980. Mandrajji was born in Vienna and received his artistic training in Europe. He practiced monumental art, completing 12 frescoes in European churches and non-religious frescoes in Amsterdam and Vienna. Many of his smaller works are now in private collections in Austria, Sweden, Germany, Canada and the United States. Marsten was born in Los Angeles and studied art at U.C.L.A. She has exhibited in California and New York, and has paintings in private collections. Marsten and Mandrajji work together not only as painters, but also as designers for many world-famous companies, including Wedg-

wood and Cartier. In 1986, they created their first plate series for the Knowles China Company, *American Innocents*, which is a tribute to the traditional American folk art of the nineteenth century.

MASSERIA, Francisco J.J.C.
(1926–   ) Francisco Masseria won his first gold medal at the age of fourteen in the *Salon Annuale de Entre Rios* in his native Argentina. He emigrated to Italy in 1936, made his home in Rome, and studied the works of the Italian and Spanish Renaissance masters. Today he studies the faces of people he sees on the streets. In Royal Doulton's *Portraits of Innocence* series, Masseria mixes two distinct techniques to form his own style, painting classically smooth faces against boldly Impressionistic backgrounds. His numerous awards include NALED's Lithograph of the Year in 1982. He has exhibited in South, Central and North America and in Europe.

MAYS, Maxwell (1918–   )
Maxwell Mays, designer of the 1976, 1977 and 1978 plates in Reed & Barton's *Christmas* collector's plate series, specializes in Americana. His art has appeared in such magazines as *Collier's*, *Yankee*, *Cosmopolitan* and *New England*.

McCLELLAND, John (1919–   )
In 1980, Reco artist John McClelland's plate "Mary, Mary," first in the *McClelland's Mother Goose* series, out-performed all others on the Bradford Exchange and was named Plate of the Year. It was also named "Best All-Around Collectible" and "Best Plate" by the National Association of Limited Edition Dealers, and McClelland won their "Best Artist" title as well. But he made his mark as a magazine illustrator and portraitist of politicians and artists long before he designed his first collector's plate. McClelland works almost exclusively from live models, whom he may meet by chance, to capture the individuality of children—he saw the model for "Mary, Mary" at a church day-care centre. He studied at Auburn University and at Grand Central Art School and Art Career School, in New York, but considers portrait artist Jerry Farnsworth his most valuable teacher. He is the author of books on flower and portrait painting and has had numerous exhibits, primarily on the East Coast. His other plate series include *McClelland Children's Circus Collection* and *Becky's Day*, for Reco.

PLATE ARTIST INFORMATION

METTLER, Dölf (1934 –) Dölf Mettler lives in a small village at the bottom of Mount Säntis in Switzerland and grew to love all that is Appenzell while watching the processions to the mountain pastures as a child at his parents' side.

After completing his education, Mettler was apprenticed at St. Gallen, the world-famous center for Swiss Embroideries, but soon began to paint in his free time, propping up his easel by the roadside during the summer processions up the Alps and learning all he could about the history of Appenzell folk art.

His knowledge and artistry is transmitted in his first collector's plate series *Appenzell Traditions* from Langenthal Swiss China.

MEYER, Sonja (1927 –) Sonja Meyer is considered to be a great artist of animal and nature painting who has turned a childhood dream into reality, when she spent hours at the zoo, sketching the beloved animals. After she completed her art training in Zürich she was still fascinated with animals as subjects. Sonja Meyer first gained public attention with a remarkable series of cards. *Marmots on the Watch* opens her first collector's plate series, *Alpine Wildlife* from Langenthal Swiss China. Academic knowledge and artistic achievement is expressed in her work — but the closeness to nature and the vitality of her art may even be more important.

MONEY, Rusty (1939?–) In 1981, the Ernst plate series *Seems Like Yesterday* introduced artist Rusty Money to the collector's market. Money was born in Oak Park, Illinois and now lives and paints in Escondido, California. She studied at Arizona State University and the Washington School of Art. Her favourite subjects are children and turn-of-the-century period scenes. Her work is characterized by the use of delicate pastels in a semi-Impressionistic style. She won the International Fine Arts Award competition in 1980. Her works hang in numerous private collections.

MUELLER, Hans (1934–) Hans Mueller, born in Waldsassen, Bavaria, was the son of a Bareuther artist. He studied engraving and painting at the porcelain academy in Selb and the Porcelain Trade School of Bavaria and in 1952 joined Bareuther as a porcelain painter. He was promoted to chief designer for the firm in 1968. In the *Christmas* and *Father's Day* series Mueller painted castles and country scenes in blue and white.

MUNINGER, Ludwig (1929–) Ludwig Muninger has won high praise for his painting—especially his winter scenes—among collectors in many countries. He has been the focus of several one-man shows, and in 1974, the government of Ireland officially honored him for his works. He has also been included in some of Europe's most prestigious collective shows. His work is noted for its mastery of the laws of color and air perspective, as well as the juxtaposition of the grandeur of nature with humbler creations of humankind.

Muninger was born in Augsburg, Bavaria. From there, he relentlessly pursued his dream of painting from childhood on, studying in Germany, France, Italy, Switzerland, and Austria. Although he was surrounded by dizzying changes in the modern art world, he found his inspiration in an earlier era. His mentors were not cubists or abstractionists, but the 17th-century Dutch landscape artists and the Dutch masters. His works evoke a more simple time and place, a world in which man and nature coexist in perfect harmony. His first series for Furstenberg, titled *Muninger's Romantic Winter Impressions,* exemplifies this viewpoint.

NEIMAN, LeRoy (1927–   ) The creator of Royal Doulton's *Commedia Dell' Arte Series* also created the Olympian murals at the 1976 and 1980 Olympics and was named official artist for the 1984 Olympics. He was a gold medallist at the *Salon d'Arte Moderne* in Paris and an illustrator for such magazines as *Vogue, Harper's Bazaar, Glamour, Time, Newsweek* and *The Saturday Evening Post.* His works hang in some of the world's great museums, including the Hermitage Museum in Leningrad, and in private collections. Neiman attended the St. Paul Art Centre, the University of Chicago and the Art Institute of Chicago.

NEUBACHER, Gerda (1945–   ) The creator of Kaiser's *Classic Fairy Tales Collection* also introduced Austrians to moccasins. Gerda Neubacher was born in the small Austrian mountain village of Pols and intended to make fashion design her career. She studied for four years at the Grace Kelly School of Art in Zurich and has designed shoes, perfume ads and shopping bags. Now she is a realist painter well-known for her scenes of forests, children and wildlife. She moved to Canada with her husband, Fred, also a painter, and has won numerous awards in the many Canadian shows where she has exhibited. Her work, on canvas and on porcelain, is in galleries and private homes all over the world.

NEWMAN, Colin (1952–   ) Born in the Fen region of East Anglia, England, Colin Newman so loved the tranquil English countryside that he lives there now with his wife and son. The land inspires his wildlife paintings, which have won him renown in England. His paintings hang in many galleries in Cambridge and London—and are gaining him a respectable reputation in Europe and North America.

Newman received first-class honors at both the Cambridge School of Art and the Hornsey College of Art. He is featured in both the '85–'86 *Illustrator's Annual* and *European Annual of Illustrators.* He has contributed color illustrations to the *Illustrated Animal Encyclopedia* published by MacMillian, as well as to numerous Reader's Digest Field Guides. His ability to bring the creatures he illustrates to life without forsaking critical scientific detail has brought him to the forefront of promising young European illustrators.

A private and retiring man, Newman's interests include angling in local streams, working for neighborhood conservation causes, and sketching the wildlife that can be seen from his doorstep and window. This perspective was his inspiration for the *Colin Newman's Country Panorama* series from Wedgwood.

NG, Kee Fung The story of Kee Fung Ng is the story of an artist who wanted to bring beauty into a grey world.

Born in Canton, China, before World War II., Kee Fung Ng's artistic talent earned him a place in the state-supported Fu San art school. He found out early that he was expected to create only those works that supported Maoist policy. In part because of those artistic constraints, Kee Fung Ng fell ill, and requested permission to emigrate to Hong Kong because of his failing health. Kee Fung Ng then lived and worked in Hong Kong for several years, developing his subtle mix of Eastern und Western painting techniques. Today he resides in the United States where his works can be seen at the Kee Fung Ng Gallery in San Francisco and at the Lahaina Gallery in Maui, Hawaii. Ng is no stranger to the collector's plate medium. His first plate series, Children of Aberdeen, was well received by collectors worldwide. *Chinese Childrens Games* is his second series.

PLATE ARTIST INFORMATION

NIGHTINGALE, Sandy
(1953–   ) British artist Sandy Nightingale is known in her native country as a book illustrator for a number of well-established British publishing houses, including Pan, McMillan and Hamlyn, and has exhibited her works in numerous British galleries. In the *Alice in Wonderland* series—Porcelaine Georges Boyer's first collector's series for the United States market—she incorporated scenes from her parents' garden and memories of her childhood. Nightingale studied in England and in the south of France and is a member of the Chelsea Society of Illustrators.

NITSCHKE, Detlev (1935–   )
Berlin Design artist Detlev Nitschke is widely known throughout Europe for his historically accurate paintings of turn-of-the-century Berlin. He was born in that city and studied lithography before receiving formal training as a painter and graphic artist. After studying with painter Ehrenfried Viola, Nitschke attended the Masters School for Printing and Graphics in Berlin and the State Institute for Graphics. Creator of the *Holiday Week of the Family Kappelmann* plate series, he has exhibited his work in galleries throughout Germany and the rest of Europe.

PELTRIAUX, Bernard (1921–   )
Renowned throughout the international art world for his paintings and lithographs, Bernard Peltriaux also dedicated himself, until his recent retirement, to educating artists from all over the world at the *Lycée Technique d'Etat* in Reims, the cathedral town where he was born and raised. He attended the *Ecole des Beaux-Arts* in Reims and the *Atelier Rene Jaudon* in Paris. He has numerous prizes and more than fifty solo exhibitions to his credit. *The Children of the Turn of the Century Collection*, produced by Limoges-Turgot, is his first collector's plate series.

PENTZ, Donald (1940–   )
Donald Pentz was born in Bridgewater, Nova Scotia, and studied at the Nova Scotia College of Art and Design and at Mt. Allyson University. He earned a Master's Degree in Fine Art from the University of Regina. At the age of 26, Pentz was elected to the Royal Canadian Academy and the Society of Canadian Artists. Pentz also worked as a naturalist for the Nova Scotia Department of Lands and Forests and for Kejimkujik National Park before settling into his artistic career. He has participated in numerous group and solo exhibitons, and his works are in the permanent collections of museums, corporations and academic institutions. Pentz is in demand for private commissions, magazine covers, and book illustrations for such publishers as the Nova Scotia Museum and the National Museum of Natural Science in Ottawa. The Canadian Broadcasting Corporation recently produced a documentary on his life and work. Dominion China initiated his first plate series in 1986 with the *Wings Upon the Wind* series, chronicling the life cycle of the Canada goose. The first plate in this series, "The Landing," was named Plate of Show at the 1986 Canadian Plate and Collectibles Fair.

PERILLO, Gregory (1932–   )
Gregory Perillo has been an artist fascinated by the Old West since his father, an Italian immigrant, told him stories of the Indian Wars and Perillo sketched the details in crayon. Today he is a successful oil painter who paints proud, strong Plains Indians as they used to be. He was born in New York City. He studied at the Pratt Institute, the School of Visual Arts and the Art Student's League. He is also the

only living artist to have studied under renowned Western painter William R. Leigh. His collector's plate series for Kern Collectibles and Vague Shadows include *The Professionals*, *The Storybook Collection*, *The Chieftains I* series, a Christmas series and a wildlife series.

PETER, Nori (1934–   ) Nori Peter, well-known for her portrayals of life in the Arctic, became entranced with the Innuit people when she saw them and their carvings at an art show. She makes frequent trips to the North from her Ontario, Canada home. Born in Hungary, she fled her country at the age of 21 after the Budapest uprising of 1956. Soon after arriving in Toronto, she began doing children's portraits. Her first collector's plate series was *People of the Midnight Sun* for Kaiser; her second, for Anna-Perenna, was *Arctic Spring*. She also has done *Mother's Day* series plates and twelve figurines for Kaiser. She studied at the Academy of Fine Arts in Budapest.

QUELLIER, André (1925–   ) André Quellier, creator of *Quellier's Morals of Perrault* series for Limoges-Turgot, was born in Paris. He received his classical training at *L'Ecole des Beaux Arts* and studied under the direction of Jean Dupas and Edmond Heuze. His work has been shown in the major cities of the world—in the United States, Japan, the Soviet Union, Spain and

France, including one of the first exhibits at the Theatre des Champs Elysees in Paris. His portrait of Jean Cocteau is in the home of Jean Marais. His numerous prizes include the *Prix Internationale du Gemmeil d'Art Sacré à Lourdes*, the *Médaille d'Or des Artists Français*, *Pris Casa Vealsquez, a Madrid*, and, in 1945, *Prix de l'Institute*.

RESTIEAU, André (1912–1981) André Restieau was a world authority on the techniques of re-creating medieval stained-glass colouration in porcelain, as seen in his *Stained Glass Christmas (Noel Vitrail)* series for D'Arceau-Limoges. He studied with such masters as Lavelle and Fournier. His commissions also include *The Lafayette Legacy Collection* for D'Arceau-Limoges. In 1966 he exhibited at the *Cercle de la Librairie* in Paris.

ROCKWELL, Norman (1894–1978) One of the most widely-known artists of the twentieth century, Norman Rockwell possessed an uncanny—and perhaps unmatched—ability to capture the spirit of American life in its most ordinary and its most festive moments. Rockwell created well over 3,000 works in his long and illustrious career. He drew his first *Saturday Evening Post* cover in 1916, followed by more than 300 more. He also drew numerous illustrations for *Life*, *Look* and *Boy's Life*, and was well-known for his annual Boy Scouts calendar illustrations. Rockwell studied at Chase School of Fine and Applied Arts, the National Academy of Design and the Art Student's League, all in New York. He had a one-man show in 1941 at the Milwaukee Art Institute and a one-man exhibition at the Dannenberg Galleries in New York City. His works hang in the Smithsonian Institution, the Metropolitan Museum of Art, the Corner House Museum in Stockbridge, Massachusetts, and in other museums throughout the United States. In addition to the well-known and very popular collector's plate series by The Rockwell Society of America, Rockwell's work is also featured on collector's plates by Franklin Mint, Gorham and Royal Devon.

PLATE ARTIST INFORMATION

RODERICK, Merri (1948–   )
Merri Roderick has spent many years in the formal study of art. Her work is included in many private collections, and she recently won a major award at the Invitational Fine Arts Exhibition in the Midwest. She spent several years as an apprentice to sculptor Perrin Gerber, and her *Treasures of the Doré Bible* series in fused bronze relief represents the fulfilment of a long time dream; Ms. Roderick was awed by Doré's biblical etchings even as a child.

Living in the Chicago area, Ms. Roderick hopes to expand into figurine design and is planning a lead crystal Christmas series for plates. She works for a gallery, and last year returned to the University of Illinois. Art is her life she says, it is "What I do."

ROLLER, Carole (1953–   ) The first American artist to design plates for Danish company Bing & Grøndahl, Carole Roller has also designed printed fabrics, dinnerware, rugs, towels, Christmas ornaments and stationery. She earned a bachelor's degree in fine arts at the Pratt Institute in New York City. Her plate series include *Children's Day* for Bing & Grøndahl. The company has also produced her figurines and pendants.

ROMANELLI, Carl (1913–   )
The sculptor of Incolay's *Great Romances of History Collection* has works on display in memorials, churches, galleries and private collections throughout the world. Romanelli learned his art in a five-year apprenticeship with his father, sculptor Carlo Romanelli. One of his most famous works is a bronze bust of John Henry Cardinal Newman on display in the Vatican. His other commissions include a life-size bronze of Elvis Presley for the Las Vegas Hilton. He has exhibited in galleries across the United States and is a board member of the California Art Club and the American Institute of Fine Arts.

RUGGERI, Gino (1918–   )
Gino Ruggeri, a sculptor in the neo-Classical tradition, is best known for his work "The Crucifix," sculpted from the Casa Serena Institute of Cecina Mare, and his two sculptures "Memorials to the Fallen," which pay tribute to World War I victims. He sculpted the 1976-1980 issues in Studio Dante di Volteradici's *Grand Opera Series*. Ruggeri studied at the Academy of Fine Arts in Sienna and the Art Institute in Volterra, Italy. His awards include three first prizes from the Academy of Fine Arts. He has been director of the Cooperative Artien since 1942.

RUSSELL, Frank (1921–   )
Frank Russell and his wife, Gertrude Barrer, have blended their talents to become a successful art-producing team. They met at the Art Student's League in New York and five years later were reunited in New York's art centre, Greenwich Village. Together they have created lithographs, photographs, frescos, serigraphs, ceramics, sculptures and two plate series for Anna-Perenna, the *Triptych* and *Romantic Love* series. Their work has been exhibited at the Art Institute of Chicago and the Whitney Museum of American Art, and hangs in the private collections of Cyrus Vance, Helmut Schmidt and the U.N. Interfaith Chapel in New York.

SANTANGELA, Alberto (1936–   ) When Alberto Santangela was an art student in Florence he was so captivated by the baptistery doors sculpted by 15th-century artist Lorenzo Ghiberti that they inspired him to become a sculptor instead of a painter. Years later he recreated scenes from Ghiberti's doors on collector's plates in the *Ghiberti's Doors* series for Studio Dante di Volteradici. He also sculpted the *Living Madonnas* series. He was born in Italy. Santangela apprenticed to his uncle, Amilcare Santini, at an early age before studying informally in Florence.

SCHOENER, Toni (1913–1978) Toni Schoener's first love was porcelain. At the end of elementary school he was appointed chief designer for Altrohlauer Porzellanfabrik, one of the best-known Bavarian porcelain houses of the time. This "non-essential" industry came to a halt in 1939, and after the war Schoener wandered across Europe restoring war-damaged paintings before returning to Bavaria in 1955, when he joined Kaiser as chief designer. His Kaiser creations include *Christmas* and *Mother's Day* plates.

SCHULZ, Charles (1922–   )
Cartoonist Charles Schulz' "Peanuts" characters have endeared themselves to millions of Americans through comic strips, television specials, a *Time* magazine cover, and many other media, including collector's plate series produced by Schmid. Schulz's television creations have won various Peabody and Emmy awards; the "Peanuts" strip won Best Humour Strip of the Year from the National Cartoonists Society in 1962; Yale University voted Schulz Humourist of the Year in 1958; and as governor of California Ronald Reagan proclaimed a Charles Schulz Day in 1967. Schulz studied at Art Instruction, Inc. in Minneapolis and has been awarded honorary degrees by Anderson College in Indiana and St. Mary's College in California. He was Grand Marshal of the Tournament of Roses Parade in 1976. He also won the National Cartoonists' Society "Reuben" Award in 1955 and 1964, the School Bell Award from the National Education Society in 1960 and the Big Brother of the Year Award in California in 1973.

SHERWOOD, Stewart
(1941–   ) Because of his love of variety, Stewart Sherwood works in a number of styles and mediums, sometimes combining several techniques in a single piece. A self-taught artist born in Toronto, Canada he commonly works with such mediums as oil, water color, gouache, line, marker, and pastel. He has created illustrations for children's books and greeting cards, but his best works consists of portraits—his portraits of Pope John Paul II, Menachem Begin, John F. Kennedy, Anwar Sadat and Pierre Trudeau are only a few of his pieces that have appeared on the cover of *Maclean's Magazine*. His illustrations have also appeared in *The Toronto Star*, *Reader's Digest*, and *Legion Magazine*.

Still living in Toronto, Sherwood's interests include photography and bike riding. Another hobby is landscape painting; he keeps a rustic cottage "up north" where he finds inspiration.

SKELTON, Red (1913–   ) Many people regard film, stage and television comedian and artist Red Skelton as a vital part of America's entertainment heritage. He has made Americans laugh for decades with his portrayals of such characters as Freddie the Freeloader, Clem Kadiddlehopper, Willie Lump-Lump, Sheriff Deadeye, Bolivar Shagnasty, San Fernando Red, George Appleby and Junior the Mean Widdle Kid. Skelton is also a photographer and filmmaker, a recorded composer, a children's fiction writer (with 40 published titles to his credit) and, of course, a painter whose works, reproduced on collector's plates, have endeared him to thousands. His plate series include the *Freddie the Freeloader* and *Freddie's Adventures* series for Crown Parian and the *Famous Clowns* series for Fairmont. Born in Vincennes, Indiana, the son of a clown who died before he was born, Skelton began his career dancing for pennies on the street and joined a travelling medicine show at age ten. Since then he has entertained on vaudeville, stage, screen, radio and television. He is a self-taught artist who paints anytime, anyplace—even on airplanes.

PLATE ARTIST INFORMATION

SMITH, Jessie Willcox (1863–1935) Born in Philadelphia, Jesse Willcox Smith studied in that city under Thomas Eakins at the Pennsylvania Academy of Fine Arts. She was also influenced by the work of Howard Pyle at the Drexel Institute of Arts and Sciences. Smith became the most highly-paid woman illustrator of her time, and the most admired. She illustrated many classic children's books, including *A Child's Book of Verses, The Water Babies, Heidi* and *Little Women.* Although she was in constant demand to paint portraits of the children of wealthy Philadelphia families, she is best-known for the "ordinary" children she painted for the covers of *Good Housekeeping* magazine' from 1918 until 1932. Although she never married, Smith devoted her life to expressing the joys and delights of childhood. This theme is the basis of the *Jessie Willcox Smith Childhood Holiday Memories* series, introduced by the Knowles China Company in 1986.

SPAULDING, Don (1926–   ) Edwin M. Knowles artist Don Spaulding is a Norman Rockwell protege and a leading exponent of authentic historical detail in painting. He began study at New York City's Art Student's League on the G.I. Bill at the end of World War II when he was in his early 20's. He was among half a dozen students chosen to study and live with Rockwell for a summer, and Rockwell became one of his heroes and an example for his approach to

Western art. Each of the props and costumes in his seven-plate *Americana Holidays* series is handpicked and true to the 19th century. He has won several awards at shows of Western painting.

SPENCER, Irene (1940?–   ) Irene Spencer received her training at the American Academy of Art and the Art Institute of Chicago, where she developed her distinctive style, reminiscent of the Old Masters. In addition to her accomplishments as a fine artist, she has written and illustrated children's books and worked as a newspaper cartoonist. Her collector's plates include the *Mother's Love* and *Symphony of Roses* series for Pickard and plates for Fairmont and Gorham. In 1979 she won NALED's "Lithograph of the Year" award and in 1980, NALED's "Plate of the Year" award, as well as The Bradford Exchange's award for New Edition of the Year.

STOBART, John (1938–   ) John Stobart, artist for Royal Doulton's *The Log of the "Dashing Wave"* series, grew up in the English shipping town of Liverpool. He attended Derby College of Arts and won a scholarship to the Royal Academy of Art in London. He has travelled extensively by sea and some of the most exotic ports in the world have served as settings for his paintings. His works hang in such prestigious collections as the Marine Museum of Upper Canada in Toronto, the

National Maritime Museum in Greenwich, England, and the Royal Naval College. His paintings have been featured as cover art for many magazines.

TELLIER, Liliane (1924–   ) Noted watercolourist Liliane Tellier, creator of Haviland's *1001 Arabian Nights* series, has an extensive following among connoisseurs of the medium. A native Parisienne, she studied watercolour and gouache at L'École Camondo in Paris and refined her techniques in Sweden. Later she worked for the International Society for Education through Art as a consultant to UNESCO.

THELANDER, Henry (1902–   ) Artist Henry Thelander's association with Bing & Grøndahl is unparalleled on the collector's plate market. The 1984 issue marked his twenty-second consecutive design for the *Christmas* series. He also has designed every Bing & Grøndahl *Mother's Day* issue. A self-taught artist, Thelander has spent his five-decade-long career living and working in Copenhagen, London and Stockholm, benefitting from the variety of cultures and artistic influences. Known as the "equivalent of the poet laureate" in the Danish visual arts, he has designed government-sponsored postage stamps and posters.

TOOTLE, Douglas (1950–)
Davenport Pottery artist Douglas Tootle was born and raised in Staffordshire, England, and schooled at one of the region's finest institutions, the Burslen College of Art. He was awarded a number of scholarships and left Staffordshire to study fine art and sculpture in London and Florence. Since returning to his native region he has done extensive modelling for some of its most prestigious potteries, including Coalport, a division of Wedgwood, and Hereford. He modelled "Jack Tar" for the *Toby Plate Collection.*

TRAUTH, Gero (1942–) Born in Neurode/Selesia, Gero Trauth began studying art there at the age of five. In 1960 he entered the Gutenberg University in Mainz, West Germany, where for five years he studied graphic design, painting, sculpture, the history of book illustration and visual communications, after which he earned his Master of Arts degree summa cum laude.

Since 1966 he has won first place in seven competitions for graphic design at the International Frankfurt Fair, and has participated in numerous prestigious exhibitions throughout Germany and Switzerland. He has designed fabrics, wall coverings, lighting, flatware, and collector's plates, including Villeroy & Boch's *Dreams of Katharina* series.

Gero Trauth lives and works in Siegen, West Germany, with his favourite model (his wife) and their two daughters. In his spare time he actively enjoys ice-dancing, ballet, and adding to his collection of rare and exotic butterflies.

UOSIKKINEN, Raija (1925–)
Born in Hollola, Finland, Raija Uosikkinen is widely regarded as a master ceramicist. She studied at the Institute of Industrial Arts in Helsinki. In 1947 she joined the Arabia design department, and in 1952 she received a grant scholarship from the Arabia-Decora factory to study in Germany. She has taken subsequent study trips to Australia, Turkey, England and Indonesia. A 1954 Helsinki exhibit was devoted exclusively to her creations. Her distinctive contemporary folk art style is exemplified in her plate series *Kalevala.*

VESTERGAARD, Sven
(1932–) As head artist and chief designer for Royal Copenhagen, Sven Vestergaard is a guardian of the centuries-old tradition of hand-painted ceramics. He enrolled with Royal Copenhagen as an apprentice decorator in 1948 at the age of 16 and four years later had attained the pinnacle of the decorator's art. In 1976, when he was head of the drawing department, his artwork was chosen for the annual Christmas plate, "Danish Watermill." His works of the last decade include the Historical Plates, the Olympic Plates, the *Motherhood* series and the *Hans Christian Andersen* series. Beginning in 1985, Vestergaard has been responsible for the *Christmas* series.

VICKERS, Mary (1940–)
Wedgwood artist Mary Vickers credits a German bomb that fell on London during World War II as her inspiration for becoming an artist. Born in a war-torn suburb of London, she soon set out to create beauty in an often violent, ugly world. Today she is one of the leading contemporary Romantic painters, and is also accomplished in lithographs and etching. She studied at England's St. Martin's School of Art, the New York Art Student's League and the Pratt Institute. Her works are exhibited in major galleries on both sides of the Atlantic and in private collections such as that of the Duke and Duchess of Marlborough. Her collector's plates include *The Blossoming of Suzanne, My Memories* and *Portraits of First Love* series.

PLATE ARTIST INFORMATION

WEBER, Sarah Stilwell (1878–1939) Sarah Stilwell Weber was born near Philadelphia, Pennsylvania. She studied art at the Drexel Institute in Philadelphia under the tutelage of American illustrator Howard Pyle and was one of the founders of the American Realist movement. Between 1900 and 1930, Weber's work appeared in children's books and on the covers of such magazines as *Collier's* and the *Saturday Evening Post*. Her artwork appears on the plates in Newell Pottery's *Sarah Stilwell Weber Calendar* series.

WETTEROTH, Ernst (1928–) Born in 1928 in the Frankfurt suburb of Niederrad in a large family, he started earning to help support his family of nine at a very early age as a caddy for the golf course in Niederrad. In his off-duty breaks he made sketches and drawings of trees and landscapes.
At Christmas 1938 the gift of a paintbox brought out his talent as a painter. His joy in colours and his talent for painting and sketching led to a decision to start as apprentice to a commercial artist. After his apprenticeship he was called up in spite of his youth. For three years from 1946 Wetteroth became a pupil of the artist Johann Heinrich Pfaff. Ernst Wetteroth has freelanced as a painter and graphic artist since 1969, and since the early 1970s he has lived with his family at Odenwald, where he can devote himself entirely to art in this delightful and beautiful countryside. In 1987 he created the motives for the collection *Ancient Giants* from Tirschenreuth.

WIINBLAD, Bjorn (1918–) Danish artist Bjorn Wiinblad graduated from the Royal Academy of Art in 1944 and worked for *Nymolle Art Fajance* Factory from 1946 to 1956. His creations attracted the attention of Philipp Rosenthal, Jr., head of the Rosenthal company, who, after extensive negotiation, persuaded Wiinblad to design works for the German maker. He was assigned to create products for the Studio-Linie, a high quality, high-priced line of Rosenthal ware. His distinctive collector's plates are world renowned, and the "Lotus" pattern of dinnerware he designed won the 1965 American Interior Design Award. His creations include the *Wiinblad Christmas* series produced by Rosenthal. His works are in the collections of museums throughout Europe.

WORRALL, Linda (1951–) Linda Worrall graduated with distinction from the Bolton College of Art Design in England, the country of her birth. She has completed major private commissions as well as participating in public exhibitions of her work. Worrall is a diploma member of the Society of Industrial Artists and Designers. Her work has been presented at the prestigious Northwest Association of Illustrators exhibition in Liverpool. In 1986, Davenport Pottery issued her first work in the medium of collector's plates, *The Poetry Society of London's Treasury of Classic Children's Verse* series.

WÜLFING, Sulamith (1901–   )
Sulamith Wülfing was born in 1901 in Elberfeld (now part of Wuppertal), Germany and has lived in that area all of her life. She studied at the Art College in Wuppertal and is known for her art that has been reproduced on numerous cards, books and calendars. Much of her original work was lost during World War II, but this did not discourage her long and distinguished career. Her collector's plates include *Sulamith's Love Song*, *Sulamith's Christmas* and *A Woman's Love and Life* series for Königszelt Bayern. She has exhibited at the Spring Fair in Frankfurt.

XARAS, Ted (1945–   ) Theodore "Ted" Xaras has been enamoured of the steam engine since he was a child, when his father told him bedtime tales of building locomotives in Eddystone, Pennsylvania, and took him in borrowed cars to chase their clouds of smoke across the countryside—a pastime he still enjoys. Xaras' plate "Symphony in Steam: Canadian Pacific Railway," first issue in Christian Bell's *Age of Steam* series, won CALED's 1981 Plate of the Year title and became the first Bradex-listed plate produced in Canada. Xaras holds a B.F.A. in illustration from Philadelphia College of Art and an M.F.A. in painting from the Tyler School of Art in Philadelphia. He is a professor and chairman of the art department at Ursinus College in Pennsylvania. His credits include a cover for *Time* magazine and illustrations for various other books and railroad magazines.

YATES, Michael (1927–   ) Michael Yates was born in Pennsylvania. He studied at the Art Institute of Pittsburgh. His works appear in numerous public buildings and churches throughout America as well as in many private collections. His art has been commissioned for the homes of such prominent figures as Gerald Ford, Golda Meir, Johnny Cash and former First Lady Pat Nixon. He designed *Michael Yates' Country Ladies* series, Morgantown Crystal's first limited-edition collector's plate series, in double intaglio-carved crystal.

ZHAO Huimin (1919–   ) Zhao Huimin was born into a desperately poor home in China (ED. NOTE: Chinese surnames always precede given names; hence "Zhao" is the artist's surname). He dreamed of becoming an artist, but the family had no money for lessons. Zhao worked during the day and taught himself to paint at night. He became skilled at gouache and traditional watercolour painting, as practiced for centuries by the great Chinese masters. His work became more widely known and in 1958 Zhao was awarded the title of Porcelain Painter in the factory in Ching-te Chen (Jingdezhen). In 1983, he was acclaimed as Master Artisan. Examples of Zhao's work are in porcelain collections all over the world. The *Beauties of the Red Mansion* series, with artwork by Zhao, was initiated in 1986 by Imperial Ching-te Chen Porcelain. It is the first collector's plate series from the People's Republic, and features the beautiful heroines of *The Dream of Red Mansions*, a classic romantic novel and one of China's great literary masterpieces.

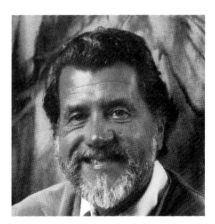

ZOLAN, Donald (1936–   )
Donald Zolan is consistently rated one of the most popular collector's plate artists living in the United States, for his poignant pictures of special moments in the lives of contemporary children. His first plate, "Erik and Dandelion" in Viletta's *Zolan's Children* series, was released in 1978. In 1979 "Sabina in the Grass" made history when it became the first non-first-issue to receive the Bradford Exchange's

PLATE ARTIST INFORMATION

"Plate of the Year"' award. Zolan's *Wonder of Childhood Collection, Children at Christmas Collection,* and *Children and Pets* series are produced by Pemberton & Oakes. He and his brother, Richard Zolan (who has produced plates for Modern Masters), are the fifth generation of artists in their family. He studied at the Art Institute of Chicago and won a scholarship to the American Academy of Art. His works hang in numerous galleries throughout the United States and in private collections in Mexico, Australia, France, Italy, South Korea and Colombia.

ZVORYKIN, Boris (1872–1950) Russian artist Boris Vasilevich Zvorykin was born in Moscow and was one of the last great book illustrators of Tsarist Russia. He was also noted for his murals in the Cathedral at Simferopol. Forced to leave Russia during the 1917 revolution, he settled in Paris in 1920 and became an integral figure in an expatriate movement to retain Imperial Russia's cultural heritage. He elaborately illustrated four books of Russian fairy tales, later published as *The Firebird and Other Russian Fairy Tales* when they caught the eye of book editor Jaqueline Kennedy Onassis. Some of his illustrations appear on collector's plates in Heinrich/Villeroy & Boch's *Russian Fairy Tales* series.

GLOSSARY OF COMMONLY USED TERMS

A

Aftermarket. See *Market*.

Alabaster. A dense, fine-grained form of gypsum (calcium sulfate) stone, usually white pink and slightly translucent. Alabaster stone can be carved in fine detail for ornamental objects and hardened by intense heat. Italian alabaster is also called Florentine marble. Ivory alabaster is composed of alabaster but is non-translucent and acquires a patina with age like that of old ivory.

Allotment. A number of plates, all alike and usually at issue, allocated by a maker to a distributor or dealer. See *Lot*.

Alloy. Two or more metals combined while molten. Alloying is done to achieve hardness, toughness, or lustre. See *Pewter*.

Annual. A plate issued once each year as part of a series. The term is most often used when a plate does not commemorate a specific holiday.

Annular kiln. A round oven made from brick used to fire ceramic plates.

Art Deco, Art Décoratif. A style of decoration popular in Europe and America from 1920 to 1945. The Art Deco movement sought to glorify progress and the future by using as motifs such shapes as the cylinder, circle, rectangle, and cone.

Art Nouveau. A style of decoration in Europe and America from 1890 to 1920. The Art Nouveau movement used twining floral patterns as its primary decorative motifs.

Asked Price, Ask. The offering price posted for a plate by a seller on the Exchange.

At Issue. A plate being offered for sale at the time of its manufacture and at the original price set by the maker.

B

Back Issue. See *Issue*.

Backstamp. The information on the back of a plate, usually including the maker's signature, name, or trademark (logo-type). It may also record serial number, title, artist's signature, edition limit, explanation of the plate, sponsor, production techniques, awards, or release initials. It may be hand-applied, stamped, incised (cut or pressed), or applied as a decalcomania.

Banding. A method for hand-application of precious metals, such as gold, silver, or platinum, to the edge or other parts of a glazed plate. The decorator uses a camel's hair brush to apply a liquid metal suspended in special oils. The plate is then fired to adhere the metal to the glaze.

Baroque. An elaborate style of decoration developed in Europe the seventeenth and eighteenth centuries and noted for exaggerated gesture and line. Example: Dresden **(22-D68-0.0)**.

Bas-relief. See *Relief Sculpture*.

Bavaria (Bayern). A province in the southwest corner of Germany long known as a centre for porcelain factories. The region contains large deposits of kaolin, the key porcelain component.

Bearish. Marked by declining prices, either actual or expected. A bear market is one of declining prices.

Bedroom Dealer. A trade term for a small dealer who usually operates from his home, buys discounted plates, and resells them for a small profit.

Bid Price, Bid. The amount a prospective buyer offers to pay for a plate on the Exchange.

Bisque, Biscuit. A plate that has been fired but not glazed, leaving it with a matt texture. So called because of the biscuit-like appearance. Example: Lladró **(72-L41-0.0)**.

Blue Chip. An established series by a well-known maker in which nearly every issue shows a steady sequence of price rises above issue price, usually over an extended period of time.

Body. 1. The formula or combination of substances that make up potter's clay, generally referring to stoneware and earthenware. 2. The basic plate form to which ornamentation is applied.

Bone Ash. Calcium phosphate, a component of bone china, added to give whiteness and translucency. It is obtained by calcinating (reducing to powder by heat) animal bones, usually those of oxen.

Bone China (Bone Porcelain). A type of china developed by Josiah Spode in England in the 1790s. By replacing part of the caolin in the china formula with bone ash, greater translucency and whiteness is obtained at lower firing temperatures. The finest bone china contains up to 50% bone ash. It is the most commonly made china in England. Example: Royal Doulton **(26-R62-0.0)**

Bradex. Common term for the *Bradford Exchange Current Quotations,* a periodic listing of the current market prices of collector's plates now listed on the Exchange. *See Listed Plate, Exchange.*

Broker. A representative of the Bradford Exchange who logs buy-orders, seeks out an appropriate seller and confirms all transactions.

Bullish. Marked by rising prices, either actual or expected, and optimistic atmosphere. A bull market is one ofrising prices.

Buy order. An offer by an individual or dealer to purchase one or more plates on the secondary market. See *Bid Price, Exchange.*

C

Cameo Effect. Ornamentations in relief on a background of contrasting colour to resemble a cameo. Examples: Wedgwood Jasper ware **(26-W90-0.0)** and Incolay Studios **(84-I31-0.0).**

Carnelian. A hard translucent quartz that has a reddish colour.

Celsius, Centigrade. The thermometric scale in which 0° represents the freezing point of water and 100° the boiling point. Celsius temperature is denoted by ''C ''after the number.

Ceramic. A general term applying to all of the various plates made from clay and hardened by firing.

Certificate. An attestation of authenticity which may accompany each plate in an edition. A certificate authenticates a plate as being part of an issue and usually confirms the plate's individual number within the edition.

China, Chinaware. A hard, vitreous ceramic, whose main components are kaolin and china stone fired at high temperature. Originally the term was used for those ceramics which only came from China. Later it was applied to all ''hard'' and ''soft'' porcelain. China is often used as a generic term which includes porcelain, but is properly distinguished from it by a high bisque firing temperature and lower glaze firing temperature. The main firing (bisque) of china is approximately 7% lower than the main firing (glaze) of porcelain. In china production, the glaze is applied after the main firing and fixed with a second lower-temperature firing. A typical china formular is 40% kaolin, 10% ball clay, and varying proportions of china stone, feldspar, and flint. See *Porcelain.*

China Clay. See *Kaolin.*

China Stone, Petuntse. A feldspathic material in china formulas. China stone acts as a flux which helps dissolve and fuse the other components into a vitreous mass.

Christmas Plates, Christmas Series. Annual plates issued to commemorate Christmas, usually as part of a series. Plate names for Christmas include Noël (French), Weihnachten (German), Jul (Danish), Navidad (Spanish and Portuguese), and Natale (Italian). The oldest Christmas series is that of Bing & Grøndahl, produced continuously since 1895 **(14-B36-1.0).**

Clay. Any of various plastic, viscous earths used to make plates. It is formed by the decomposition, due to weathering, of igneous rocks such as granite, feldspar, and pegmatite.

Close. Last traded price on the Exchange.

Closed-End Series. A series of plates with a predetermined number of issues. Example: D'Arceau-Limoges *Douze Sites Parisiens de Louis Dali (Twelve Parisian Places)* **(18-D15-6.0).**

Cobalt Blue. Cobalt oxide in the form of a dark black powder which, when fired, turns a deep blue. It was the first known and still the most commonly used ceramic underglaze colour because of its ability to withstand high firing temperatures. It can produce a variety of shades. Examples: Kaiser cobalt blue **(22-K4-0.0)**, Bing & Grøndahl Copenhagen blue **(14-B36-0.0)**, Royal Copenhagen Danish Blue **(14-R59-0.0)**, and Rörstrand Scandia blue **76-R54-0.0).**

Collector's Plate. A decorative plate produced in a limited edition for the purpose of being collected. Although the earliest plates were not produced with this objective, they have since acquired the name by virtue of being collected and are now produced for this purpose.

Commemorative Plate. A plate produced in remembrance of an event. Example: Wedgwood *Bicentennial of American Independence.* **(26-W90-3.0).**

Coterie Plate. A collector's plate with a limited following which is traded too infrequently to be listed on the Exchange.

Crystal. See *Lead Crystal.*

Cut Glass. Glass decorated by the cutting of grooves and facets, usually done with a copper engraver's wheel.

D

Damascene. An electroplating effect, created and patented by Reed & Barton **(84-R18-0.0)**, of etching and then depositing layers of gold, copper, and silver on bronze. Originally the term referred to the art, developed in Damascus, of ornamenting iron or steel with inlaid precious metals.

Dealer. A marketer of plates who buys primarily from makers or distributors and sells primarily to the public.

Dealer-Broker. A dealer who acts as an agent of the Bradford Exchange to transact secondary market purchases and sales for his customers.

Decalcomania. The printed reproduction of original artwork which is produced by individual colour separations, either in offset lithography, silk-screen printing, or a combination of both.

Delftware. Earthenware covered with an opaque white glaze made of stannic oxide, and oxide of tin. Originally developed in Delft, Holland, in the sixteenth century, Delftware has the appearance of being covered with a thick white paint. Similar ware is the majolica of Italy and faience of France and Germany. See *Faience, Majolica, Tin Glaze.*

Dilute Colours. Solutions of metallic salts which are absorbed by the bisque body of a plate when it is glazed and fired, producing soft, impressionistic tones. Perfected in Copenhagen in about 1883. Examples: Royal Copenhagen **(14-R59-0.0)**, Bing & Grøndahl **(14-B36-0.0)**, and Grande Copenhagen **(14-G65-0.0)**.

Distributor. A marketer of plates who buys from manufacturers and sells to dealers. Some distributors also act as makers and as dealers.

Dresden, Meissen. Neighbouring cities now in East Germany where the first hard-paste porcelain outside of China was produced by Johann Friedrich Böttger in 1708.

Dresden, China. Term used in England beginning in the eighteenth century to describe true hard-paste porcelain. See *Dresden, Porcelain.*

E

Earthenware. A term for any ceramics which are not vitrified. Typical components of earthenware are 43% ball clay, 24% kaolin, 23% flint, and 10% pegmatite. Fired earthenware is normally covered with either a transparent or opaque glaze. Highfired earthenware is fired at a higher temperature to produce a harder ware. Example: Royal Doulton *Beswick Christmas* series **(26-R62-1.0)**.

Edition. The total number of plates, all with the same decoration, produced by a maker. Editions of collector's plates are normally limited to a fixed number and are not repeated. To do so would constitute a violation of the edition limit.

Electroplating. A process by which metal plates are coated with another metal by electrical charges.

Embossed Design. Raised ornamentation produced by the plate mould or by stamping a design into the body of the plate. Example: Belleek **(26-B18-0.0)**.

Enamel. A glaze material coloured with suspended mineral oxides for decorating plates.

Engraved Design. Decoration produced by cutting into the surface of metal, glass, or china plates with either a tool or acid, as in etching. See *Intaglio.*

Etched Design. Decoration produced by cutting into the surface of a plate with acid. The plate is first covered with an acid-resistant paint or wax, and the design is carved through this coating. When the plate is immersed in acid, the acid ''bites'' into the plate surface in the shape of the design. Example: Franklin Mint silver plates **(84-F64-0.0)**. See *Intaglio.*

Exchange. A place where plates are traded, most commonly the Bradford Exchange, the world's largest trading centre in limited-edition collector's plates. Incorporated in 1962, it was formerly known as Bradford Galleries Exchange. See *Trading Floor.*

F

Faience. Tin-enamelled earthenware from France, Germany, or Spain developed in the seventeenth century and named for the Italian town of Faenza, a centre for majolica, another name for this ware. See *Delftware.*

Feldspar. A mineral composed of aluminium silicates with either potassium, sodium, calcium, or barium. Feldspar decomposes to form kaolin, the key ingredient of china and porcelain. The addition of undecomposed feldspar to china formulas gives the ware greater hardness.

Fine China. A designation of quality which is made after firing; those plates which do not merit the designation are simply called ''china.''

Fire. The heating process which hardens ceramic plates in a kiln. Ceramic clay begins to undergo chemical change at 500° C and vitrifies at around 1300° C.

First Edition. The first, and presumably the only, edition of a collector's plate. The term (or its abbreviation, ''FE'') is sometimes used for the edition which is the first issue in a series of collector's plates. However, since no edition is normally ever reopened and therefore no ''second edition'' is possible, all issues of collector's plates are properly termed first editions.

First Issue. Chronologically, the first plate in a series, i.e., the plates issued in the first year of an annual series.

Flint Glass. See *Lead Crystal.*

Flux. Finely ground material added to porcelain formulas which lowers the vitrification temperature and helps fuse the components. See *Feldspar.*

Foot Rim. A slightly projected ring on the convex side of a plate. The foot rim raises the plate in the kiln during firing.

G

Glaze. Glassy, hard surface coating on plates made of silicates (glassforming compounds) and

411

mineral oxides. Glaze is put on ceramic ware to make it wear-resistant, waterproof, decorative, and to seal the pores. Glaze material suspended in water is applied after the first firming and is heated to the glaze's vitrification point when it fuses to the plate body. Glaze is applied by dipping, spraying, or painting. Decorating is added under, over, or with the glaze layer. See *Underglaze Decoration, Overglaze Decoration*.

I

Incised Design. Ornamentation cut into the body of the plate. Example: Veneto Flair **(38-V22-0.0)**.

Incolay Stone. The material from which the cameo-like plates produced by Incolay Studios are made. Incolay stone may contain, among other minerals, semi-precious carnelian and crystal or topaz quartz. Example: Incolay Studios **(84-I31-0.0)**.

Inlaid. Decoration on a plate created by etching, incising, or engraving a design on the surface and filling with another material.

Instaquote Trading System.™ The computerized auction market for collector's plates that is an exclusive service of the Bradford Exchange Trading Floor in the U.S.A. Both individual collectors and dealers may trade on the system.

Intaglio. Decoration created by cutting beneath the surface of the plate. Example: Morgantown Crystal **(84-M58-0.0)**. See *Engraved Design, Etched Design*.

Iridescence. A rainbow effect on a plate's surface caused by the diffraction of light. True iridescent colour effects are readily distinguished from a plate's inherent colour because the pattern will change as the plate is moved. Example: Belleek **(26-B18-0.0)**.

Issue. 1. The release for sale of an edition of plates by a maker.
2. A plate in an edition.
3. An edition within a series.
A new issue is the release of the

most recent plate in a continuing series. A back issue is a plate other than the most recently-issued plate in a series. Back issue usually denotes a plate that has sold out at issue price and is available only on the secondary market. See *Market*.

Issue Price. Original or first price of the plate established by the maker at the time the plate is released for sale.

J

Jasper Ware. Hard, fine-grained, unglazed stoneware made by adding barium sulfate to clay, developed by Josiah Wedgwood in the 1770s. The term ''jasper'' does not indicate the presence of jasper stone but most likely denotes the variety of colours in which Jasper ware can be produced. Though white in its original form, Jasper ware can be stained in blue, green, lilac, yellow, maroon, pink, taupe, or black to serve as a background for embossments of white Jasper relief for cameo effect. When stained throughout, the body of it is called solid Jasper ware. Example: Wedgwood **(26-W90-0.0)**.

Jigger. A machine with a revolving mould on which plates are formed. Semi-malleable clay is thrown on the revolving mould forming the top of the plate. The bottom of the plate is formed by a metal blade which is fastened to a pivotal arm.

K

Kaolin. The only clay which yields a white material when fired and the indispensable element of porcelain and china plates. Also called true clay or china clay, it is formed by the complete decomposition by weathering of feldspar. Kaolin is a refractory clay which can be fired at high temperatures without deforming. It produces a vitreous, translucent ceramic when fired with fluxes (fusible rocks) such as feldspar. The components of kaolin clay are 50% silica, 33% alumina, 2% oxides, 1% magnesia, 2% alkali, and 12% water.

KPM. The trademark on plates from Königliche Porzellan-Manufaktur, Berlin, Germany. Plates made by this manufacturer date from as early as 1763.

L

Lead Crystal. Extremely transparent fine quality glass, also called flint glass and lead glass, which contains a high proportion of lead oxide to give extra weight, better refractiveness and a clear ringing tone when tapped. Full lead crystal is the term used to identify glass with a 24% or greater lead contient. Example: Lalique **(18-L3-0.0)**.

Lead Glass. See *Lead Crystal*.

Limited-Edition Plates. Plates produced in a fixed quantity, either predetermined by number or determined by a specific period of issue or by a period of production. All true collector's plates are limited-editions.

Limoges. A town in south central France famous for its porcelain production since the discovery of kaolin deposits nearby in 1768. Limoges porcelain manufacturers have joined together to enforce quality standards. Examples: D'Arceau-Limoges **(18-D15-0.0)**, Haviland **(18-H6-0.0)**, **Haviland & Parlon (18-H8-0.0)**, and Limoges-Turgot **(18-L52-0.0)**.

Listed Plate. A plate listed and regularly quoted on the *Bradford Exchange Current Quotations*. Such a plate is often referred to as being ''Bradex-listed.'' See *Bradex, Exchange, Over-The-Counter Plate*.

Lot. A number of plates, all in the same edition and represented by a sell order on the Exchange, usually on the secondary market and not at issue. See *Allotment*.

Lustre. Decoration applied to a plate surface by application of metallic oxides such as gold, silver, platinum, or copper over the glaze. When gently fired, this leaves a thin metallic film.

M

Majolica, Maiolica. Earthenware finished with opaque white enamel, similar to faience and Delftware, but first made in the Spanish island of Majorca. See *Delftware.*

Maker. The name by which a plate is known or under which it is issued, e.g., manufacturer, distributor, or sponsor. In most cases the "maker" is the actual manufacturer, e.g., Bing & Grøndahl **(14-B36-0.0)**. However, it can also be a commissioner or distributor, e.g., Schmid **(22-S12-0.0)**, using a trade name, while the physical production is in fact done by a sub-contractor.

Market. The structure within which plates are bought and sold. The primary market consists of new issues which are sold by the makers or their sales representatives to dealers and distributors. Dealers and distributors in turn normally sell the new issues to the public at issue price. Secondary market or after-market refers to the buying and selling of plates previously sold, and usually sold out, on the primary market. In many cases secondary market prices are higher than those of the primary market.

Market Bradex. A kind of "Dow Jones" index of the overall collector's plate market expressed as a percentage, based on the current price/issue price ratio of twelve key indicator series.

Market Price. The price at which a plate is currently traded, regardless of its issue price. See *Issue Price.*

Market Price Order. An open bid posted on the Exchange to purchase an issue at the price the market demands. Only over-the-counter plates are currently traded in this way on the Exchange. See *Over-The-Counter-Plate.*

Meissen. See *Dresden.*

Mint Condition. A plate in new or like-new condition (free of manufacturer defects and damage) accompanied by any original certificates and packing materials included at issue.

Modelling. The process of making the original pattern from the

which the master mould is made for a sculptured plate.

Mould. A general term for the form which gives a plate its shape. Clay, metal or glass is pressed into a mould to form a blank (without ornamentation). Intaglio decoration or raised ornamentation may also be formed in the mould. China or porcelain slip-casting is done in plaster-of-paris moulds. Slip (diluted clay formula) is poured into the mould, and the excess water is absorbed into the plaster-of-paris. When the plate is jiggered, the mould forms the back and a tool forms the front using a moist clay mixture. See *Slip.*

N

New Issue. See *Issue.*

O

Open-End Series. A continuing series of annual plates with no established termination. Example: Royal Copenhagen *Christmas* series **(14-R59-1.0)**.

Open Stock. Plates available in or produced in unlimited numbers or for an unlimited time period (and therefore not considered collector's plates).

Overglaze Decoration. A decoration consisting of precious metals such as gold, platinum, or silver and/or lithographic patterns in up to twentyfive colours, applied by hand to a porcelain piece after it has been glazed and fired a second time (glost fired). Hand-applied lithographic decoration—the most widely used form of overglaze decoration—can also be used underglaze. See *Glaze, Underglaze Decoration.*

Over-The-Counter Plate. A collector's plate not traded in sufficient volume to be *listed* on the Exchange. The majority of such plates, however, are *traded* on the Exchange and can be obtained, when available, at the prevailing market prices. See *Listed Plate.*

P

Parian China. A highly vitrified, translucent china characterized

by an iridescent lustre and rich, creamy tint much like that of parain marble, for which it is named. The process for making parian ware was invented by the Copeland and Garrett firm in England in the mid-nineteenth century. Example: Belleek **(26-B18-0.0)**.

Paste. The combination of substances that make up potter's clay, generally that for porcelain or china.

Pewter. An alloy of tin with copper and antimony as hardeners. The greater the amount of copper and antimony, the harder the ware. Fine pewter is composed of 80% tin and 20% antimony and brass or copper. See *Alloy.*

Plate, Exchange. See *Swap'n'Sell.* Point, Bradex Point. One percentage point of the Market Bradex.

Porcelain. The hardest vitreous ceramic fired at the highest temperatures. Although the term porcelain is often interchanged with china, true porcelain, as the term is used in the field, is distinguished from china by its very high glaze firing and low bisque firing temperature compared with the high bisque firing and lower glaze firing of china. The main firing (glaze) of porcelain is approximately 7% higher than the main firing (bisque) of china. The glaze fuses with the porcelain plate body and produces an extremely hard surface. Hard-paste or true porcelain is made from a formula whose primary components are kaolin and china stone (petuntse). When fired, the china stone vitrifies producing a hard, glassy ceramic. True porcelain is translucent when thin, white unless coloured, impervious to scratching, and transmits a ringing tone when struck. A typical porcelain formula is 50% kaolin, 25% quartz and 25% feldspar. Soft-paste porcelain was developed in Renaissance Europe in an attempt to imitate the true porcelain of China. Soft-paste porcelain was a mixture of white sand, gypsum, soda, alum, salt, and niter, fired until it vitrified. It had a soft texture, great sensitivity to sudden temperature changes, was warmer to the touch than true porcelain, and

GLOSSARY OF COMMONLY USED TERMS

could be scratched with a file. The terms "hard" and "soft" porcelain refer to the "hard" firing temperature (around 1450° C) required for true porcelain and the "soft" firing temperature (around 1150° C) used for soft-paste porcelain. See *China*.

Pottery. 1. A general term used for all ceramic ware, but in fact properly applied only to earthenware and non-vitrified ceramics. 2. The place where ceramic objects are made and fired.

Primary Market. See *Market*.

Q

Queen's Ware. An earthenware of ivory or cream colour developed by Josiah Wedgwood. The name "Queen's Ware" was adopted by other potters for similar stoneware; also often referred to as "white ware."

Quote. The Exchange's best imitate of market price at the close of the current bi-monthly trading period.

R

Relief Sculpture. Sculpture in which the design or figure is not freestanding but is raised from a background. There are three degrees of relief sculpture: Alto-relievo or high relief, where the design is almost detached from the background; Basso-relievo or basrelief, where the design is raised somewhat; and Relievostiacciato, where the design is scarcely more than scratched. Relief designs on plates may be formed in the plate mould or formed separately and applied to the plate body. Examples. Davenport Pottery *Toby Plate Collection* **(26-D8-1.0)** and Edwin M. Knowles *Biblical Mothers Collection* **(84-K41-6.0).**

S

Saggers. Boxes of fire-clay into which objects to be glost fired are put for protection against direct contact with the flames.

Second, Second, Sorting. A plate judged to be a grade below first quality, usually indicated by a scratch or gouge through the 1glaze over the backstamp on the back.

Secondary Market. See *Market.*

Sell Order. An offer at an asked price given by an individual or dealer to sell one or more plates on the secondary market. See *Asked Price, Exchange.*

Slip. Ceramic paste or body diluted with water to a smooth, creamy consistency used for slip-casting. See *Mould.*

Sponsor. Authoritative body (prestigious organization, museum, or person) which attests to the authenticity of the artwork depicted on a plate.

Steatite, Soapstone. A natural rock whose primary component is talc. Steatite is used in porcelain formulas as a flux.

Stoneware. A hard ceramic fired to vitrification but not translucency. Typical components of stoneware are 30% ball clay, 32% kaolin, 15% flint, and 23% cornish stone. Example: Wedgwood's Jasper Ware **(26-W90-0.0).**

Supermarket Plate. Common term for a plate edition of dubious limitations, cheaply produced and not considered a true collector's plate.

Swapn 'n' Sell Event. An open buy and sell auction for the trading of plates from one collector to another. Swap 'n' Sell events have been organized periodically throughout the country often in conjunction with a dealer outlet.

T

Terra Cotta. A general term for any kind of fired clay. Strictly speaking, terra cotta is an earthenware produced from a clay which fires to a dull ochre or red colour. The ware, left unglazed is coarse and porous. Example: Veneto Flair **(38-V22-0.0).**

Tin Glaze. A glaze, coloured white by oxide of tin, which produces a heavy opaque surface when fired. See *Delftware.*

Toriart. The process by which wood shavings and resin are combined to form a wood material which is then moulded and carved into threedimensional forms. Example: Anri **(38-A54-0.0).**

Trader. An individual or a dealer who buys, sells, or bids on plates through the Exchange. See *Trading Floor, Exchange.*

Trading Floor. The physical area of The Bradford Exchange where the trading of plates takes place.

Transfer-Printing. Method by which an engraved design may be transferred from an engraver's plate or lithographer's block to the surface of a plate. Originally, thin papers were inked with a mixture of metallic oxide in an oily medium, or sometimes used with a greasy substance onto which metallic oxide could be dusted. Transfer-printing may be overglaze or underglaze.

Translucency. The quality of transmitting light without transparence. In a plate, translucency depends on the quality of the china or porcelain, thickness of the plate, and firing temperature. Underfired porcelain is not translucent.

Triptych. A set of three panels hinged side by side, bearing paintings or carvings, usually on a religious theme and originally used as a portable altarpiece. Example: Anna-Perenna **(22-A3-3.0).**

True Clay. See *Kaolin.*

U

Underglaze Decoration. Decoration applied after a plate has been fired once (bisque fired) but before it is glazed and fired a second time. Underglaze painting is most commonly done in cobalt blue pigment (although other colours can be used) because this is the most stable colour and can withstand high firing temperatures. True underglaze technique indicates that such painting was done by hand. See *Glaze, Overglaze Decoration.*

V

Vitrification. A fusion of potters clay at temperatures between 1250° C and 1450° C to form a glassy, nonporous substance. With continued heating, the substance will become translucent.

OVER-THE-COUNTER ISSUES

Over-the-counter plates are issues which are not listed on the *Current Quotations,* or "Bradex", but may still be traded on The Bradford Exchange. Over-the-counter issues are nonetheless true collector's plates, issued in verifiable limited editions. They differ from Bradex-listed plates only in that they are traded far less frequently than Bradex issues. Over-the-counter issues are arranged alphabetically by country, then alphabetically by maker or maker/sponsor, then chronologically by series. Each entry includes the series name, the year and name of the plate, the edition limit. In view of potential currency fluctuations, all issue prices (where available) have been stated in U.S. Dollars. Please remember, when converting these to Pounds Sterling, that issue price variations between the United Kingdom and the U.S.A. are possible. Therefore always check prices with the Brokerage Department of The Bradford Exchange first.

	Edition Limit	Issue Price (US)
ARGENTINA		
Porcelana Granada		
Peace on Earth		
1971 Annunciation	9,300	12.00
1972 Mary and Elizabeth	6,000	13.00
1973 Road to Bethlehem	5,000	14.00
1974 No Room at Inn	5,000	15.00
1975 Shepherds in Field	5,000	16.50
1976 Nativity	5,000	17.50
1977 Three Kings	5,000	18.00
1978 Young Carpenter	5,000	18.00
1979 Calling of Disciples	5,000	19.00
1980 Loaves and Fishes	5,000	20.00
1981 Suffer Little Children	5,000	21.00
1982 Triumphal Entry	5,000	22.50
1983 Gethsemane	5,000	23.50
1984 Golgotha	5,000	24.00
1985 Ascension	5,000	24.50

	Edition Limit	Issue Price (US)
AUSTRIA		
Arta		
Mother's Day		
1973 Family with Puppy	1,500	50.00
Christmas		
1973 Nativity–In Manger	1,500	50.00
BELGIUM		
Val St. Lambert		
American Heritage		
1969 Pilgrim Fathers	500	200.00
1970 Paul Revere's Ride	500	200.00
1971 Washington on Delaware	500	200.00
Annual Old Masters		
1969 Rubens & Rembrandt (Pair)	5,000	50.00

	Edition Limit	Issue Price (US)
1969 Van Gogh & Van Dyck (Pair)	5,000	50.00
1970 Da Vinci & Michelangelo (Pair)	5,000	50.00
1971 El Greco & Goya (Pair)	5,000	50.00
1972 Reynolds & Gainsborough (Pair)	5,000	50.00
(Single issue)		
1970 Rembrandt	Year	25.00
CANADA		
Canadian Collector Plates		
Discover Canada		
1980 Sawmill-Kings Landing	10,000	98.00
1981 Quebec Winter	10,000	98.00
1981 Before Bath	10,000	125.00
1982 Grist Mill, Delta	10,000	125.00

	Edition Limit	Issue Price (US)
1982 Anglican Church at Magnetawan	10,000	125.00
1983 Majestic Rockies	10,000	125.00
1983 Habitants Driving Sleigh	10,000	125.00
1984 Autumn Memories	10,000	125.00
1984 After Bath	10,000	125.00
1985 Postman	10,000	125.00
1985 Pedlar	10,000	125.00
1986 Winter Memories	10,000	125.00
Children of Classics		
1982 Anne of Green Gables	15,000	70.00
1983 Tom Sawyer	15,000	70.00
Days of Innocence		
1982 He Loves Me . . .	15,000	70.00
1982 Butterflies Are Free	15,000	70.00
Winter Romance (set of 2)		
1986 Male/Female Cardinal (framed and signed)	3,500	160.00

OVER-THE-COUNTER ISSUES

Christian Bell (Schumann)

Preserving a Way of Life–Chapter I
	Edition Limit	Issue Price (US)
1980 Making Way for Cars	5,000	60.00
1980 Atop Hay Wagon	5,000	60.00
1980 Turning Sod	5,000	60.00
1980 Winter's Morning	5,000	60.00

Preserving a Way of Life–Chapter II
1981 Sugarbush	10,000	70.00
1981 Fishing for Redfin	10,000	70.00
1981 Wheat Harvest	10,000	70.00
1981 Returning from Village	10,000	70.00

Preserving a Way of Life–Chapter III
1985 New Horse	10,000	65.00
1986 To the Sawmill	10,000	65.00
1987 Day's End	10,000	65.00

American Steam
1982 Hiawatha	15,000	65.00
1983 Hittin' Diamond	15,000	65.00
1983 Morning at Depot	15,000	65.00
1984 Boston and Maine	15,000	65.00
1985 On Horseshoe Curve	15,000	65.00

Men of Rails
1982 Engineer	30 Days	39.50
1983 Conductor	30 Days	39.50
1983 Pullman Porter	30 Days	39.50
1983 Night Operator	30 Days	39.50
1984 Brakeman	30 Days	39.50

Vanishing Africa
1983 Sentinel	15,000	55.00

Wild North
1983 Emperor of North	15,000	55.00

Men of Sea
1984 Helmsman	NA	39.50
1984 Dorryman	NA	39.50

(Single issue)
1984 Royal Hudson "2860"	25,000	75.00

Last Spike Centennial (Set of two)
1986 Spiral Tunnel		
1986 Big Hill	7,500	135.00

Steam on CNR
1986 When I Grow Up	15,000	65.00
1986 Frosty Morning	15,000	65.00

Bengough

Christmas
1972 Charles Dickens Christmas Carol	490	$125.00

Northwest Mounted Police
1972 1898 Dress Uniform	1,000	140.00
1972 First Uniform	1,000	140.00

Royal Canadian Police
1972 Order Dress	1,000	140.00

Goldcrown Ceramics

Wild West
1981 Horse and Rider	5,000	49.95
1982 Bucking Horse	5,000	49.95
1983 Cowboy	10,000	49.95
1983 Chuckwagon Race	10,000	49.95
1984 Bull Rider	10,000	49.95

Bush Pilot Planes
1983 Fokker Universal	10,000	49.95
1983 DeHavilland DH80 Puss Moth	10,000	49.95
1984 Ford 6-AT-AS Tri-Motor	10,000	49.95
1984 Fairchild 71B	10,000	49.95

Endangered American Wildlife
1983 Bald Eagle	15,000	59.95

Famous Fighter Aircraft of World War II
1983 P-51 D Mustang	10,000	49.95
1983 Chance Vought F4U Corsair	10,000	49.95
1984 Lockheed P-38 Lightning	10,000	49.95
1984 Supermarine Spitfire	10,000	49.95

Keirstead Gallery Ltd.

The Sisters
1987 Brenda's Mill	4,000	55.00

Prairie Collectibles

Canada, Featuring Saskatchewan
1986 Wascana Park	5,000	50.00

Old Fashioned Threshing Bee
	Edition Limit	Issue Price (US)
1986 Threshing Scene	15,000	50.00

Rare Bird

Canadian Dream
1983 Going to Rink	7,500	70.00
1984 Lacing Up	7,500	70.00
1984 Face Off	7,500	70.00
1985 Winning Goal	7,500	70.00

Birds of Distinction
1987 Pause From the Journey	NA	45.00

Christmas in Canada
1986 The Windmill	5,000	45.00

Royal Doulton

Aged in Wood
1984 Sugarbush	5,000	55.00
1984 Peggy's Cove	5,000	55.00
1985 Weathering Storm	5,000	55.00
1985 Thunder in Air	5,000	55.00

Captured Moments
1984 Treasure Seekers	5,000	45.00
1984 Seascape	5,000	45.00

Encore
1985 Gabriella	10,000	95.00

Reefton Meadows
1986 All in a Days Work	5,000	45.00

The Dorothy Francis Annual
1987 Happy Days	7,500	45.00

Sorrina

Christmas
1981 Gingerbread House	5,000	40.00
1982 Christmas Eve at Jesuit House	5,000	42.50
1983 Main Street, Barkerville	5,000	45.00

Country Friends
1983 Meeting at Fence	10,000	65.00

Viletta Canada

A Brush with Life
1987 Racoon Family	9,800	49.50
1987 Fawn at Rest	9,800	49.50

Waldenburg Porcelain

Punkinhead Happy Little Bear
1983 Punkinhead and His Friends	5,000	39.50
1983 Punkinhead and Santa Claus	5,000	39.50
1984 School's Out	5,000	39.95

Western Authentics

Tribute to R.C.M.P.
1986 Scarlet and Gold	19,500	49.95

Iron Pioneers
1986 CPR No. 374	15,000	49.95
1986 Countess of Dufferin	15,000	49.95

The Iron Giants
1985 The Royal Lady	15,000	40.00

Guns at Sea
1986 H.M.C.S. Haida	5,000	39.95
1987 H.M.C.S. Bonaventure	5,000	55.00

(Single issue)
1986 Douglas DC-3	7,500	39.95

(Single issue)
1986 Pacific Belle	5,000	45.00

CHINA (TAIWAN)

Royal Cornwall

Five Perceptions of Weo Cho
1979 Sense of Touch	19,500	55.00
1979 Sense of Sight	19,500	55.00
1979 Sense of Taste	19,500	55.00
1979 Sense of Hearing	19,500	55.00
1979 Sense of Smell	19,500	55.00

CZECHOSLOVAKIA

Bohemia

Mother's Day
1974 Mother's Day	500	130.00
1975 Mother's Day	500	140.00
1976 Mother's Day	500	150.00

Koschevak Bros.

Mary Gregory Christmas
	Edition Limit	Issue Price (US)
1973 Christmas	1,000	55.00
1974 Christmas	1,000	60.00
1975 Christmas	1,000	60.00
1976 Christmas	500	65.00

Mary Gregory Mother's Day
1973 Mother's Day	500	55.00
1974 Mother's Day	300	60.00
1975 Mother's Day	300	60.00
1976 Mother's Day	500	65.00

Moser

Christmas (Vanoce)
1970 Hradcany Castle	400	75.00
1971 Karlstein Castle	1,365	75.00
1972 Old Town Hall	1,000	85.00
1973 Karlovy Vary Castle	500	90.00

Mother's Day (Den Matek)
1971 Peacocks	350	75.00
1972 Butterflies	750	85.00
1973 Squirrels	200	90.00

DENMARK

Bing & Grøndahl

Olympic Games
1972 Olympiade–Munich	Year	20.00
1976 Olympic Montreal	Year	29.50
1980 Moscow by Night	Year	43.00
1984 Los Angeles	Year	45.00

Bicentennial
1976 E. Pluribus Unum	Year	50.00

Heritage
1976 Norseman	5,000	30.00
1977 Navigators	5,000	30.00
1978 Discovery	5,000	39.50
1979 Exploration	5,000	39.50
1980 Helmsman	NA	45.00
1981 Swordsman	NA	49.50

Carl Larsson (Sets of four)
1977 Flowers on Windowsill		
1977 Breakfast under Big Birch		
1977 Yard & Warehouse		
1977 Kitchen	7,500	150.00
1978 First Born		
1978 Room for Mother and Children		
1978 Portrait of Inga-Maria Thiel		
1978 Iduna	7,500	170.00
1979 Forestry		
1979 Cutting Grass		
1979 Potato Harvest		
1979 Fishery	7,500	165.00

(Single issue)
1977 Madonna	10,000	45.00

(Single issue)
1978 Seagull	7,500	75.00

Classical Composers
1979 Beethoven	Year	37.50
1980 Bach	Year	37.50
1981 Brahms	Year	37.50
1982 Chopin	Year	37.50
1983 Haydn	Year	37.50
1984 Grieg	Year	37.50

Windjammers
1980 Danmark	10,000	95.00
1980 Eagle	10,000	95.00
1981 Gladan	10,000	95.00
1981 Gorch/Fock	10,000	95.00
1982 Amerigo Vespucci	10,000	95.00
1982 Christian Radich	10,000	95.00

Year of Viking (Single issue)
1980 Viking	10,000	65.00

New Generation
1982 Fledglings	10,000	29.50
1982 Kittens	10,000	29.50
1982 Bunnies	10,000	29.50
1982 Fawns	10,000	29.50

Country Garden Calendar
1984 September	12,500	55.00
1984 October	12,500	55.00
1984 November	12,500	55.00
1984 December	12,500	55.00

	Edition Limit	Issue Price (US)
1984 January	12,500	55.00
1984 February	12,500	55.00
1984 March	12,500	55.00
1984 April	12,500	55.00
1984 May	12,500	55.00
1984 June	12,500	55.00
1984 July	12,500	55.00
1984 August	12,500	55.00

Seasons Remembered
1984 Promise of Spring	7,500	35.00
1984 Wildflowers of Summer	7,500	35.00

Gentle Love
1985 Joanna and Jon	9,500	45.00
1985 Alexandra and Amy	9,500	45.00
1985 Ingrid and Lise	9,500	45.00
1986 Elizabeth and David	9,500	45.00

(Single issue)
1985 Give Me Liberty	10,000	60.00

Christmas in America
1986 Christmas Eve in Williamsburg	NA	29.50

Carl Larson Miniature
1986 Flower Window	15,000	15.00
1986 Lunch Under Birch Tree	15,000	15.00
1986 Winter and the Old Barn	15,000	15.00
1986 Mama's Room	15,000	15.00
1986 Iduna's New Dress	15,000	15.00
1986 Working in the Woods	15,000	15.00
1986 Harvest	15,000	15.00
1986 Potato Harvest	15,000	15.00
1986 Fishing	15,000	15.00
1986 Opening Day of the Crayfish Season	15,000	15.00
1986 Azalea	15,000	15.00
1986 Apple Harvest	15,000	15.00

See also: Ghent Collection (U.S.A.)

Grande Copenhagen

Bicentennial (Single issue)
1976 Great Seal	Year	35.00

Grande Danica

Mother's Day
1977 Dog with Puppies	10,000	25.00
1978 Storks	10,000	25.00
1979 Badgers	10,000	25.00

Georg Jensen

Christmas
1972 Doves	Year	15.00
1973 Christmas Eve	Year	15.00
1974 Christmas Story	Year	?.??
1975 Winter Scene	Year	2.50
1976 Christmas in Country	Year	2.50

Chagall (Single issue)
1972 Lovers	12,500	50.00

Mother's Day
1973 Mother & Child	Year	5.00
1974 Sweet Dreams	Year	15.00
1975 Mother's World	Year	?.??

Svend Jensen

Christmas
1970 H.C. Andersen House	Year	14.50
1971 Little Match Girl	Year	15.00
1972 Mermaid of Copenhagen	Year	16.50
1973 Fir Tree	Year	22.00
1974 Chimney Sweep	Year	25.00
1975 Ugly Duckling	Year	27.50
1976 Snow Queen	Year	27.50
1977 Snowman	Year	29.50
1978 Last Dream of Old Oak	Year	32.00
1979 Old Street Lamp	Year	36.50
1980 Willie Winky	Year	42.50
1981 Uttermost Parts of Sea	Year	49.50
1982 Twelve by Mailcoach	Year	54.50
1983 Story of Year	Year	54.50
1984 Nightingale	Year	54.50

Mother's Day
1970 Bouquet for Mother	Year	14.50
1971 Mother's Love	Year	15.00
1972 Good Night	Year	16.50
1973 Flowers for Mother	Year	20.00
1974 Daisies for Mother	Year	25.00

	Edition Limit	Issue Price (US)
1975 Surprise for Mother	Year	27.50
1976 Complete Gardener	Year	27.50
1977 Little Friends	Year	29.50
1978 Dreams	Year	32.00
1979 Promenade	Year	36.50
1980 Nursery Scene	Year	42.50
1981 Daily Duties	Year	49.50
1982 My Best Friend	Year	54.50
1983 An Unexpected Meeting	Year	54.50
1984 Who Are You?	Year	54.50
1985 Mother's Day	Year	50.00
1986 Meeting on Meadow	Year	50.00
Anniversary		
1980 Hans Christian Andersen's Home	NA	60.00

Kera
	Edition Limit	Issue Price (US)
Christmas		
1967 Kobenhavn	Year	6.00
1968 Forste	Year	6.00
1969 Andersen's House	Year	6.00
1970 Langelinie	Year	6.00
1971 Lille Peter	Year	6.00
Moon		
1969 Apollo 11	Year	6.00
1970 Apollo 13	Year	6.00
Mother's Day		
1970 Mother's Day	Year	6.00
1971 Mother's Day	Year	6.00

Lund & Clausen
	Edition Limit	Issue Price (US)
Moon		
1969 Moon Landing–Apollo 11	Year	10.00
1971 Apollo 13	Year	15.00
Mother's Day		
1970 Rose	Year	10.00
1971 Forget-Me-Nots	Year	10.00
1972 Bluebell	Year	15.00
1973 Lily of Valley	Year	16.00
Christmas		
1971 Animal Garden	Year	13.50
1972 Stave Church	Year	13.50
1973 Christmas Scene	Year	13.50

Palisander
	Edition Limit	Issue Price (US)
Christmas		
1971 Red Robin on Holly	1,200	50.00
1972 Flying Geese	1,200	50.00
1973 Christmas	1,200	50.00
Presidential		
1971 George Washington	1,000	50.00
1972 Thomas Jefferson	1,000	50.00
1973 John Adams	1,000	50.00
(Single issue)		
1973 Bicentennial	250	50.00

Royal Copenhagen
	Edition Limit	Issue Price (US)
Historical		
1975 R. C. Bicentennial	Year	30.00
1976 U.S. Bicentennial	Year	35.00
1977 Electro-Magnetism	Year	35.00
1978 Capt. Cook	Year	37.50
1979 Adam Oehlenschlager	Year	42.50
1980 Amagertorv	Year	52.50
National Parks of America		
1978 Yellowstone	5,000	75.00
1979 Shenandoah	5,000	75.00
1980 Yosemite	5,000	75.00
1980 Mt. McKinley	5,000	75.00
1981 Everglades	5,000	75.00
1981 Grand Canyon	5,000	75.00
(Single issue)		
1980 Year of Viking	5,000	55.00
Hans Christian Andersen		
1983 Shepherdess and Chimney Sweep	Year	39.50
1984 Thumbelina	Year	39.50
1985 Little Mermaid	Year	44.50
1986 The Princess and the Pea	NA	44.50

FINLAND
Arabia
	Edition Limit	Issue Price (US)
Christmas 100 Years Ago		
1978 Inland Village Scene	Year	49.00
1979 Forest Village Scene	Year	72.00
1980 Seaside Village Scene	Year	79.00
1981 Farm Village Scene	Year	87.00
1982 Country Village Scene	Year	95.00
Pictures of Lapland		
1981 Laplander Village	7,000	175.00
Christmas Annual		
1986 Christmas 1986	NA	90.00
(Single issue)		
1981 Rose	2,000	360.00

FRANCE
Bayel of France
	Edition Limit	Issue Price (US)
Flowers		
1972 Rose	300	50.00
1973 Lilies	300	50.00
1973 Orchid	300	50.00
Bicentennial		
1974 Liberty Bell	500	50.00
1975 Independence Hall	500	60.00
1976 Spread Eagle	500	60.00
Eagles		
1974 Eagle Head	300	50.00
1974 Eagle in Flight	300	50.00

Betourne Studios
	Edition Limit	Issue Price (US)
Jean-Paul Loup Christmas		
1971 Noel	300	125.00
1972 Noel	300	150.00
1973 Noel	300	175.00
1974 Noel	400	200.00
1975 Noel	250	250.00
1976 Noel	150	300.00
Mother's Day (Champleve)		
1974 Mother & Child	500	250.00
Mother's Day (Enamel)		
1975 Mother's Day	400	285.00
1976 Mother & Child	250	300.00

Cartier
	Edition Limit	Issue Price (US)
Cathedral		
1972 Chartres Cathedral	12,500	50.00
1974 Chartres, Millous	500	130.00

Cristal D'Albret
	Edition Limit	Issue Price (US)
Four Seasons		
1972 Summer	1,000	75.00
1973 Autumn	648	75.00
1973 Spring	312	75.00
1974 Winter	1,000	88.00
(Single issue)		
1972 Bird of Peace	3,700	64.00

Daum
	Edition Limit	Issue Price (US)
Four Seasons		
1969 Autumn (Amethyst)	2,000	150.00
1970 Winter (Aquamarine)	2,000	150.00
1970 Spring (Emerald)	2,000	150.00
1970 Summer (Topaz)	2,000	150.00
Famous Musicians		
1970 Bach (Emerald)	2,000	60.00
1970 Beethoven (Amethyst)	2,000	60.00
1971 Mozart (Tourmaline)	2,000	60.00
1971 Wagner (Peridot)	2,000	60.00
1972 Debussy (Topaz)	2,000	60.00
1972 Gershwin (Sapphire)	2,000	60.00
Dali		
1971 Ceci N'est Pas Une Assiette	2,000	200.00
1971 Triomphale	2,000	200.00
Art Nouveau		
1979 Waterlilies	4,000	125.00
1980 Lily Pond	4,000	150.00
1981 Swan	4,000	170.00

Gourinat-Dolan
	Edition Limit	Issue Price (US)
(Single issue)		
1978 Doves of Peace	3,000	60.00

Haviland
	Edition Limit	Issue Price (US)
Historical		
1968 Martha Washington	2,500	35.00
1969 Lincoln	2,500	100.00
1970 Grant	3,000	100.00
1971 Hayes	2,500	110.00
Bicentennial		
1972 Burning of Gaspee	10,000	39.95
1973 Boston Tea Party	10,000	39.95
1974 First Continental Congress	10,000	39.95
1975 Ride of Paul Revere	10,000	40.00
1976 Declaration of Independence	10,000	48.00
French Collection		
1973 Breakfast	10,000	29.95
1974 Wash	10,000	29.95
1975 In Park	10,000	30.00
1976 To Market	10,000	38.00
1977 A Wash Before Dinner	10,000	38.00
1978 An Evening at Home	10,000	40.00
1979 Happy Mother's Day	10,000	45.00
Theatre Des Saisons		
1978 Spring	5,000	120.00
1978 Summer	5,000	120.00
1978 Autumn	5,000	120.00
1978 Winter	5,000	120.00
Mother's Day		
1980 Child and His Animals	Year	55.00
Visit from Saint Nicholas		
1980 Twas Night Before Christmas	Year	55.00
1981 Children Were Nestled	Year	60.00
1982 Tore Open Shutters	Year	60.00
1983 What to Wondering Eyes	Year	60.00
1984 Up Chimney	Year	60.00
1985 Happy Christmas to All	Year	60.00
Fleurs et Rubens		
1980 Orchidée	7,500	120.00
1981 Hibiscus	7,500	120.00
1982 Poppy	7,500	120.00
Traditional Christmas Carols		
1986 Deck the Halls	2,000	75.00

Haviland & Parlon
	Edition Limit	Issue Price (US)
Nan Lee (Single issue)		
1973 Peaceable Kingdom	5,000	30.00
Mother's Day		
1975 Laura and Child	15,000	37.50
1976 Pinky and Baby	15,000	42.50
1977 Amy and Snoopy	10,000	45.00
King Tut (Single issue)		
1977 Scarab	2,500	80.00
Zodiac (Single issue)		
1977 Astrological Man	5,000	50.00
Enchanted Forest		
1982 Entrance to Forest	10,000	65.00
1983 Birds of Forest	10,000	65.00

See also: Kern Collectibles (U.S.A.)

HB—Henriot Quimper
	Edition Limit	Issue Price (US)
The Chapels of Brittany		
1986 The Chapel of Tronoen	250	75.00

Josair
	Edition Limit	Issue Price (US)
Bicentennial		
1972 American Eagle	400	250.00
1973 American Flag	400	250.00
1974 Abraham Lincoln	400	250.00
1975 George Washington	400	250.00
1976 Declaration of Independence	400	250.00

Poillerat
	Edition Limit	Issue Price (US)
Christmas		
1972 Three Kings	500	350.00
1973 Rose	250	350.00

Puiforcat
	Edition Limit	Issue Price (US)
Cartes a Jouer		
1972 (Set of five)	2,000	300.00
(Single issue)		
1973 Exodus (Silver)	2,000	200.00

Raynaud-Limoges
	Edition Limit	Issue Price (US)
Castles		
1979 Bodiam Castle	5,000	48.00
1979 Glamis Castle	5,000	48.00
1979 Tower of London	5,000	48.00
Wildlife Collection		
1978 Tiger Bouquet	Year	50.00

Royal Limoges
	Edition Limit	Issue Price (US)
Christmas		
1972 Nativity	5,000	25.00
1973 Three Wise Men	5,000	27.50

Sabino
	Edition Limit	Issue Price (US)
Annual Crystal		
1970 King Henry IV & Maria De Medici	1,500	65.00
1971 Milo & Beasts	1,500	65.00

GERMANY
Anna-Perenna
	Edition Limit	Issue Price (US)
Birds of Fancy		
1978 Firebird	5,000	110.00
Floral Fantasies		
1978 Empress Gold	5,000	110.00
Enchanted Gardens		
1978 June Dream	5,000	75.00
1979 Summer Day	5,000	95.00
Oriental Tranquility		
1978 Chun Li at Pond	5,000	100.00
1979 Ming Tao on Path of Faith	5,000	110.00
Joy of Motherhood		
1979 Gesa and Children	5,000	165.00
1980 Alexandra and Children	5,000	175.00
American Silhouettes I–Children		
1981 Fiddlers Two	5,000	75.00
1981 Mary with Lambs	5,000	75.00
1981 Waiting for Tom	5,000	75.00
1981 Ring Around Rosie	5,000	75.00
American Silhouettes II–Family		
1982 Family Outing	5,000	75.00
1982 John and Mary	5,000	75.00
1982 Homemakers A- Quilting	5,000	75.00
1982 Leisure Time	5,000	75.00
American Silhouettes III–Valley Life		
1983 Frosty Frolic	5,000	75.00
1983 Hayride	5,000	75.00
1983 Sunday Ride	5,000	75.00
1983 Market Day	5,000	75.00
Bashful Bunnies		
1981 Spring's Surprise	15,000	62.50
1981 Summer's Sunshine	15,000	62.50
1982 Fall's Frolic	15,000	62.50
1982 Winter's Wonder	15,000	62.50
Children of Mother Earth		
1982 Spring	2,500	250.00
1982 Summer	2,500	250.00
1982 Autumn	2,500	250.00
1982 Winter	2,500	250.00
Happy Village		
1982 Spring Picnic	5,000	55.00
1982 Summer on Pond	5,000	55.00
1982 Autumn Harvest Dance	5,000	55.00
1982 Winter Snow Kids	5,000	55.00
Masquerade Fantasy		
1982 Masquerade Party	9,800	95.00
1982 Clowns and Unicorns	9,800	95.00
1982 Merry-Go-Round Ballet	9,800	95.00
Uncle Tad's Holiday Cats		
1982 Jingle Bells	9,800	75.00
1983 Pollyanna	9,800	75.00
1984 Pumpkins	9,800	75.00
1985 Perry, Buttercup and Black-Eyed Susan	9,800	75.00
Arctic Spring		
1983 Patience	9,500	75.00
1984 Proud Mother	9,500	75.00

OVER-THE-COUNTER ISSUES

	Edition Limit	Issue Price (US)
1985 We Like It	9,500	75.00
1986 The Race	9,500	75.00

Rhythm and Dance

	Edition Limit	Issue Price (US)
1983 Ballroom	5,000	29.50
1983 Two-Step	5,000	29.50
1983 Strut	5,000	29.50
1983 Swing	5,000	29.50
1983 Aerobics	5,000	29.50
1983 Jazz	5,000	29.50
1983 Charleston	5,000	29.50
1983 Cake-Walk	5,000	29.50

Moss Christmas

	Edition Limit	Issue Price (US)
1984 Noel, Noel	5,000	69.00
1985 Helping Hands	5,000	69.00
1986 Night Before Christmas	5,000	75.00

Reflections of Youth

	Edition Limit	Issue Price (US)
1984 Swimmers	9,500	69.00
1985 Daydreamer	9,500	69.00
1985 Challenging Log	9,500	69.00
1985 End of Run	9,500	69.00

Me and My Shadow

	Edition Limit	Issue Price (US)
1985 Jason and Ginger	7,500	75.00

Celebration

	Edition Limit	Issue Price (US)
1986 Wedding Joy	5,000	100.00
1987 The Christening	5,000	100.00

Bareuther

Mother's Day

	Edition Limit	Issue Price (US)
1969 Mother & Children	5,000	12.00
1970 Mother & Children	5,000	12.00
1971 Mother & Children	5,000	13.50
1972 Mother & Children	5,000	15.00
1973 Mother & Children	5,000	15.00
1974 Musical Children	5,000	19.00
1975 Spring Outing	5,000	21.50
1976 Rocking Cradle	5,000	23.00
1977 Noon Feeding	5,000	24.50
1978 Blind Man's Bluff	5,000	27.50
1979 Mother's Love	5,000	35.00
1980 First Cherries	5,000	37.50
1981 Playtime	5,000	39.50
1982 Suppertime	5,000	39.50
1983 On Farm	5,000	39.50
1984 Village Children	5,000	42.50
1985 Sunrise	5,000	42.50
1986 Playtime	5,000	42.50
1987 Pets	5,000	46.50

Thanksgiving

	Edition Limit	Issue Price (US)
1971 First Thanksgiving	2,500	13.50
1972 Harvest	2,500	14.50
1973 Country Road in Autumn	2,500	15.00
1974 Old Mill	2,500	19.00
1975 Wild Deer in Forest	2,500	21.50
1976 Thanksgiving on Farm	2,500	23.50
1977 Horses	2,500	24.50
1978 Apple Harvest	2,500	27.50
1979 Noontime	2,500	35.00
1980 Longhorns	2,500	37.50
1981 Gathering Wheat	2,500	39.50
1982 Autumn	2,500	39.50

Barthmann

Christmas

	Edition Limit	Issue Price (US)
1977 Mary with Child	300	236.00
1978 Adoration of Child	500	326.00
1979 Holy Mother of Kasanskaja	500	361.00
1980 Holy Mother by Kykos	500	385.00

Berlin Design

Father's Day (Historical)

	Edition Limit	Issue Price (US)
1971 Brooklyn Bridge on Opening Day	12,000	14.50
1972 Continent Spanned	3,000	15.00
1973 Landing of Columbus	2,000	18.00
1974 Adorn's Balloon	Year	25.00
1975 Washington Crossing Delaware	Year	30.00
1976 Tom Thumb	Year	32.00
1977 Zeppelin	Year	32.00
1978 Carl Benz	Year	36.00
1979 Johannes Gutenberg at Mainz	Year	47.50

Danish Church

Church

	Edition Limit	Issue Price (US)
1968 Roskilde Cathedral	Year	12.00
1969 Ribe Cathedral	Year	13.00
1970 Marmor Church	Year	13.00
1971 Ejby Church	Year	13.00
1972 Kalundborg Church	Year	13.00
1973 Grundtvig Church	Year	15.00
1974 Broager Church	Year	15.00
1975 Sct. Knuds Church	Year	18.00
1976 Osterlars Church	Year	22.00
1977 Budolfi Church	Year	15.95
1978 Haderslev Cathedral	Year	19.95
1979 Holmens Church	Year	19.95
1980 Sct. Bendts Church	Year	24.00
1981 Vor Frue Church	Year	32.50
1982 Fjennesler Church	Year	33.00
1983 Udby Church	Year	39.50

Dresden

Christmas

	Edition Limit	Issue Price (US)
1971 Shepherd Scene	3,500	14.50
1972 Niklas Church	6,000	18.00
1973 Schwanstein Church	6,000	18.00
1974 Village Scene	5,000	20.00
1975 Rothenberg Scene	5,000	24.00
1976 Bavarian Village Church	5,000	26.00
1977 Old Mill in Hexenloch	5,000	28.00

Mother's Day

	Edition Limit	Issue Price (US)
1972 Doe and Fawns	8,000	15.00
1973 Mare and Colt	6,000	16.00
1974 Tiger and Cub	5,000	20.00
1975 Dachshund Family	5,000	24.00
1976 Mother Owl and Young	5,000	26.00
1977 Chamois	5,000	28.00

Fürstenberg

Easter

	Edition Limit	Issue Price (US)
1971 Sheep	3,500	15.00
1972 Chicks	4,000	15.00
1973 Bunnies	4,000	16.00
1974 Pussywillow	4,000	20.00
1975 Village Church	4,000	24.00
1976 Country Watermill	4,000	25.00

Christmas

	Edition Limit	Issue Price (US)
1971 Rabbits	7,500	14.00
1972 Snowy Village	6,000	15.00
1973 Christmas Eve	3,000	18.00
1974 Sparrows	4,000	20.00
1975 Deer Family	4,000	24.00
1976 Winter Birds	4,000	25.00

Deluxe Christmas

	Edition Limit	Issue Price (US)
1971 Three Wise Men	1,500	45.00
1972 Holy Family and Angel	2,000	45.00
1973 Christmas Eve	2,000	60.00

Mother's Day

	Edition Limit	Issue Price (US)
1972 Hummingbird	5,000	15.00
1973 Hedgehogs	5,000	16.00
1974 Doe with Fawn	4,000	20.00
1975 Swan Family	4,000	24.00
1976 Koala Bear	4,000	25.00

Olympic

	Edition Limit	Issue Price (US)
1972 Olympics–Munich	5,000	20.00
1976 Olympics–Montreal	5,000	37.50

New York City Landscape

	Edition Limit	Issue Price (US)
1981 City Hall	3,500	75.00
1981 Central Park	3,500	75.00

Glaskunst/Schott-Zwiesel

Christmas

	Edition Limit	Issue Price (US)
1977 Three Wise Man	NA	105.00
1978 Holy Family	NA	112.50
1979 Shepherd of Field	NA	115.00
1980 Annunciation of Maria	NA	118.00

Goebel

Charlot Byj

	Edition Limit	Issue Price (US)
1973 Santa at Tree	Year	16.50
1974 Santa and Girl	Year	22.00
1975 Up and Away	Year	25.00
1976 Boy with Teddy Bear	Year	25.00
1977 Joy to World	Year	25.00

Wildlife

	Edition Limit	Issue Price (US)
1974 Robin	Year	45.00
1975 Blue Titmouse	Year	50.00
1976 Barn Owl	Year	50.00
1977 Bullfinch	Year	50.00
1978 Sea Gull	Year	55.00
1979 Mallard	10,000	90.00
1980 Cardinal	10,000	90.00
1981 Peregrine Falcon	10,000	90.00

Mothers

	Edition Limit	Issue Price (US)
1975 Rabbits	Year	45.00
1976 Cats	Year	45.00
1977 Panda Bears	Year	45.00
1978 Doe and Fawn	Year	50.00
1979 Long-Eared Owl	10,000	65.00
1980 Raccoon and Baby	10,000	75.00
1981 Ringed Seal	10,000	80.00
1982 Swan	10,000	80.00
1983 Walrus	10,000	80.00

Robson Christmas

	Edition Limit	Issue Price (US)
1975 Flight to Egypt (Porcelain)	Year	50.00
1975 Flight to Egypt (Pewter)	Year	45.00

Annual Crystal

	Edition Limit	Issue Price (US)
1978 Praying Girl	Year	45.00
1979 Praying Boy	Year	50.00
1980 Praying Angel	15,000	50.00
1981 Girl with Teddy Bear	10,000	50.00

Old Testament Themes

	Edition Limit	Issue Price (US)
1978 Twelve Tribes of Israel	10,000	125.00
1979 Ten Commandments	10,000	175.00
1980 Traditions	10,000	225.00
1981 Prophet	10,000	275.00

American Heritage

	Edition Limit	Issue Price (US)
1979 Freedom & Justice Soaring	15,000	100.00
1980 Wild & Free	10,000	120.00
1981 Where Buffalo Roam	5,000	125.00

Crystal Mother's Day

	Edition Limit	Issue Price (US)
1979 Butterfly	15,000	50.00
1980 Sparrow	15,000	50.00
1981 Doves	5,000	50.00

(Single issue)

	Edition Limit	Issue Price (US)
1979 Christmas	200	500.00

Bratsoff

	Edition Limit	Issue Price (US)
1979 Star Steed	15,000	125.00

Bavarian Forest

	Edition Limit	Issue Price (US)
1980 Owls	7,500	150.00
1981 Deer	7,500	150.00
1982 Pheasants	7,500	150.00

North American Wildlife

	Edition Limit	Issue Price (US)
1980 Beaver	10,000	125.00
1981 Harp Seal	10,000	125.00
1982 Polar Bear	10,000	125.00
1983 Fox and Kits	10,000	125.00
1984 Lynx	10,000	75.00

Christmas in Kinderland

	Edition Limit	Issue Price (US)
1982 A Gift of Joy	10,000	49.50
1983 A Midnight Clear	10,000	49.50
1984 Three Wee Kings	10,000	49.50
1985 Christmas Starglow	10,000	49.50

Christmas Morning in Dingle Dell

	Edition Limit	Issue Price (US)
1982 Dolly Dingle	10,000	30.00
1983 Billy Bumps	10,000	30.00

Dolly Dingle World Traveler

	Edition Limit	Issue Price (US)
1982 Dolly Visits Germany	10,000	30.00
1982 Dolly Visits Italy	10,000	30.00
1982 Dolly Visits Holland	10,000	30.00
1982 Dolly Visits Spain	10,000	30.00

Native Companions

	Edition Limit	Issue Price (US)
1982 Rachel	10,000	49.50
1983 Hummingbird	10,000	49.50
1983 Rabbit Dancer	10,000	49.50
1984 Celebration	10,000	49.50

Winged Fantasies

	Edition Limit	Issue Price (US)
1982 Strawberries	10,000	49.50
1983 Bacchanalia	10,000	49.50
1983 Cerises	10,000	49.50
1983 Brambleberries	10,000	49.50

Blue-Button Twins Christmas

	Edition Limit	Issue Price (US)
1983 By Fireplace	10,000	30.00
1983 Down Stairs	10,000	30.00

English Countryside Cat

	Edition Limit	Issue Price (US)
1983 James	10,000	35.00
1983 Henry	10,000	35.00
1983 Lucy	10,000	35.00

(Single issue)

	Edition Limit	Issue Price (US)
1984 Skater's Waltz	10,000	33.00

Little Hugs

	Edition Limit	Issue Price (US)
1985 Dolly Dearest	7,500	34.50
1986 First Puppy	7,500	34.50

Grafburg

Christmas

	Edition Limit	Issue Price (US)
1975 Black-Capped Chickadee	5,000	20.00
1976 Squirrels	5,000	22.00

Little Music Makers

	Edition Limit	Issue Price (US)
1987 Band Leader	NA	90.00

Heinrich

UNICEF Children in World

	Edition Limit	Issue Price (US)
1977 Europe	Year	30.00
1978 Asia	Year	30.00
1979 Africa	Year	30.00
1980 America	Year	30.00
1981 Malaysia	Year	30.00
1982 India	Year	35.00
1983 Mexico	Year	35.00

(Single issue)

	Edition Limit	Issue Price (US)
1979 International Year of Child	Year	35.00

Flower Fairies Collection

	Edition Limit	Issue Price (US)
1979 Lavender Fairy	21 Days	35.00
1980 Sweet Pea Fairy	21 Days	35.00
1980 Candytuft Fairy	21 Days	35.00
1980 Heliotrope Fairy	21 Days	35.00
1981 Black Thorne Fairy	21 Days	35.00
1981 Apple Blossom Fairy	21 Days	35.00

Famous Sea Battles

	Edition Limit	Issue Price (US)
1981 Battle of Trafalgar	Year	42.00
1982 Battle/Flamborough Head	Year	42.00
1983 Battle of Lepanto	Year	42.00

Flower Fairies

	Edition Limit	Issue Price (US)
1983 Columbine	21 Days	39.00
1983 Cornflower	21 Days	39.00
1984 Mallow	21 Days	39.00
1984 Black Medick	21 Days	39.00
1985 Canterbury Bell	21 Days	39.00
1985 Fuschia	21 Days	39.00

Hibel Studio (Kaiser)

Tribute to Classical Greek Beauty

	Edition Limit	Issue Price (US)
1980 Diana	3,000	350.00

World I Love

	Edition Limit	Issue Price (US)
1981 Leah's Family	17,500	85.00
1982 Kaylin	17,500	85.00
1983 Edna's Music	17,500	85.00
1984 O-Hana	10,000	85.00

A Tribute to All Children

	Edition Limit	Issue Price (US)
1984 Giselle	19,500	55.00
1985 Gerard	19,500	55.00
1985 Wendy	19,500	55.00

Flower Girl

	Edition Limit	Issue Price (US)
1985 Lily	15,000	79.00
1986 Iris	15,000	79.00

To Life

	Edition Limit	Issue Price (US)
1986 Golden's Child	5,000	99.00

Hibel Studio (Rosenthal)

Famous Women and Children

	Edition Limit	Issue Price (US)
1980 Pharoah's Daughter and Moses	3,000	350.00
1981 Cornelia and Jewels	2,500	350.00
1982 Anna and Children	2,500	350.00
1983 Mozart and Maria	2,500	350.00

Hutschenreuther

	Edition Limit	Issue Price (US)
1972 On Way to Egypt	5,000	NA
1973 Adoration	5,000	NA
1974 Annunciation	5,000	NA

Christmas

Gunther Granget Annual

	Edition Limit	Issue Price (US)
1972 Sparrows	5,000	50.00
1973 Killdeer	2,500	75.00
1973 Squirrel	2,500	75.00
1974 Partridge	2,500	75.00
1975 Rabbits	2,500	90.00
1976 Wrens	2,500	100.00
1976 Freedom in Flight	5,000	100.00
1977 Bears	2,500	100.00
1978 Foxes	1,000	125.00

Songbirds of America

	Edition Limit	Issue Price (US)
1972 Eastern Bluebird and Goldfinch (Pair)	5,000	100.00

	Edition Limit	Issue Price (US)
1973 Mockingbird and Robin (Pair)	5,000	100.00

Canada Christmas

	Edition Limit	Issue Price (US)
1973 Parliament Building	Year	15.00
1974 Moose	Year	16.00
1975 Basilica	Year	21.00
1976 Winter on Prairies	Year	23.00
1977 Bluenose	Year	23.00
1978 Lost Lagoon	Year	27.00
1979 Yukon Highway Bridge	Year	33.00
1980 Covered Bridge	Year	38.00
1981 Saskatchewan Winter	Year	38.00
1982 Christmas to Celebrate	Year	38.00
1983 Province House	Year	38.00
1984 Christmas in Winnipeg	Year	38.00

Bicentennial

	Edition Limit	Issue Price (US)
1976 Freedom in Flight	5,000	100.00
1976 Freedom in Flight (Gold)	200	200.00

Plates of Month (Set of 12)

	Edition Limit	Issue Price (US)
1977 January–December	5,000	780.00

Mother and Child Annual

	Edition Limit	Issue Price (US)
1978 Mother and Child	Year	55.00
1979 Mother and Child	Year	65.00
1980 Mother and Child	Year	87.50
1981 Mother and Child	Year	87.50

Birthday Annual

	Edition Limit	Issue Price (US)
1978 Birthday Plate	10,000	165.00

Winter Christmas

	Edition Limit	Issue Price (US)
1978 Silent Night	Year	260.00
1979 Saint Lucia	Year	295.00
1980 Christmas Pavillion	Year	325.00
1981 Christmas Sleigh	Year	400.00
1982 Joy to World	Year	400.00

Friendship Annual

	Edition Limit	Issue Price (US)
1978 Friendship Plate	Year	80.00

Dolores Valenza Enchantment

	Edition Limit	Issue Price (US)
1979 Princess Snowflake	5,000	50.00
1979 Blossom Queen	5,000	62.50
1980 Princess Marina	5,000	87.50
1980 Princess Starbright	5,000	87.50
1981 Princess Aura	5,000	87.50
1981 Harvest Queen	5,000	87.50

Wedding Annual

	Edition Limit	Issue Price (US)
1978 Wedding Plate	10,000	210.00

Zodiac Collection (Set of 12)

	Edition Limit	Issue Price (US)
1978 Aries–Pisces	1,500	1500.00

Hans Achtziger Annual

	Edition Limit	Issue Price (US)
1979 Heading South	4,000	150.00
1980 Playful Flight	5,000	187.50
1981 Tropical Skies	5,000	245.00
1982 Carried by Wind	2,500	250.00
1983 Toward Sun	5,000	250.00

Arzberg Christmas

	Edition Limit	Issue Price (US)
1979 Christmas	2,500	60.00

To Life

	Edition Limit	Issue Price (US)
1986 Golden's Child	5,000	99.00

Hibel Studio (Rosenthal)

Famous Women and Children

	Edition Limit	Issue Price (US)
1980 Pharoah's Daughter and Moses	3,000	350.00
1981 Cornelia and Jewels	2,500	350.00
1982 Anna and Children	2,500	350.00
1983 Mozart and Maria	2,500	350.00

Hutschenreuther

Christmas

	Edition Limit	Issue Price (US)
1972 On Way to Egypt	5,000	NA
1973 Adoration	5,000	NA
1974 Annunciation	5,000	NA

Gunther Granget Annual

	Edition Limit	Issue Price (US)
1972 Sparrows	5,000	50.00
1973 Killdeer	2,500	75.00
1973 Squirrel	2,500	75.00
1974 Partridge	2,500	75.00
1975 Rabbits	2,500	90.00
1976 Wrens	2,500	100.00
1976 Freedom in Flight	5,000	100.00
1977 Bears	2,500	100.00
1978 Foxes	1,000	125.00

Songbirds of America

	Edition Limit	Issue Price (US)
1972 Eastern Bluebird and Goldfinch (Pair)	5,000	100.00

	Edition Limit	Issue Price (US)
1973 Mockingbird and Robin (Pair)	5,000	100.00

Canada Christmas

	Edition Limit	Issue Price (US)
1973 Parliament Building	Year	15.00
1974 Moose	Year	16.00
1975 Basilica	Year	21.00
1976 Winter on Prairies	Year	23.00
1977 Bluenose	Year	23.00
1978 Lost Lagoon	Year	27.00
1979 Yukon Highway Bridge	Year	33.00
1980 Covered Bridge	Year	38.00
1981 Saskatchewan Winter	Year	38.00
1982 Christmas to Celebrate	Year	38.00
1983 Province House	Year	38.00
1984 Christmas in Winnipeg	Year	38.00

Bicentennial

	Edition Limit	Issue Price (US)
1976 Freedom in Flight	5,000	100.00
1976 Freedom in Flight (Gold)	200	200.00

Plates of Month (Set of 12)

	Edition Limit	Issue Price (US)
1977 January–December	5,000	780.00

Mother and Child Annual

	Edition Limit	Issue Price (US)
1978 Mother and Child	Year	55.00
1979 Mother and Child	Year	65.00
1980 Mother and Child	Year	87.50
1981 Mother and Child	Year	87.50

Birthday Annual

	Edition Limit	Issue Price (US)
1978 Birthday Plate	10,000	165.00

Winter Christmas

	Edition Limit	Issue Price (US)
1978 Silent Night	Year	260.00
1979 Saint Lucia	Year	295.00
1980 Christmas Pavillion	Year	325.00
1981 Christmas Sleigh	Year	400.00
1982 Joy to World	Year	400.00

Friendship Annual

	Edition Limit	Issue Price (US)
1978 Friendship Plate	Year	80.00

Dolores Valenza Enchantment

	Edition Limit	Issue Price (US)
1979 Princess Snowflake	5,000	50.00
1979 Blossom Queen	5,000	62.50
1980 Princess Marina	5,000	87.50
1980 Princess Starbright	5,000	87.50
1981 Princess Aura	5,000	87.50
1981 Harvest Queen	5,000	87.50

Wedding Annual

	Edition Limit	Issue Price (US)
1978 Wedding Plate	10,000	210.00

Zodiac Collection (Set of 12)

	Edition Limit	Issue Price (US)
1978 Aries–Pisces	1,500	1500.00

Hans Achtziger Annual

	Edition Limit	Issue Price (US)
1979 Heading South	4,000	150.00
1980 Playful Flight	5,000	187.50
1981 Tropical Skies	5,000	245.00
1982 Carried by Wind	2,500	250.00
1983 Toward Sun	5,000	250.00

Arzberg Christmas

	Edition Limit	Issue Price (US)
1979 Christmas	2,500	60.00

(Single issue)

	Edition Limit	Issue Price (US)
1979 Celebration Plate	Year	67.50

(Single issue)

	Edition Limit	Issue Price (US)
1979 Anniversary Plate	Year	120.00

(Single issue)

	Edition Limit	Issue Price (US)
1977 Allegro Ensemble	7,500	120.00

Hibel Museum (Single issue)

	Edition Limit	Issue Price (US)
1977 Flower Girl of Provence	12,750	175.00

Floral Heirlooms

	Edition Limit	Issue Price (US)
1978 Zinnias in Sugar Bowl	5,000	65.00
1979 Pansies in Antique Tin	5,000	70.00
1981 Primroses in Staffordshire Pitcher	5,000	75.00
1982 Asters	5,000	75.00

Birds of Paradise

	Edition Limit	Issue Price (US)
1981 Bluebird of Paradise	10,000	175.00
1982 Raggis Great Bird of Paradise	10,000	175.00

Glory of Christmas

	Edition Limit	Issue Price (US)
1982 Nativity	25,000	80.00
1983 Angels	25,000	80.00
1984 Shepherds	25,000	80.00
1985 Wiseman	25,000	80.00

Legendary Animals (Set of four)

	Edition Limit	Issue Price (US)
1982 Unicorn		
1982 Griffin		
1982 Dragon		
1982 Pegasus	12,500	175.00

Songbirds of North America

	Edition Limit	Issue Price (US)
1982 Eastern Bluebird	12,500	60.00
1982 Mockingbird	12,500	60.00
1982 American Goldfinch	12,500	60.00
1982 Rosebreasted Grosbeak	12,500	60.00

Early Memories

	Edition Limit	Issue Price (US)
1983 Do They Bite?	7,500	75.00
1983 Tug of War	7,500	75.00
1984 Explorers	7,500	75.00
1984 My Turn	7,500	75.00

Water Babies

	Edition Limit	Issue Price (US)
1983 Tom and Dragon-Fly	15 Days	45.00
1983 Fairies Take Care of Tom	15 Days	45.00
1983 Tom and Mrs. Do-As-You-Would	15 Days	45.00
1983 Tom and Mrs. Be-Done-By	15 Days	45.00
1984 Tom and Sweet Chest	15 Days	45.00
1984 Ellie Teaches Tom	15 Days	45.00
1984 Tom Takes Care of Baby	15 Days	45.00
1984 Tom and Ellie	15 Days	45.00

Unicorns in Dreamer's Garden (Set of five)

	Edition Limit	Issue Price (US)
1984 Sound of Melodies		
1984 Sight of Wonders		
1984 Smell of Roses		
1984 Taste of Sweetness		
1984 Touch of a Dream	12,500	197.50

Women of Four Seasons

	Edition Limit	Issue Price (US)
1984 Woman of Spring	7,500	70.00

Legend of St. George

	Edition Limit	Issue Price (US)
1985 Knight	5,000	100.00
1985 Lady	5,000	100.00
1985 Contest	5,000	100.00
1985 Wedding	5,000	100.00

Spring in World of Birds

	Edition Limit	Issue Price (US)
1985 Pheasants	2,500	325.00

Concert of Angels

	Edition Limit	Issue Price (US)
1986 Singing Angel	7,500	80.00

Wagner Operas

	Edition Limit	Issue Price (US)
1986 Tristan and Isolde	5,000	125.00

See also:
Hamilton Collection (U.S.A.)

Kaiser

(Single issue)

	Edition Limit	Issue Price (US)
1970 Oberammergau Passion Play	Year	25.00

(Single issue)

	Edition Limit	Issue Price (US)
1970 Royal Horse Show–Toronto	1,000	29.00

Great Yachts

	Edition Limit	Issue Price (US)
1971 Cetonia	1,000	50.00
1971 Westward	1,000	50.00

Anniversary

	Edition Limit	Issue Price (US)
1972 Love Birds	Year	16.50
1973 In Park	Year	18.00
1974 Canoeing Down River	7,000	22.00
1975 Tender Moment	7,000	25.00
1976 Serenade for Lovers	Year	25.00
1977 A Simple Gift	Year	25.00
1978 Viking Toast	Year	30.00
1979 Romantic Interlude	Year	32.00
1980 Love at Play	Year	40.00
1981 Rendezvous	Year	40.00
1982 Betrothal	Year	40.00
1983 Sunday Afternoon	Year	40.00

Feathered Friends

	Edition Limit	Issue Price (US)
1978 Blue Jays	10,000	70.00
1979 Cardinals	10,000	80.00
1980 Cedar Waxwings	10,000	80.00
1981 Goldfinches	10,000	80.00

King Tut

	Edition Limit	Issue Price (US)
1978 Golden Mask	15,000	65.00

People of the Midnight Sun

	Edition Limit	Issue Price (US)
1978 Northern Lullaby	15,000	65.00
1979 Ilaga, My Friend	15,000	75.00
1980 Motherhood	15,000	85.00
1981 Odark and Son Samik	15,000	90.00
1982 Anana with Little Nutak	15,000	90.00
1983 Hunter's Reward	15,000	90.00

Yesterday's World

	Edition Limit	Issue Price (US)
1978 Time for Dreaming	5,000	70.00

	Edition Limit	Issue Price (US)
1979 Summer Is Forever	5,000	75.00
1980 Sunday Afternoon	5,000	80.00
1981 Breath of Spring	5,000	80.00

(Single issue)

	Edition Limit	Issue Price (US)
1980 Oberammergau Passion Play	Year	40.00

Little Men

	Edition Limit	Issue Price (US)
1980 Magical Moment	9,500	60.00
1983 A Day to Remember	9,500	60.00

Four Seasons (Set of four)

	Edition Limit	Issue Price (US)
1981 Spring		
1981 Summer		
1981 Fall		
1981 Winter	NA	200.00

Happy Days

	Edition Limit	Issue Price (US)
1981 Aeroplane	5,000	75.00
1982 Julie	5,000	75.00
1983 Winter Fun	5,000	75.00
1984 Lookouts	5,000	75.00

Little Clowns

	Edition Limit	Issue Price (US)
1981 Red Mask	9,500	35.00
1982 Pigtails and Puppies	9,500	35.00
1983 Concertina	9,500	35.00

Nativity

	Edition Limit	Issue Price (US)
1981 Old Country Christmas	Year	20.00

Romantic Portraits

	Edition Limit	Issue Price (US)
1981 Lilie	5,000	175.00
1982 Camelia	5,000	175.00
1983 Rose	5,000	175.00
1984 Daisy	5,000	175.00

Children's Prayers

	Edition Limit	Issue Price (US)
1982 Now I Lay Me Down to Sleep	5,000	29.50
1983 Saying Grace	10,000	25.00

Memories of Christmas

	Edition Limit	Issue Price (US)
1983 Wonder of Christmas	19,500	42.50
1984 Christmas Dreams	19,500	42.50
1985 Christmas Eve	19,500	39.50
1986 Visit with Santa	19,500	39.50

Famous Horses

	Edition Limit	Issue Price (US)
1983 Snow Knight	3,000	95.00

Traditional Fairy Tales

	Edition Limit	Issue Price (US)
1983 Cinderella	NA	39.50
1983 Jack and Beanstalk	NA	39.50
1984 Three Little Pigs	NA	39.50
1984 Tom Thumb	NA	39.50

Racing for Pride and Profit

	Edition Limit	Issue Price (US)
1984 Aging Victor	9,500	50.00
1985 Second Goes Hungry	9,500	50.00
1986 No Time to Boast	9,500	50.00
1987 First Fish to Market	9,500	50.00

Woodland Creatures

	Edition Limit	Issue Price (US)
1984 Springtime Frolic	10 Days	34.95
1984 Fishing Trip	10 Days	34.95

Bird Dogs

	Edition Limit	Issue Price (US)
1985 Cocker Spaniel	15,000	39.50
1985 Beagle	15,000	39.50
1985 English Setter	15,000	39.50
1985 Black Labrador	15,000	39.50
1985 German Pointer	15,000	39.50
1985 Golden Labrador	15,000	39.50
1985 English Pointer	15,000	39.50
1985 Irish Setter	15,000	39.50

Water Fowl

	Edition Limit	Issue Price (US)
1985 Mallard Ducks	19,500	55.00
1985 Canvas Back Ducks	19,500	55.00
1985 Wood Ducks	19,500	55.00
1986 Pintail Ducks	19,500	55.00

Harmony in Nature

	Edition Limit	Issue Price (US)
1985 Spring Encore	NA	39.50

Wild Flowers

	Edition Limit	Issue Price (US)
1985 Trillium	9,500	39.50
1986 Spring Beauty	9,500	45.00

See also:
Ghent Collection (U.S.A.)
Hibel Studio (Ger.)

Lihs-Lindner

Christmas

	Edition Limit	Issue Price (US)
1972 Little Drummer Boy	6,000	25.00
1973 Little Carolers	6,000	25.00
1974 Peace on Earth	6,000	25.00
1975 Christmas Cheer	6,000	30.00
1976 Joy of Christmas	6,000	30.00

	Edition Limit	Issue Price (US)
1977 Holly-Jolly Christmas	6,000	30.00

Mother's Day

	Edition Limit	Issue Price (US)
1972 Mother and Child	1,000	25.00
1973 Mother and Child	2,000	25.00
1974 Bouquet for Mother	2,000	25.00
1975 We Wish You Happiness	2,000	28.00

Union Pacific Railroad

1972 Union Pacific	1,500	22.00
1973 Union Pacific Big Boy	1,500	25.00

History

1973 Tribute to Flag	3,000	60.00
1974 Golden Spike Centennial	1,500	40.00

Easter

1973 Happy Easter	1,500	25.00
1974 Springtime	1,500	25.00
1975 With Love to You at Easter	1,500	28.00

America Beautiful

1975 Independence Hall	1,500	42.00
1975 Statue of Liberty	1,500	42.00
1975 Niagara Falls	1,500	42.00
1975 Grand Canyon	1,500	42.00
1975 Golden State	1,500	42.00
1975 Capitol	1,500	42.00

Bicentennial

1976 Freedom Train	1,500	45.00
1976 Spirit of America	3,500	45.00

Playmates

1976 Timmy and His Pal	5,000	45.00
1977 Heidi and Playmate	5,000	45.00

Golden Spike Centennial

1977 Central Pacific Jupiter	1,500	25.00
1977 Union Pacific 119	1,500	25.00

A Child's Christmas

1978 Holy Night	5,000	40.00

Marmot

Father's Day

1970 Stag	3,500	12.00
1971 Horse	3,500	12.50

Christmas

1970 Polar Bear	5,000	13.00
1971 Buffalo	5,000	14.00
1972 Boy & Grandfather	5,000	20.00
1973 Snowman	3,000	20.00
1974 Dancing Children	2,000	24.00
1975 Covey of Quail	2,000	30.00
1976 Windmill	2,000	30.00

Presidents

1971 Washington	1,500	25.00
1972 Jefferson	1,500	25.00
1973 John Adams	1,500	25.00

Mother's Day

1972 Seal	6,000	16.00
1973 Polar Bear	2,000	20.00
1974 Penguins	2,000	24.00
1975 Raccoons	2,000	30.00
1976 Ducks	2,000	40.00

Mueller

Christmas

1971 Christmas in Tyrol	Year	20.00
1972 Christmas Messenger	Year	15.00
1973 Bringing Home Tree	Year	20.00
1974 Trimming Tree	Year	25.00
1975 Family on Christmas Morning	Year	27.50
1976 Christmas Fire	Year	28.50
1977 Ice Skating	Year	28.50

Father's Day

1973 Three Generations	NA	17.50
1974 Fishing	NA	20.00
1975 Hiking	NA	27.50

Porcelaine Ariel

See: Hamilton Collection (U.S.A.)

Rosenthal

Annual (Porcelain)

1971 Tapio Wirkkala	3,000	NA
1972 Natale Sapone	3,000	NA
1973 Otto Piene	3,000	NA
1974 Gunther Fruhtrunk	3,000	NA
1975 Srivastava Narendra	3,000	NA
1976 Salvador Dali	3,000	NA

	Edition Limit	Issue Price (US)
1977 Victor Vasarely	3,000	NA
1978 E. Paolozzi	3,000	NA
1979 Arnold Leissler	3,000	NA
1980 O.H. Hajek	3,000	NA

Annual (Crystal)

1974 Otto Piene (Clear)	3,000	200.00
1974 Otto Piene (Gold Inlaid)	3,000	250.00
1974 Otto Piene (Platinum Inlaid)	3,000	250.00
1975 G. Uecker	3,000	200.00
1976 Bjørn Wiinblad	3,000	NA
1977 Gunter F. Ris	3,000	NA
1978 Ivan Rapuzin	3,000	600.00
1979 Salvador Dali	3,000	NA
1980 Ernst Fuchs	3,000	NA

Lorraine Trester

1975 Once Upon a Summertime	5,000	60.00
1976 One Lovely Yesterday	5,000	70.00

Fantasies and Fables

1976 Oriental Night Music	NA	50.00
1977 Mandolin Players	NA	55.00

Wiinblad Studio-Linie

1976 Madonna	2,000	150.00
1977 Annunciation	2,000	195.00
1978 Three Kings	2,000	225.00
1979 Holy Family	2,000	230.00
1980 Appearance of Angels	2,000	240.00
1981 Adoration of Shepherds	2,000	295.00

Aladdin

1979 Aladdin and Lamp	NA	65.00
1979 Aladdin and Street Urchins	NA	65.00
1980 Aladdin and Magician	NA	65.00
1980 Aladdin in Garden	NA	65.00
1981 Aladdin and Spirit	NA	85.00
1981 Aladdin and Princess	NA	85.00
1982 Aladdin's Mother and Genie	NA	85.00
1982 Aladdin's Mother and Sultan	NA	85.00
1983 Aladdin Rides to Palace	NA	85.00
1983 Genie Builds Palace	NA	85.00

Christmas Carols

1983 Silent Night	NA	195.00
1984 Jingle Bells	NA	195.00
1985 We Three Kings of Orient Are	NA	195.00
1986 O Tannenbaum	NA	225.00

Parables in Glass

1986 Rich Man and Beggar	NA	295.00

See also:
Hibel Studio (Ger.)
Kern Collectibles (U.S.A.)

Royal Bayreuth

See: Kern Collectibles (U.S.A.)

Royal Tettau

Papal Plates

1971 Pope Paul VI	5,000	100.00
1972 Pope John XXIII	5,000	100.00
1973 Pope Pius XII	5,000	100.00

Christmas (Single issue)

1972 Carriage in Village	NA	12.50

Royale

Christmas

1969 Christmas Fair in Ebeltoft	6,000	12.00
1970 Kalundborg Church	10,000	13.00
1971 Christmas Night	8,000	16.00
1972 Elks	8,000	16.00
1973 Christmas	6,000	20.00
1974 Village at Christmas	5,000	22.00
1975 Feeding Time	5,000	26.00
1976 Christmas at Seaport	5,000	27.50
1977 Sledding	5,000	30.00

Mother's Day

1970 Swan and Brood	6,000	12.00
1971 Doe and Fawn	9,000	13.00
1972 Rabbit Family	9,000	16.00
1973 Owl Family	6,000	18.00
1974 Duck Family	5,000	22.00
1975 Lynx Family	5,000	26.00

	Edition Limit	Issue Price (US)
1976 Woodcock and Young	5,000	27.50
1977 Koala Bear	5,000	30.00

Father's Day

1970 U.S. Frigate Constitution	5,000	13.00
1971 Man Fishing	5,000	13.00
1972 Mountain Climber	6,000	16.00
1973 Camping	4,000	18.00
1974 Eagle	2,500	22.00
1975 Regatta	2,500	26.00
1976 Hunting Scene	2,500	27.50
1977 Fishing	5,000	30.00

Game

1972 Setters Pointing Quail	500	180.00
1973 Fox	500	200.00
1974 Osprey	250	250.00
1975 California Quail	250	265.00

Royale Germania

Annual

1970 Orchid (Blue)	600	200.00
1971 Cyclamen (Red)	1,000	200.00
1972 Silver Thistle (Green)	1,000	250.00
1973 Tulips (Lilac)	600	275.00
1974 Sunflowers (Topaz)	500	300.00
1975 Snowdrops (Amber)	350	450.00
1976 Flaming Heart (Red)	350	450.00

Mother's Day

1971 Roses (Red)	250	135.00
1972 Elephant (Green)	750	180.00
1973 Koala Bear (Lilac)	600	200.00
1974 Squirrels (Topaz)	500	240.00
1975 Swan Family (Amber)	350	250.00

Schmid

Bavarian Christmas

1971 Family Portrait	5,000	25.50
1972 On Horseback	5,000	26.50
1973 Bringing Home Tree	5,000	26.50
1974 Decorating Tree	5,000	26.50
1975 Opening Presents	5,000	26.50
1976 By Fireside	5,000	26.50
1977 Skating	5,000	28.50
1978 Family Picking Tree	5,000	36.00
1979 Breakfast by Tree	5,000	45.00
1980 Feeding Animals	5,000	55.00

Ferrandiz Christmas

1972 Christ in Manger	Year	30.00
1973 Christmas	Year	30.00

Golden Moments

1978 Tranquility	15,000	250.00

Christmas (Pewter)

1977 Santa	5,000	30.00
1978 Beautiful Snow	5,000	45.00
1979 I Hear America Singing	6,000	50.00

Ferrandiz Mother and Child

1977 Orchard Mother	10,000	65.00
1978 Pastoral Mother	10,000	75.00
1979 Floral Mother	10,000	95.00
1980 Avian Mother	10,000	100.00

Beatrix Potter (Pewter)

1978 Peter Rabbit	5,000	50.00
1979 Jemima-Puddle Duck	5,000	50.00

Reflections of Life

1980 Quiet Reflections	10,000	85.00
1981 Tree of Life	10,000	85.00

Country Pride

1981 Surprise in Cellar	7,500	35.00
1981 Plum Tuckered Out	7,500	35.00
1981 Duke's Mixture	7,500	35.00
1982 Bustin with Pride	7,500	35.00

Music Makers

1981 Flutist	10,000	25.00
1982 Entertainer	10,000	25.00
1982 Magical Medley	10,000	25.00
1982 Sweet Serenade	10,000	25.00

My Name Is Star

1981 Star's Spring	10,000	30.00
1981 Star's Summer	10,000	30.00
1982 Star's Autumn	10,000	30.00
1982 Star's Winter	10,000	30.00

Beautiful Bounty

1982 Summer's Golden Harvest	10,000	40.00

	Edition Limit	Issue Price (US)
1982 Autumn's Blessing	10,000	40.00
1983 A Mid-Winter's Dream	10,000	40.00
1983 Spring Blossoms	10,000	40.00

Cat Tales

1982 Right Church, Wrong Pew	12,500	37.50
1982 Company's Coming	12,500	37.50
1983 Flew Coop	12,500	37.50
1983 On Move	12,500	37.50

Prairie Women

1982 Maiden	12,500	35.00
1982 Courtship Blanket	12,500	35.00
1983 Mother Now	12,500	35.00
1983 Passing of Moons	12,500	35.00

Carousel Fantasies

1983 A Fairy Tale Princess	7,500	50.00

Lowell Davis Christmas

1983 Country Christmas	7,500	45.00
1984 Country Christmas	7,500	45.00
1985 Christmas at Foxfire	7,500	45.00
1986 Christmas at Red Oak	7,500	45.00
1987 Blossom's Gift	7,500	47.50

(Single issue)

1983 Critics	12,500	45.00

Gift of Happiness

1984 Lilies of Field	7,500	125.00
1984 Morning Glories	7,500	125.00

Good Ol' Days (Set of two)

1984 Waiting for Master		
1984 Minutes Like Hours	5,000	60.00

Nature's Treasures

1984 Rose Haven/Sparrow	5,000	45.00
1984 Tulip Nest/Robin	5,000	45.00
1984 Leafy Bower/Oriole	5,000	45.00
1984 Nesting/Mockingbird	5,000	45.00

Prime Time

1984 Love Boat	NA	30.00
1984 Dynasty	NA	30.00
1984 Dallas	NA	30.00

Statuette

1984 Hark Herald	Year	40.00

Red Oak Sampler

1986 General Store	5,000	45.00
1987 Country Wedding	5,000	47.50

(Single issue)

1986 Home from Market	7,500	55.00

(Single issue)

1987 Snow White and the Seven Dwarfs	5,000	47.50

See also: Addams Family (U.S.A.)

Schumann

Composers

1970 Beethoven	NA	8.00
1972 Mozart	NA	13.00

Christmas

1971 Snow Scene	10,000	12.00
1972 Deer in Snow	15,000	12.00
1973 Weihnachten	5,000	12.00
1974 Church in Snow	5,000	12.00
1975 Fountain	5,000	12.00

See also:
Christian Bell (Can.)
Calhoun's Collector's Society (U.S.A.)

Stumar

Christmas

1970 Angel	10,000	8.00
1971 Old Canal	10,000	8.00
1972 Countryside	10,000	8.00
1973 Friendship	10,000	10.00
1974 Making Fancy	10,000	10.00
1975 Preparation	10,000	10.00
1976 Drummer Boy	10,000	10.00
1977 Joyful Expectations	10,000	15.00
1978 Christmas	10,000	19.50

Mother's Day

1971 Amish Mother & Daughter	10,000	8.00
1972 Children	10,000	8.00
1973 Mother Sewing	10,000	10.00
1974 Mother Cradle	10,000	10.00
1975 Baking	10,000	10.00
1976 Reading to Children	10,000	15.00
1977 Comforting Child	10,000	15.00

	Edition Limit	Issue Price (US)
1978 Tranquility	10,000	19.50
Egyptian		
1977 Ancient Egyptian Trilogy	5,000	45.00
1978 Charioteer	5,000	54.00

Tirschenreuth

Christmas

	Edition Limit	Issue Price (US)
1969 Homestead	3,500	12.00
1970 Church	3,500	12.00
1971 Star of Bethlehem	3,500	12.00
1972 Elk Silhouette	2,000	13.00
1973 Christmas	Year	14.00

Villeroy & Boch

Christmas

	Edition Limit	Issue Price (US)
1977 Holy Family	10,000	175.00
1978 Three Holy Kings	20,000	175.00
1979 Mary with Child	10,000	198.00
1980 Madonna in Glory	10,000	200.00
1981 Mary Glorious	10,000	210.00

World Wildlife

	Edition Limit	Issue Price (US)
1983 Panda Bear	Year	38.00
1983 Tiger	Year	38.00
1984 Otter	Year	38.00
1984 Orangutan	Year	38.00
1985 Seal	Year	38.00

Enchanted Fairyland Lovers

	Edition Limit	Issue Price (US)
1982 Prince	NA	39.00
1982 Ivan and Horse	NA	39.00
1982 Princess and Stag	NA	39.00
1983 Goose Girl	NA	39.00
1983 Cinderella	NA	39.00
1983 Prince Ahmed and Peri	NA	39.00
1984 Ta-Khai and Bird Feng	NA	39.00
1984 Fisherman and Dragon King's Daughter	NA	39.00

French Fairy Tales

	Edition Limit	Issue Price (US)
1983 Fortunata and Hen	19,750	70.00
1983 King of Peacocks	19,750	70.00
1983 King and Puss in Boots	19,750	70.00
1984 In Search of Phoenix	19,750	70.00
1984 Princess Radiant and Phoenix	19,750	70.00
1985 Monkeys in Garden	19,750	70.00
1985 Florina and Fairy Pie	19,750	70.00
1986 Uglinette and Pagodies	19,750	70.00

Exotic Birds

	Edition Limit	Issue Price (US)
1984 Fiery Parakeet	15,000	70.00
1984 Long-Billed Cockatoo	15,000	70.00
1985 Black-Billed Cockatoo	15,000	70.00

Dreams of Katharina

	Edition Limit	Issue Price (US)
1985 Katharina Receives Love	20,000	75.00
1986 Dream Castle	NA	75.00

Famous Sea Battles

	Edition Limit	Issue Price (US)
1986 Battle of East India	NA	42.00

(Single issue)

	Edition Limit	Issue Price (US)
1985 Golden Lady	1,000	150.00

(Single issue)

	Edition Limit	Issue Price (US)
1986 Symbols of Freedom	21 Days	38.00

(Single issue)

	Edition Limit	Issue Price (US)
1986 Liberty Bas Relief	21 Days	32.00

(Single issue)

	Edition Limit	Issue Price (US)
1986 Liberty Centennial	21 Days	35.00

WMF Geislingen

Annual

	Edition Limit	Issue Price (US)
1978 Rose-Motif I	2,500	117.50
1979 Rose-Motif-II	2,500	120.00
1980 Rose-Motif III	2,500	120.00

Christmas

	Edition Limit	Issue Price (US)
1978 Birth of Christ	2,500	117.50
1979 Praising King	2,500	120.00
1980 Praising Shepherd	2,500	120.00

GREAT BRITAIN

Belleek

Irish Countryside Christmas

	Edition Limit	Issue Price (US)
1984 Irish White Beam	10,000	95.00
1985 Irish Heather	10,000	95.00
1986 Wild Irish Rose	10,000	95.00

St. Patrick's Day Annual

	Edition Limit	Issue Price (US)
1985 Slemish Mountain	10,000	75.00
1986 Banishing Snakes	10,000	75.00

(Single issue)

	Edition Limit	Issue Price (US)
1986 First Sight of Liberty	NA	55.00

Boehm Studios

European Bird Plates

	Edition Limit	Issue Price (US)
1973 Swallow	5,000	48.75
1973 Chaffinch	5,000	48.75
1973 Coal Tit	5,000	48.75
1973 Tree Sparrow	5,000	48.75
1973 King Fisher	5,000	48.75
1973 Gold Crest	5,000	48.75
1973 Blue Tit	5,000	48.75
1973 Linnet	5,000	48.75

Honor America

	Edition Limit	Issue Price (US)
1974 American Bald Eagle	12,000	85.00

Butterfly

	Edition Limit	Issue Price (US)
1975 Blue Mountain Swallowtails	100	450.00
1975 Jezabels	100	450.00
1976 Comma with Loops	100	450.00
1976 African Butterflies	100	450.00
1976 Solandras Maxima	100	450.00

Hard Fruit

	Edition Limit	Issue Price (US)
1975 Plums	100	450.00
1975 Pears	100	450.00
1976 Peaches	100	450.00
1976 Apples	100	450.00

Oriental Birds

	Edition Limit	Issue Price (US)
1975 Bluebacked Fairy Bluebirds	100	400.00
1975 Azure-Winged Magpies	100	400.00
1976 Golden-Fronted Leafbird	100	400.00
1976 Golden-Throated Barbet	100	400.00

Seashell

	Edition Limit	Issue Price (US)
1975 Violet Spider Conch	100	450.00
1975 Rooster Tail Conch	100	450.00
1976 Orange Spider Conch	100	450.00
1976 Cheragra Spider Conch	100	450.00

Soft Fruit

	Edition Limit	Issue Price (US)
1975 Loganberries	100	450.00
1975 Cherries	100	450.00
1976 Strawberries	100	450.00
1976 Grapes	100	450.00

Butterflies of World

	Edition Limit	Issue Price (US)
1978 Monarch and Daisy	5,000	62.00
1978 Red Admiral and Thistle	5,000	62.00

Flower

	Edition Limit	Issue Price (US)
1975 Lilies	100	450.00
1975 Passion Flowers	100	450.00
1976 Double Clematis	100	450.00

Favorite Floral

	Edition Limit	Issue Price (US)
1978 Clematis	2,500	58.00
1978 Rhododendron	2,500	58.00
1979 Boehm Orchid	2,500	58.00
1979 Yellow Rose	2,500	58.00
1980 Spider Orchid	2,500	58.00
1980 Dahlia	2,500	58.00

Musical Maidens of Imperial Dynasties

	Edition Limit	Issue Price (US)
1984 Balloon Guitar	15,000	65.00
1984 Three-Stringed Guitar	15,000	65.00
1984 Harp	15,000	65.00
1984 Gong	15,000	65.00
1984 Reen Organ	15,000	65.00
1984 Ceremonial Flute	15,000	65.00
1984 Lute	15,000	65.00
1984 Common Flute	15,000	65.00

See also: Hamilton Collection (U.S.A.)

Caithness Glass

America's Favorite Birds

	Edition Limit	Issue Price (US)
1979 Crystal Wren	5,000	79.50

Coalport

(Single issue)

	Edition Limit	Issue Price (US)
1972 Indy 500	2,000	49.95

Poole Pottery

Medieval Calendar

	Edition Limit	Issue Price (US)
1972 Drinking Wine by Fire (January)	1,000	100.00

	Edition Limit	Issue Price (US)
1972 Chopping Wood (February)	1,000	100.00
1973 Digging in Fields and Setting Seeds (March)	1,000	125.00
1973 Carrying Flowering Branch (April)	1,000	125.00
1974 Hawking (May)	1,000	125.00
1974 Mowing Hay (June)	1,000	125.00
1975 Cutting Corn with Sickle (July)	1,000	125.00
1975 Threshing with Flail (August)	1,000	125.00
1976 Picking Grapes (September)	1,000	125.00
1976 Sowing Winter Corn (October)	1,000	125.00
1977 Gathering Acorns to Feed Pigs (November)	1,000	125.00
1977 Pig Killing (December)	1,000	125.00

Cathedral

	Edition Limit	Issue Price (US)
1973 Christ on Cross	11,000	125.00

Christmas

	Edition Limit	Issue Price (US)
1973 Adoration of Magi	1,000	125.00
1973 Flight into Egypt	1,000	125.00

Home at Christmas

	Edition Limit	Issue Price (US)
1978 Santa's Helpers	10,000	37.50
1979 Three Wisemen	10,000	37.50

Birds of North America

	Edition Limit	Issue Price (US)
1979 Great Horned Owl	10,000	37.50

Mother's Day

	Edition Limit	Issue Price (US)
1979 Tenderness	10,000	37.50

Rhea Silva

Feline Favourites

	Edition Limit	Issue Price (US)
1982 Long Haired Ladies	10,000	47.00
1983 Siamese & Apple Blossoms	10,000	47.00
1984 Abyssinian Playmates	10,000	47.00

Child's Garden of Verses

	Edition Limit	Issue Price (US)
1983 Land of Counterpane	17,500	39.00

Portraits of Countryside

	Edition Limit	Issue Price (US)
1983 Autumn Wayside	5,000	79.00

Endangered Birds

	Edition Limit	Issue Price (US)
1984 Whooping Crane	5,000	60.00

Royal Doulton

Flower Garden

	Edition Limit	Issue Price (US)
1975 Spring Harmony	15,000	60.00
1976 Dreaming Lotus	15,000	65.00
1977 Poet's Garden	15,000	70.00
1978 Country Bouquet	15,000	70.00
1980 From My Mother's Garden	15,000	85.00

Ports of Call

	Edition Limit	Issue Price (US)
1975 San Francisco	15,000	60.00
1976 New Orleans	15,000	65.00
1977 Venice	15,000	70.00
1978 Montmartre	15,000	70.00

Reflections on China

	Edition Limit	Issue Price (US)
1976 Garden of Tranquility	15,000	70.00
1977 Imperial Palace	15,000	70.00
1978 Temple of Heaven	15,000	75.00
1980 Lake of Mists	15,000	85.00

I Remember America

	Edition Limit	Issue Price (US)
1977 Pennsylvania Pastorale	15,000	70.00
1978 Lovejoy Bridge	15,000	70.00
1979 Four Corners	15,000	75.00
1980 Marshlands	15,000	95.00

All God's Children

	Edition Limit	Issue Price (US)
1978 Brighter Day	10,000	60.00
1980 Village Children	10,000	65.00
1981 Noble Heritage	10,000	85.00
1982 Buddies	10,000	85.00
1983 Little Brother	10,000	95.00
1985 Sisterly Love	10,000	95.00

American Tapestries

	Edition Limit	Issue Price (US)
1978 Sleigh Bells	10,000	70.00
1979 Pumpkin Patch	10,000	70.00
1980 General Store	10,000	95.00
1981 Fourth of July	10,000	95.00

Jungle Fantasy

	Edition Limit	Issue Price (US)
1979 Ark	10,000	75.00
1980 Compassion	10,000	95.00

	Edition Limit	Issue Price (US)
1981 Patience	10,000	95.00
1982 Refuge	10,000	95.00

(Single issue)

	Edition Limit	Issue Price (US)
1980 Winning Colors	15,000	80.00

Behind Painted Masque

	Edition Limit	Issue Price (US)
1982 Painted Feelings	10,000	95.00
1983 Make Me Laugh	10,000	95.00
1983 Minstrel Serenade	10,000	95.00
1984 Pleasing Performance	10,000	95.00

Celebration of Faith

	Edition Limit	Issue Price (US)
1982 Rosh Hashanah	7,500	250.00
1982 Passover	7,500	250.00
1983 Yom Kippur	7,500	250.00
1983 Chanukah	7,500	250.00

Children of Pueblo

	Edition Limit	Issue Price (US)
1983 Apple Flower	10,000	60.00
1983 Morning Star	10,000	60.00

Christmas Carol

	Edition Limit	Issue Price (US)
1983 Silent Night	Year	39.95
1984 While Shepherds Watched	Year	39.95
1985 Oh, Little Town of Bethlehem	NA	39.95
1986 I Saw Three Ships	NA	39.95

Festival Children of World

	Edition Limit	Issue Price (US)
1983 Mariani (Bali)	15,000	65.00
1983 Magdalena (Mexico)	15,000	65.00
1984 Michiko (Japan)	15,000	65.00
1984 Monika (Poland)	15,000	65.00
1985 Maureen	15,000	65.00
1985 Marijke	15,000	65.00

Grandest Gift

	Edition Limit	Issue Price (US)
1984 Reunion	10,000	75.00
1985 Storytime	10,000	75.00

Royal Worcester

Doughty Bird

	Edition Limit	Issue Price (US)
1972 Redstarts and Beech	2,750	125.00
1973 Myrtle Warbler/Cherry	3,000	175.00
1974 Blue-Grey Gnatcatchers	3,000	195.00
1975 Blackburnian Warbler	3,000	195.00
1976 Blue-Winged Sivas	3,000	195.00
1977 Paradise Wydah	3,000	195.00
1978 Bluetits/Witch Hazel	3,000	195.00
1979 Mountain Bluebird	3,000	195.00
1980 Cerulean Warblers	3,000	315.00
1981 Willow Warbler	3,000	330.00
1982 Ruby-Crowned Kinglets	3,000	330.00
1983 Bewick's Wren	3,000	330.00

Bicentennial

	Edition Limit	Issue Price (US)
1976 Independence	10,000	150.00

Fabulous Birds

	Edition Limit	Issue Price (US)
1976 Peacocks I	10,000	65.00
1977 Peacocks II	10,000	65.00

Audubon Birds

	Edition Limit	Issue Price (US)
1977 Warbler & Jay	5,000	150.00
1978 Kingbird & Sparrow	10,000	150.00

Chinoiserie

	Edition Limit	Issue Price (US)
1977 Bishop Summer	Year	65.00

English Christmas

	Edition Limit	Issue Price (US)
1979 Christmas Eve	Year	60.00
1980 Christmas Morning	Year	65.00
1981 Christmas Day	Year	70.00
1982 Christmas Evening	Year	70.00

Kitten Classics

	Edition Limit	Issue Price (US)
1985 Cat Nap	14 Days	29.50

Spode

Ray Harm Birds (Set of 12)

	Edition Limit	Issue Price (US)
1970 Rufus-Sided Towhee		
1970 Winter Wren		
1971 Eastern Bluebird		
1971 Stellar's Jay		
1971 Eastern Mockingbird		
1971 Barn Swallow		
1971 Rose-Breasted Grosbeak		
1971 Cardinal		
1972 Western Tanager		
1972 Woodpecker		
1972 Chickadee		
1972 American Goldfinch	5,000	300.00

Maritime Plates (Set of six)

	Edition Limit	Issue Price (US)
1980 USS United States and HMS Macedonian		

	Edition Limit	Issue Price (US)
1980 USS President and HMS Little Belt		
1980 HMS Shannon and USS Chesapeake		
1980 USS Constitution and HMS Guerriere		
1980 USS Constitution and HMN Java		
1980 HMS Pelican and USS Argus	2,000	300.00

Christmas Pastimes
1982 Sleigh Ride	Year	75.00

World of Charles Dickens
1987 Oliver Twist	NA	29.50

Wedgwood

Children's Story
1971 Sandman	Year	7.95
1972 Tinder Box	Year	9.00
1973 Emperor's New Clothes	Year	9.00
1974 Ugly Duckling	Year	10.00
1975 Little Mermaid	Year	12.00
1976 Hansel & Gretel	Year	12.00
1977 Rumpelstiltskin	Year	15.00
1978 Frog Prince	Year	15.00
1979 Golden Goose	Year	15.00
1980 Rapunzel	Year	16.00
1981 Tom Thumb	Year	18.00
1982 Lady and Lion	Year	20.00
1983 Elves and Shoemaker	Year	20.00
1984 King Roughbeard	Year	20.00
1985 Little Tailor	Year	20.00

Bicentennial
1972 Boston Tea Party	Year	30.00
1973 Paul Revere's Ride	Year	35.00
1974 Battle of Concord	Year	40.00
1975 Across Delaware	Year	45.00
1975 Victory at Yorktown	Year	45.00
1976 Declaration Signed	Year	45.00

(Single issue)
1978 Tri-Color Decade Christmas	10,000	325.00

(Single issue)
1978 Anniversary Christmas	Year	130.00

Trophy
1978 Tutankhamun	500	1000.00
1978 Ankhesenamum	500	1000.00

Child's Christmas
1979 Snowman	Year	35.00
1980 Bringing Home Tree	Year	35.00
1981 Tobogganing	Year	35.00
1982 Skaters	Year	35.00
1983 Carolers	Year	35.00
1984 Christmas Baking	Year	35.\

Remarkable World of Charles Dickens
1980 Oliver Twist and Fagin	19,500	60.00
1980 Scrooge and Marley's Ghost	19,500	60.00
1980 Bob Cratchit	19,500	60.00
1980 David Copperfield	19,500	60.00
1981 Micawber/Uriah Heep	19,500	60.00
1981 Little Nell	19,500	60.00
1981 Madame Defarge	19,500	60.00
1981 Mr. Pickwick	19,500	60.00

Valentine's Day
1982 Lilac on White	Year	55.00
1983 White on Pink	Year	55.00
1984 White on Teal	Year	55.00

Eyes of Child
1983 Little Lady Love	15,000	65.00
1984 My Best Friend	15,000	65.00
1985 I Wish Upon a Star	15,000	65.00
1985 In a Child's Thoughts	15,000	65.00
1985 Puppy Love	15,000	65.00

(Single issue)
1983 200 Years of Ballooning	Year	35.00

INDIA

Sarna

Christmas
1975 Holy Family	4,000	17.50

ITALY

Anri

Mother's Day
1972 Alpine Mother & Children	5,000	35.00
1973 Alpine Mother & Children	5,000	40.00
1974 Alpine Mother & Children	5,000	50.00
1975 Alpine Stroll	5,000	60.00
1976 Knitting	5,000	60.00

Father's Day
1972 Alpine Father & Children	5,000	35.00
1973 Alpine Father & Children	5,000	40.00
1974 Cliff Gazing	5,000	50.00
1975 Sailing	5,000	60.00

Ferrandiz Birthday
1972 Birthday Girl	Year	15.00
1972 Birthday Boy	Year	15.00
1973 Birthday	Year	20.00
1974 Birthday Girl	Year	22.00
1974 Birthday Boy	Year	22.00
1975 Birthday Girl	Year	35.00

Ferrandiz Mother's Day
1972 Mother Sewing	2,500	35.00
1973 Mother and Child	1,500	40.00
1974 Mother and Child	1,500	50.00
1975 Mother Holding Dove	1,500	60.00
1976 Mother and Child	1,500	60.00
1977 Girl with Flowers	1,500	65.00
1978 Beginning	3,000	77.50
1979 All Hearts	3,000	120.00
1980 Spring Arrivals	3,000	150.00
1981 Harmony	3,000	150.00
1982 With Love	3,000	150.00

Ferrandiz Christmas
1972 Christ in Manger	Year	30.00
1973 Boy with Lamb	Year	30.00
1974 Nativity	Year	50.00
1975 Flight into Egypt	Year	60.00
1976 Mary and Joseph Pray	Year	60.00
1977 Girl with Tree	4,000	65.00
1978 Leading Way	4,000	77.50
1979 Drummer Boy	4,000	120.00
1980 Rejoice	4,000	150.00
1981 Spreading Word	4,000	150.00
1982 Shepherd Family	4,000	150.00
1983 Peace Attend Thee	4,000	150.00

Ferrandiz Wedding Day
1972 Wedding	Year	40.00
1973 Wedding	Year	40.00
1974 Wedding	Year	48.00
1975 Wedding	Year	60.00
1976 Wedding	Year	60.00

(Single issue)
1982 Riding Thru Rain	2,500	550.00

Ferrandiz Annual
1984 Pastoral Journey	2,000	180.00
1985 Tender Touch	2,000	170.00

Sarah Kay Annual
1984 A Time for Secrets	2,500	120.00
1985 Carousel Magic	2,500	120.00

Capo Di Monte

Christmas
1972 Cherubs	500	55.00
1973 Bells & Holly	500	55.00
1974 Christmas	1,000	60.00
1975 Christmas	1,000	60.00
1976 Christmas	250	65.00

Mother's Day
1973 Mother's Day	500	55.00
1974 Mother's Day	500	60.00
1975 Mother's Day	500	60.00
1976 Mother's Day	500	65.00

Carlo Monti

Mother's Day
1973 Madonna & Child	2,000	35.00

Count Agazzi

Famous Personalities
1968 Famous Personalities	600	8.00
1970 Famous Personalities	1,000	12.50
1973 Famous Personalities	600	15.00

(Single issue)
1969 Apollo II	1,000	17.00

Children's Hour
1970 Owl	2,000	12.50
1971 Cat	2,000	12.50
1972 Pony	2,000	12.50
1973 Panda	2,000	12.50

Easter
1971 Playing Violin	600	12.50
1972 At Prayer	600	12.50
1973 Winged Cherub	600	12.50

Mother's Day
1972 Mother's Day	144	35.00
1973 Mother's Day	720	19.50

Father's Day
1972 Father's Day	144	35.00
1973 Father's Day	288	19.50

Christmas
1973 Christmas	1,000	19.50

(Single issue)
1973 Peace	720	12.50

Kings

Mother's Day
1973 Dancing Girl	1,500	100.00
1974 Dancing Boy	1,500	115.00
1975 Motherly Love	1,500	140.00
1976 Maiden	1,500	180.00

Christmas
1973 Adoration	1,500	150.00
1974 Madonna	1,500	150.00
1975 Heavenly Choir	1,500	160.00
1976 Girl and Brother	1,500	200.00

Veneto Flair

Christmas
1971 Three Kings	1,500	45.00
1972 Shepherds	2,000	45.00
1973 Christ Child	2,000	55.00
1974 Angel	2,000	55.00

Wildlife
1971 Deer	500	37.50
1972 Elephant	1,000	37.50
1973 Puma	2,000	37.50
1974 Tiger	2,000	40.00

Birds
1972 Owl	2,000	37.50
1973 Falcon	2,000	37.50
1974 Mallard Duck	2,000	45.00

Dogs
1972 German Shepherd	2,000	37.50
1973 Poodle	2,000	37.50
1974 Doberman	2,000	37.50
1975 Collie	2,000	40.00
1976 Dachshund	2,000	45.00

Mother's Day
1972 Madonna and Child	2,000	55.00
1973 Madonna and Child	2,000	55.00
1974 Mother and Son	2,000	55.00
1975 Daughter and Doll	2,000	45.00
1976 Son and Daughter	2,000	55.00
1977 Mother and Child	2,000	50.00

Easter
1973 Rabbits	2,000	50.00
1974 Chicks	2,000	50.00
1975 Lamb	2,000	50.00
1976 Composite	2,000	55.00

Goddess
1973 Pomona	1,500	75.00
1974 Diana	1,500	75.00

Mosaic
1973 Justinian	500	50.00
1974 Pelican	1,000	50.00
1977 Theodora	500	50.00

Cats
1974 Persian	2,000	40.00
1975 Siamese	2,000	45.00
1976 Tabby	2,000	45.00

Christmas Card
1975 Christmas Eve	5,000	45.00
1976 Old North Church	5,000	50.00
1977 Log Cabin Christmas	5,000	50.00
1978 Dutch Christmas	5,000	50.00

Valentine's Day
1977 Valentine Boy	3,000	45.00
1978 Valentine Girl	3,000	45.00
1979 Hansel	3,000	60.00
1980 Gretel	3,000	67.50

Flower Children
1978 Rose	3,000	45.00
1979 Orchid	3,000	60.00
1980 Camillia	3,000	65.00

La Belle Femme
1978 Lily	9,500	70.00
1978 Gigi	9,500	76.50
1980 Dominique	9,500	76.50
1980 Gabrielle	9,500	76.50

American Landscape
1979 Hudson Valley	7,500	75.00
1980 Northwest Cascade	7,500	75.00

Children's Christmas
1979 Carolers	7,500	60.00
1980 Heading Home	7,500	70.00
1981 Night Before	7,500	95.00
1982 A Visit to Santa	7,500	80.00

Mother and Child
1981 Buffalos	5,000	95.00
1981 Elephants	5,000	95.00
1981 Koalas	5,000	95.00
1981 Lions	5,000	95.00
1981 Loons	5,000	95.00
1981 Polar Bears	5,000	95.00

Lamincia Annual
1981 Young Love	5,000	95.00

JAPAN

Manjundo

Chinese Lunar Calendar
1972 Year of Rat	5,000	15.00
1973 Year of Ox	5,000	15.00

Noritake

Christmas
1975 Madonna with Child	3,000	42.00
1976 Gratia Hoso Kawa	3,000	54.00
1977 Julia Otaa	3,000	83.00
1978 Amakusa Shiro	3,000	109.00
1979 Munzio Ito	3,000	124.00
1980 Furst Takayama	3,000	125.00

Annual
1977 Paradise Birds	3,000	380.00
1978 Chrysanthemums	3,000	494.00
1979 Cranes	3,000	556.00
1980 Water Lilies and Butterflies	3,000	575.00

Sango

Christmas
1976 Undesired Slumber	7,500	25.00
1977 Togetherness	7,500	25.00

Mother's Day
1976 Spring Delight	7,500	20.00
1977 Broken Wing	5,000	22.50

See also: Kern Collectibles (U.S.A.)

Schmid

Peanuts Mother's Day
1972 Linus	Year	10.00
1973 Mom?	Year	10.00
1974 Snoopy/Wood./Parade	Year	10.00
1975 A Kiss for Lucy	Year	12.50
1976 Linus and Snoopy	Year	13.00
1977 Dear Mom	Year	13.00
1978 Thoughts That Count	Year	15.00
1979 A Special Letter	10,000	17.50
1980 A Tribune to Mom	10,000	17.50
1981 Mission for Mom	10,000	17.50
1982 Which Way to Mother?	10,000	18.50

Raggedy Ann Christmas
1975 Gifts of Love	Year	12.50
1976 Raggedy Ann Skates	Year	13.00
1977 Decorating Tree	Year	13.00
1978 Checking List	Year	15.00
1979 Little Helper	15,000	17.50

Bicentennial
1976 Peanuts	NA	13.00
1976 Disney	NA	13.00
1976 Raggedy Ann	NA	13.00

	Edition Limit	Issue Price (US)
Raggedy Ann Mother's Day		
1976 Motherhood	Year	13.00
1977 Bouquet of Love	Year	13.00
1978 Hello Mom	Year	15.00
1979 High Spirits	10,000	17.50
Peanuts Valentine's Day		
1977 Home Where Heart Is	Year	13.00
1978 Heavenly Bliss	Year	13.00
1979 Love Match	Year	17.50
1980 From Snoopy/Love	Year	17.50
1981 Hearts-a-Flutter	Year	17.50
1982 Love Patch	Year	17.50
Raggedy Ann Valentine's Day		
1978 As Time Goes By	Year	13.00
1979 Daisies Do Tell	Year	17.50
Disney Valentine's Day		
1979 Hands and Hearts	Year	17.50
1980 Mickey's I Love You	Year	17.50
1981 Be Mine	Year	17.50
1982 Picnic for Two	Year	17.50
A Year with Paddington Bear		
1979 Pyramid Presents	25,000	12.50
1980 Springtime	25,000	12.50
1981 Sandcastles	25,000	12.50
1981 School Days	25,000	12.50
Raggedy Ann Annual		
1980 Sunshine Wagon	10,000	17.50
1981 Raggedy Shuffle	10,000	17.50
1982 Flying High	10,000	18.50
1983 Winning Streak	10,000	22.50
1984 Rocking Rodeo	10,000	22.50
Peanuts 30th Anniversary (Single issue)		
1980 Happy Anniversary	15,000	27.50
Alice in Wonderland Anniversary (Single issue)		
1981 Alice in Wonderland	7,500	17.50
Disney Anniversary (Single issue)		
1981 Pluto's 50th Birthday	7,500	17.50
Four Seasons of Love		
1982 Tickets on 50 Yard Line	10,000	17.50
1982 Let it Snow	10,000	17.50
1983 Spring Bouquet	10,000	17.50
1983 Shades of Summer	10,000	17.50
A Musician's Dream		
1982 Beat Goes On	10,000	17.50
1982 Knowing Score	10,000	17.50
1983 Perfect Harmony	10,000	17.50
1983 Tickling Ivory	10,000	17.50
World's Greatest Athlete		
1982 Go Deep	10,000	17.50
1982 Puck Stops Here	10,000	17.50
1983 Way You Play Game	10,000	17.50
1983 Crowd Went Wild	10,000	17.50
Disney Annual		
1983 Sneak Preview	20,000	22.50
1984 Command Performance	20,000	22.50
1985 Snow Biz	20,000	22.50
1986 Tree for Two	20,000	22.50
1987 Merry Mouse Medley	20,000	25.00
Paddington Bear Annual		
1983 Bear's Noel	10,000	22.50
1984 How Sweet It Is	10,000	22.50
Peanuts Annual		
1983 Peanuts in Concert	20,000	22.50
1984 Snoopy/Beaglescouts	20,000	22.50
1986 Lion Tamer Snoopy	20,000	22.50
I Love Plate Collecting		
1984 A Great Beginning	20,000	22.50

See also: Addams Family (U.S.A.)

MEXICO

Bonita Silver

	Edition Limit	Issue Price (US)
Mother's Day		
1972 Mother and Baby	4,000	125.00

Roman Ceramica Excelsis

	Edition Limit	Issue Price (US)
Masterpiece Collection		
1979 Adoration	5,000	65.00
1980 Madonna with Grapes	5,000	87.50
1981 Holy Family	5,000	95.00
1982 Madonna of Streets	5,000	85.00
Ceramica Excelsis Collection		
1980 Little Children, Come to Me	15,000	45.00

NETHERLANDS

Blue Delft (Schoonhoven)

	Edition Limit	Issue Price (US)
Christmas		
1970 Drawbridge Near Binnenhof	Year	12.00
1971 St. Lauren's Church	Year	12.00
1972 Church at Bierkade	Year	12.00
1973 St. Jan's Church	Year	12.00
1974 Dongeradeel	Year	13.00
1975 Maassluis	Year	15.00
1976 Montelbaanstower	Year	15.00
1977 Harbour Tower of Hoorn	Year	19.50
1978 Binnenpoort Gate	Year	21.00
Mother's Day		
1971 Mother & Daughter of 1600s	Year	12.00
1972 Mother & Daughter of Isle of Urk	Year	12.00
1973 Rembrandt's Mother	Year	12.00
Father's Day		
1971 Francisco Lana's Airship	Year	12.00
1972 Dr. Jonathon's Balloon	Year	12.00

Crown Delft

	Edition Limit	Issue Price (US)
Christmas		
1969 Man by Tree	Year	10.00
1970 Two Sleigh Riders	Year	10.00
1971 Christmas Tree on Market Square	Year	10.00
1972 Baking for Christmas	Year	10.00
Mother's Day		
1970 Sheep	Year	10.00
1971 Stork	Year	10.00
1972 Ducks	Year	10.00
1973 Mother's Day	1,000	10.00
Father's Day		
1970 Father's Day	Year	10.00
1971 Father's Day	Year	10.00
1972 Father's Day	1,000	10.00
1973 Father's Day	1,000	10.00

Kurz (Shuler International)

	Edition Limit	Issue Price (US)
Christmas		
1972 Christmas	500	60.00
1973 Christmas	500	70.00
1974 Christmas	500	65.00
Mother's Day		
1973 Mother's Day	500	65.00

Metawa

	Edition Limit	Issue Price (US)
Christmas		
1972 Skaters	3,000	30.00
1973 One-Horse Sleigh	1,500	30.00
1974 Sailboat	Year	35.00

Royal Delft

	Edition Limit	Issue Price (US)
Christmas		
1915 Glory to God, Christmas Bells (10")	Year	NA
1915 Christmas Star (7")	Year	NA
1916 Star–Floral Design (10")	Year	NA
1916 Cradle of Child (10")	Year	NA
1917 Shepherd with Sheep in Stable (10")	Year	NA
1917 Christmas Star (10")	Year	NA
1918 Shepherd with Sheep in Stable (10")	Year	NA
1918 Christmas Star–Peace on Earth (10")	Year	NA
1919 Church (10")	Year	NA
1919 Christmas Star (10")	Year	NA
1920 Holly Wreath (10")	Year	NA
1920 Church Tower (10")	Year	NA
1921 Canal Boatman (10")	Year	NA
1921 Christmas Star (10")	Year	NA
1922 Landscape (10")	Year	NA
1922 Christmas Wreath (10")	Year	NA
1923 Shepherd (10")	Year	NA
1923 Christmas Star (10")	Year	NA
1924 Christmas Star (10")	Year	NA
1924 Town Gate with Shepherd (10")	Year	NA
1925 Towngate in Delft (10")	Year	NA
1925 Christmas Star (10")	Year	NA
1926 Christmas Star (10")	Year	NA
1926 Bell Tower (7")	Year	NA
1926 Windmill Landscape (10")	Year	NA
1927 Christmas Star (10")	Year	NA
1927 Sailing Boat (10")	Year	NA
1927 Church Tower (7")	Year	NA
1928 Christmas Poinsettia (10")	Year	NA
1928 Mill Christmas (7")	Year	NA
1928 Lighthouse Christmas (10")	Year	NA
1929 Christmas Bell (10")	Year	NA
1929 Church Spire (7")	Year	NA
1929 Small Dutch Town (10")	Year	NA
1930 Church Entrance, Delft (10")	Year	NA
1930 Christmas Rose (10")	Year	NA
1930 Sailing Boat (7")	Year	NA
1931 Christmas Star (10")	Year	NA
1931 Snow Landscape (10")	Year	NA
1931 Church Tower (7")	Year	NA
1932 Bell Tower (7")	Year	NA
1932 Fireplace (10")	Year	NA
1932 Christmas Star (10")	Year	NA
1933 Interior Scene with Exterior View (10")	Year	NA
1934 Interior Scene (10")	Year	NA
1934 Snowy Stable (10")	Year	NA
1935 Interior Scene with Exterior View (10")	Year	NA
1936 Interior Scene with Exterior View (10")	Year	NA
1937 Interior Scene with Exterior View (10")	Year	NA
1938 Interior Scene with Exterior View (10")	Year	NA
1939 Interior Scene with Well-Staircase (10")	Year	NA
1940 Interior with Christmas Tree (10")	Year	NA
1941 Interior Scene Fireplace & Tree (10")	Year	NA
1955 Christmas Star (9")	Year	NA
1955 Church Tower (10")	200	20.00
1956 Two Christmas Bells in Floral (9")	Year	NA
1956 Landscape (10")	200	20.00
1956 Flower Design (9")	Year	NA
1957 Christmas Star (9")	Year	NA
1957 Landscape (10")	225	22.00
1958 Christmas Star (9")	Year	NA
1958 View of Village at Riverside (10")	225	25.00
1959 View of Village at Riverside (10")	250	25.00
1959 Landscape with Mill (7")	400	10.00
1960 Landscape (7")	400	10.00
1960 Street in Delft (10")	250	25.00
1961 Snow Landscape (7")	500	10.00
1961 Village Scene with Church Town (10")	260	30.00
1962 Town View (7")	500	10.00
1962 Tower in Leeuwarden (10")	275	30.00
1963 Mill in Zeddam (7")	500	15.00
1963 Tower in Enkhuisen (10")	275	35.00
1964 Tower in Hoorn (10")	300	35.00
1964 Mill in Poelenburg (7")	600	15.00
1965 Towngate in Kampen (7")	600	15.00
1965 Corn-Mill in Rhoon (10")	300	35.00
1966 Towngate in Medemblik (7")	600	20.00
1966 Snuff Mill in Rotterdam (10")	325	40.00
1967 Mill in Hazerswoude (7")	700	20.00
1967 Tower in Amsterdam (10")	350	45.00
1968 Mill in Schiedam (7")	700	25.00
1968 Tower in Amsterdam "Schreierstoren" (10")	350	60.00
1969 Mill Near Gorkum (7")	800	35.00
1969 Church in Utrecht (10")	400	60.00
1970 Mill Near Haarlem (7")	1,500	25.00
1970 Cathedral in Veere (10")	500	60.00
1971 Towngate at Zierikzee (7")	3,500	25.00
1971 "Dom" Tower in Utrecht (10")	550	60.00
1972 Towngate at Elburg (7")	3,500	40.00
1972 Church in Edam (10")	1,500	70.00
1973 Towngate at Amersfoort (7")	4,500	50.00
1973 DeWaag in Alkmaar (10")	1,500	75.00
1974 Watergate at Sneek (7")	4,500	80.00
1974 Kitchen in Hindeloopen (10")	1,500	160.00
1975 Towngate at Amsterdam (7")	1,000	140.00
1975 Farmer in Laren (10")	1,500	250.00
1976 Towngate in Gorinchem (7")	4,500	115.00
1976 Farmer's Wife in Staphorst (10")	1,500	220.00
1977 Dromedaris Tower (7")	4,500	140.00
1977 Farm Family in Spakenburg (10")	1,500	277.00
1978 Winter Skating Scene (10")	1,000	277.00
1978 Christmas Fisherman (7")	1,500	140.00
1978 Christmas Angels (7")	1,500	140.00
1984 Homecoming (10")	500	230.00
1984 Figure Skating (7")	1,000	120.00
1985 Church at Woudt (10")	500	270.00
1985 The Farmhouse at Woudt (7")	1,000	140.00
1986 St. Dionysius in Asselt (10")	500	324.00
1986 Farmhouse in Asselt (7")	1,000	168.00
Mother's Day		
1971 Mother & Daughter (Volendam)	2,500	50.00
1972 Mother & Daughter (Hindeloopen)	2,500	40.00
1973 Mother & Daughter (Marken)	3,000	50.00
1974 Mother & Daughter (Zuid-Beveland)	Year	80.00
1975 Mother & Daughter (Spakenburg)	Year	100.00
1976 Mother & Daughter (Scheveningen)	Year	115.00
Father's Day		
1972 Father & Son (Volendam)	1,500	40.00
1973 Father & Son (Hindeloopen)	2,000	40.00
1974 Father & Son (Marken)	1,000	80.00
1975 Father & Son (Zuid-Beveland)	Year	80.00
1976 Father & Son (Spakenburg)	Year	140.00
Easter		
1973 Dutch Easter Palm (7")	3,500	75.00
1973 Dutch Easter Palm (10")	3,500	NA
1974 Dutch Easter Palm	1,000	110.00
1975 Dutch Easter Palm	1,000	125.00
1976 Dutch Easter Palm	1,000	175.00
Valentine		
1973 Enduring Beauty	1,500	75.00
1974 Valentine	1,000	125.00
1975 Valentine	1,000	125.00
1976 Valentine	1,000	175.00
Special Bicentenary		
1976 George Washington	2,500	350.00
1976 Eagle Plate	5,000	150.00
(Single issue)		
1986 Halley's Comet	NA	100.00

	Edition Limit	Issue Price (US)

Schoonhoven
See: Blue Delft (Neth.)

Shuler International
See: Kurz (Neth.)

Zenith Delftware

Hans Brinker
| 1972 Skating | 500 | 60.00 |
| 1973 Gretel Tending Geese | 750 | 60.00 |

Anniversary
1973 Autumn	500	45.00
1973 Spring	500	45.00
1973 Summer	500	45.00
1973 Winter	500	45.00

Birthday Boy
1973 Monday's Child	3,000	15.00
1973 Tuesday's Child	3,000	15.00
1973 Wednesday's Child	3,000	15.00
1973 Thursday's Child	3,000	15.00
1973 Friday's Child	3,000	15.00
1973 Saturday's Child	3,000	15.00
1973 Sunday's Child	3,000	15.00

Birthday Girl
1973 Monday's Child	3,000	15.00
1973 Tuesday's Child	3,000	15.00
1973 Wednesday's Child	3,000	15.00
1973 Thursday's Child	3,000	15.00
1973 Friday's Child	3,000	15.00
1973 Saturday's Child	3,000	15.00
1973 Sunday's Child	3,000	15.00

NORWAY

Porsgrund

(Single issue)
| 1909 Christmas Flowers | Year | NA |

Father's Day
1971 Fishing	Year	10.00
1972 Cookout	Year	10.00
1973 Sledding	Year	10.00
1974 Father and Son	Year	10.00
1975 Skating	Year	12.50
1976 Skiing	Year	15.00
1977 Soccer	Year	16.50
1978 Canoeing	Year	17.50
1979 Father and Daughter	Year	19.50
1980 Sailing	Year	21.50
1981 Building a Ship	Year	24.00
1982 Father and Daughter	Year	26.00
1983 Father's Day	Year	26.00
1984 Tree Planting	Year	25.00

Easter
1972 Ducks	Year	7.00
1973 Birds	Year	10.00
1974 Rabbits	Year	11.00
1975 Chicks	Year	16.00
1976 Sheep in Field	Year	18.00
1977 Butterflies	Year	23.00

Christmas
| 1983 Christmas Night | Year | 42.00 |
| 1984 Christmas Sheaf | Year | 40.00 |

SPAIN

Lladro

Christmas
1971 Caroling	Year	27.50
1972 Carolers	Year	35.00
1973 Boy and Girl	Year	45.00
1974 Carolers	Year	55.00
1975 Cherubs	Year	60.00
1976 Christ Child	Year	60.00
1977 Nativity Scene	Year	80.00
1978 Caroling Child	Year	80.00
1979 Snow Dance	Year	90.00

Santa Clara

Christmas
1970 Christmas Message	10,000	18.00
1971 Three Wise Men	10,000	18.00
1972 Children in Woods	10,000	20.00
1973 Archangel	5,000	25.00
1974 Spirit of Christmas	10,000	25.00
1975 Christmas Eve in Country	10,000	27.50
1976 Madonna and Child	10,000	25.00
1977 Mother and Child	10,000	27.50

	Edition Limit	Issue Price (US)
1978 Angel with Flowers	10,000	32.00
1979 Madonna and Angels	10,000	34.50

Mother's Day
| 1971 Mother and Child | 10,000 | 15.00 |
| 1972 Mother and Children | 12,000 | 15.00 |

SWEDEN

Kosta

Annual
1971 Madonna & Child	Year	30.00
1972 St. George & Dragon	Year	30.00
1973 Viking Ship	Year	40.00
1974 Annual	Year	40.00

Orrefors

Mother's Day
1971 Flowers for Mother	2,500	45.00
1972 Mother and Children	2,500	45.00
1973 Mother and Child	2,500	50.00
1974 Mother and Child	5,000	50.00
1975 Mother and Child	2,500	60.00
1976 Children and Puppy	2,500	75.00
1977 Child and Dove	1,500	85.00
1978 Mother and Child	1,500	90.00

Rörstrand

Christmas
1904 Christmas Night in Stockholm	Year	.27
1905 Porridge Dish for Tomten	Year	.27
1906 Star Boys Singing to Lucia	Year	.27
1907 Christmas Eve in Lapland	Year	.27
1908 Christmas Eve with Christmas Roses	Year	.27
1909 Christmas Star over Jerusalem	Year	.27
1910 Christmas Tree	Year	.27
1911 Christmas Bells and Angel	Year	.56
1912 Christmas Service	Year	.56
1913 Christmas Day Early Service Trip	Year	.56
1914 Returning Home	Year	.56
1915 On Way to Church	Year	.56
1916 Kneeling Shepherd	Year	.56
1917 Three Kings Following Star	Year	.56
1918 Sleigh-ride in Dalecarlia	Year	.87
1919 Christmas on Snow Mountain	Year	.87
1920 Mary and Child Jesus	Year	.87
1921 Knight Offering Prayers	Year	.87
1922 Christmas Bells on Gotland	Year	.87
1923 Christmas Sheaf	Year	.87
1924 Tomtefar Bearing Gifts	Year	.87
1925 Christmas Star and Angels	Year	.87

Mother's Day
1971 Mother & Child	Year	15.00
1972 Shelling Peas	Year	15.00
1973 Old Fashioned Picnic	Year	16.00
1974 Candle Lighting	Year	18.00
1975 Pontius on Floor	Year	20.00
1976 Apple Picking	Year	20.00
1977 Kitchen	Year	27.50
1978 Azalea	Year	27.50
1979 Studio Idyll	Year	31.50
1980 Lisbeth	Year	31.50
1981 Karin with Brita	Year	42.50
1982 Mother's Day	Year	36.00
1983 Little Girl	Year	42.50
1984 Mother and Crafts	Year	42.50

Father's Day
1971 Father & Child	Year	15.00
1972 Meal at Home	Year	15.00
1973 Tilling Fields	Year	16.00
1974 Fishing	Year	18.00
1975 Painting	Year	20.00
1976 Plowing	Year	20.00
1977 Sawing	Year	27.50
1978 Self Portrait	Year	27.50
1979 Bridge	Year	31.50

	Edition Limit	Issue Price (US)
1980 My Etch-Nook	Year	31.50
1981 Esbjorn with Playmate	Year	42.50
1982 Father's Day	Year	36.00
1983 Man Painting	Year	42.50
1984 Farm Life	Year	42.50

Christmas Poetry
1979 Silent Night, Holy Night	NA	173.00
1980 Three Holy Kings	NA	180.00
1981 O Holy Night	NA	280.00
1982 Shepherds in Bethlehem	NA	280.00

UNITED STATES

Abbey Press (Viletta)

Mother's Day
| 1979 Special Mothers Are God's Creation | 6,000 | 37.50 |

Christmas
| 1979 Christmas Is a Gentle Season | 6,000 | 37.50 |

Accent on Art

Mother Goose
| 1978 Jack & Jill | 5,000 | 59.50 |

Nobility of Plains
| 1978 Commanche | 12,500 | 80.00 |
| 1979 Moving Day | 3,500 | 80.00 |

Addams Family (Schmid)

Mother's Day
| 1972 On Tracks | Year | 10.00 |

Christmas
| 1972 Christmas Dinner | Year | 10.00 |

Allison

Nature's Beauty
| 1981 Winter's Peace | 7,500 | 70.00 |
| 1982 Summer's Joy | 7,500 | 70.00 |

Late to Party
1982 Piece of Cake	12,500	35.00
1983 Cheese Please	12,500	35.00
1983 Toast to a Mouse	12,500	35.00

American Archives (International Silver)

(Single issue)
| 1972 Christmas Rose | 2,500 | 100.00 |

American Artists

Famous Stallions
| 1983 Black Stallion | 19,500 | 49.50 |
| 1983 Andalusian | 19,500 | 49.50 |

Feathered Friends
| 1983 Parakeets | 19,500 | 29.50 |

Mother and Child Cats
| 1983 Kitty Love | 19,500 | 29.50 |

Noble Tribes
1983 Algonquin	19,500	49.50
1984 Sioux	19,500	49.50
1985 Cheyenne	9,500	49.50

Saturday Evening Post Covers
| 1983 Santa's Computer | 15 Days | 29.50 |

Sport of Kings
1984 Man O' War	9,500	65.00
1984 Secretariat	9,500	65.00
1985 John Henry	9,500	65.00
1985 Seattle Slew	9,500	65.00

Zoe's Cats
1984 Sniffer	12,500	29.50
1985 Waiting	12,500	29.50
1985 Sunshine	12,500	29.50
1985 Tarzan	12,500	29.50

Flower Fantasies
| 1985 Spring Blossoms | 15 Days | 24.50 |
| 1986 Cascade of Flowers | 9,500 | 27.50 |

Mare and Foal
1985 Water Trough	12,500	49.50
1985 Tranquility	12,500	49.50
1986 Pasture Pest	12,500	49.50

Feline Fantasies
| 1986 Summer Breeze | NA | 29.95 |
| 1986 May Queen | NA | 29.95 |

Cats for Cat Lovers
| 1987 Romeo and Juliet | NA | 29.95 |

	Edition Limit	Issue Price (US)

(Single issue)
| 1986 "The Shoe" | 9,500 | 75.00 |

American Arts Services (Viletta)

Children
| 1979 Last of Ninth | 5,000 | 45.00 |

American Commemorative (Gorham)

Southern Landmark
1973 Monticello	9,800	35.00
1973 Williamsburg	9,800	40.00
1974 Beauvoir	9,800	40.00
1974 Cabildo	9,800	40.00
1975 Hermitage	9,800	40.00
1975 Oak Hill	9,800	40.00
1976 Governor Tryon's Palace	9,800	40.00
1976 Montpelier	9,800	40.00
1977 Elmscourt	9,800	40.00
1977 Ashland	9,800	40.00
1978 Mt. Vernon	9,800	40.00
1978 White House	9,800	40.00
1979 Custis Lee	9,800	40.00
1979 Drayton Hall	9,800	40.00
1980 Fort Hall	9,800	40.00
1980 Liberty Hall	9,800	40.00

American Express (Gorham)

Four Freedoms
1976 Freedom to Worship	Year	37.50
1976 Freedom from Want	Year	37.50
1976 Freedom from Fear	Year	37.50
1976 Freedom of Speech	Year	37.50

Birds of North America
1978 Saw Whet Owls	9,800	38.00
1978 Bobwhite Quail	9,800	38.00
1978 October Cardinals	9,800	38.00
1978 Long-Eared Owl	9,800	38.00
1978 Eastern Bluebirds	9,800	38.00
1978 American Woodcock	9,800	38.00
1978 Ruffed Grouse	9,800	38.00
1978 House Wren	9,800	38.00

American Express (Lenox)

American Trees of Christmas
| 1976 Douglas Fir | Year | 60.00 |
| 1977 Scotch Pine | Year | 60.00 |

American Heritage Art (Crown Parian)

Battle Wagon
1982 General Quarters	15,000	39.50
1983 Last Cruise	11,103	39.50
1984 Delaware	10,000	39.50
1984 Kentucky	10,000	39.50

Celebrity Clowns
1982 Emmett	12,500	50.00
1982 Judy	12,500	50.00
1982 Jimmy	12,500	50.00
1982 Shark	12,500	50.00

Early American Sail
1982 Squall	5,000	39.50
1983 Young America	5,000	39.50
1984 Ironsides	5,000	39.50
1984 Charles W. Morgan	5,000	39.50

Lil Critters
1982 Inquisitive	10,000	39.50
1982 Sassy	10,000	39.50
1983 Vigilance	10,000	39.50
1983 Chatty	10,000	39.50

Vanishing West
1982 Hell Bent	5,000	60.00
1983 Cold Trail	5,000	60.00
1983 Horse Stick Medicine	5,000	60.00
1984 Letting 'em Blow	5,000	60.00
1984 Eyeing Back Trail	5,000	60.00

Africa's Beauties
| 1983 Elephant Family | 5,000 | 65.00 |
| 1983 Zebra Family | 5,000 | 65.00 |

America's Heritage of Flight
1983 Kitty Hawk	5,000	39.50
1983 Jenny	5,000	39.50
1984 Race	5,000	39.50
1984 Corsair	5,000	39.50

Craftsman Heritage
1983 Decoy Maker	5,000	39.50
1983 Sailmaker	5,000	39.50
1983 Farmer	5,000	39.50
1984 Platemaker	5,000	39.50

	Edition Limit	Issue Price (US)
1984 Blacksmith	5,000	39.50
1984 Spinning Wheel	5,000	39.50
1985 Gunsmith	5,000	39.50

Equestrian Love
1983 Arabian Destiny	5,000	39.50
1983 Quarterhorse Wrangler	5,000	39.50
1984 Arab Destiny	5,000	39.50

Sawdust Antics
1983 Emmett's 8 Ball	5,000	50.00
1983 Emmett with a Bang	5,000	50.00
1984 Emmett at Races	5,000	50.00
1984 Emmett at Plate	5,000	50.00

Clown Antics
1984 Comedy	10,000	19.50
1984 Tragedy	10,000	19.50

Endangered
1984 Sidney	10,000	19.50
1984 Chein	10,000	19.50

Homer's Antics
1984 Homer at Races	10,000	39.50
1984 Homer on Wall Street	10,000	39.50

Indian Greats
1984 Two Moons	10,000	19.50
1984 Chief Joseph	10,000	19.50

Kitty Kats
1984 Pansy and Sammy	10,000	19.50

Whimsical Moments
1984 Three's Company	NA	29.50

American Historical Plates (Castleton China)

Aviation
1972 Amelia Earhart	3,500	40.00
1972 Charles Lindberg	3,500	40.00

American Preservation Guild (Gorham)

Catesby Collection
1977 Cardinal	9,900	39.00

American Rose Society (Gorham)

All-American Rose
1975 Oregold	9,800	39.00
1975 Arizona	9,800	39.00
1975 Rose Parade	9,800	39.00
1976 America	9,800	39.00
1976 Cathedral	9,800	39.00
1976 Seashell	9,800	39.00
1977 Yankee Doodle	9,800	39.00
1977 Double Delight	9,800	39.00
1977 Prominent	9,800	39.00
1978 First Edition	9,800	39.00
1978 Color Magic	9,800	39.00
1978 Charisma	9,800	39.00
1979 Paradise	9,800	39.00
1979 Sundowner	9,800	39.00
1979 Friendship	9,800	39.00
1980 Love	9,800	39.00
1980 Honor	9,800	39.00
1980 Cherish	9,800	39.00
1981 Bing Crosby	9,800	49.00
1981 White Lightnin'	9,800	49.00
1981 Marina	9,800	49.00
1982 Shreveport	9,800	49.00
1982 French Lace	9,800	49.00
1982 Brandy	9,800	49.00
1983 Mon Cheri	9,800	49.00
1983 Sun Flare	9,800	49.00
1983 Sweet Surrender	9,800	49.00
1984 Olympiad	9,800	49.00
1984 Impatient	9,800	49.00
1984 Intrigue	9,800	49.00
1985 Showbiz	9,800	49.00
1985 Peace	9,800	49.00
1985 Queen Elizabeth	9,800	49.00

Antique Trader

Currier & Ives
1969 Baseball	2,000	9.00
1969 Franklin Experiment	2,000	9.00
1969 Haying Time	2,000	9.00
1969 Winter in Country	2,000	9.00

Easter
1971 Child and Lamb	1,500	10.95
1972 Shepherd with Lamb	1,000	10.95

Mother's Day
1971 Madonna and Child	1,500	10.95
1972 Mother Cat and Kittens	1,000	10.95

Father's Day
	Edition Limit	Issue Price (US)
1971 Pilgrim Father	1,500	10.95
1972 Deer Family	1,000	10.95

Thanksgiving
1971 Pilgrims	1,500	10.95
1972 First Thanksgiving	1,000	10.95

Christmas
1971 Christ Child	1,500	10.95
1972 Flight into Egypt	1,000	10.95

C. M. Russell
1971 Bad One	2,000	11.95
1971 Discovery of Last Chance Gulch	2,000	11.95
1971 Doubtful Visitor	2,000	11.95
1971 Innocent Allies	2,000	11.95
1971 Medicine Man	2,000	11.95

Bible
1973 David & Goliath	2,000	10.75
1973 Moses & Golden Idol	2,000	10.75
1973 Noah's Ark	2,000	10.75
1973 Samson	2,000	10.75

Arizona Artisan

Christmas
1974 Mexican Christmas	Year	20.00
1975 Navajo Christmas	Year	20.00

Thanksgiving
1975 Navajo Thanksgiving Feast	Year	15.00

Arlington Mint

Christmas
1972 Hands in Prayer	Year	125.00

Armstrong's

(Single issue)
1983 Seventy Years Young	15,000	85.00

Huggable Puppies
1984 Take Me Home	10,000	29.50
1985 Oh How Cute	10,000	29.50

Lovable Kittens
1984 Cat's Meow	10,000	29.50
1984 Purr-Swayed	10,000	29.50
1985 Prince of Purrs	10,000	29.50
1986 Pet and I'll Purr	10,000	29.50

Three Graces
1984 Thalia	10,000	49.50
1986 Aglia	7,500	49.50
1987 Euphrosyne	10,000	49.50

(Single issue)
1984 Freddie Torchbearer	15,000	62.50

Companions
1985 All Bark and No Bite	10,000	29.50

Reflections of Innocence
1985 Me and My Friend	10,000	37.50
1985 My RainBeau	10,000	37.50

Statue of Liberty
1985 Dedication Ceremony	10,000	39.50
1985 Immigrants	10,000	39.50
1985 Independence	10,000	39.50
1985 Re-Dedication	10,000	39.50

(Single issue)
1985 Pete Rose	10,000	45.00

Signature Collection
1986 Anyone for Tennis?	10,000	62.50

Infinite Love
1987 Once Upon a Smile	10,000	45.00

Buckhill Bears
1986 Tiddlywink and Pixie	10,000	29.50
1986 Rebecca and Friend	10,000	29.50

Zodiac Collection
1986 Pisces	NA	35.00
1986 Capricorn	NA	35.00
1986 Cancer	NA	35.00
1986 Virgo	NA	35.00

Art World of Bourgeault

Royal Literary Series
1986 John Bunyan Cottage	4,500	60.00
1987 Thomas Hardy Cottage	4,500	65.00

English Countryside Collection
1984 The Country Squire	1,500	150.00
1985 The Willows	1,500	150.00

(Single issue)
1986 Lilac Cottage	500	200.00

Artists of the World

Ruffin Annual
	Edition Limit	Issue Price (US)
1976 Navajo Lullaby	10,000	40.00
1977 Through Years	5,000	45.00
1978 Child of Pueblo	5,000	50.00
1979 Colima Madonna	5,000	50.00
1980 Sun Kachina	5,000	50.00
1981 Inner Peace	5,000	55.00
1982 Madonna of Cross	5,000	60.00
1983 Navajo Princess	5,000	60.00
1984 Americans All	7,500	60.00

World of Game Birds
1977 Mallards	5,000	45.00
1978 Gambel Quail	5,000	45.00
1979 American Autumn Ring-necked Pheasant	5,000	50.00
1980 November Journey-Canada Geese	5,000	50.00

Don Ruffin Self-Portrait
1979 Clown Also Cries	7,500	65.00

Children of Don Ruffin
1980 Flowers for Mother	7,500	50.00
1981 Little Eagle	7,500	55.00
1982 Lost Moccasins	7,500	60.00
1983 Security	7,500	60.00
1984 Americans All	7,500	60.00

Prowlers of Clouds
1981 Great Horned Owl	5,000	55.00
1981 Screech Owl	5,000	55.00
1982 Bald Eagle	5,000	60.00
1982 Golden Eagle	5,000	60.00

Anthony Sidoni
1982 Little Yankee	15,000	35.00
1983 Little Satchmo	15,000	40.00

Vel Miller
1982 Mama's Rose	15,000	35.00
1983 Papa's Boy	15,000	40.00

Woodland Friends
1983 Whitetail Deer	5,000	60.00
1984 Black Bear	5,000	60.00
1984 No Rest for Night Shift	5,000	60.00
1985 No Peace in Paradise	5,000	60.00

(Single issue)
1983 DeGrazia and His Mountain	15,000	65.00

Sweet-Hearts
1984 We Believe	10,000	40.00

(Single issue)
1984 Girl Paints DeGrazia	12,500	65.00

DeGrazia's Children at Play
1985 My First Horse	15,000	65.00
1986 Girl with Sewing Machine	15,000	65.00

Audubon Crystal

Endangered Birds
1976 Kirtland's Warbler	5,000	195.00
1976 American Eagle	5,000	195.00
1977 Peregrine Falcon	5,000	200.00

Avondale

Cameos of Childhood
1978 Melissa	28,050	65.00
1979 First Born	12,000	70.00
1980 Melissa's Brother	Year	70.00
1981 Daddy and I	Year	75.00

Myths of Sea
1979 Poseidon	15,000	70.00
1980 Maiden of Sea	15,000	75.00

Tribute to Ageless Art
1979 Court Jesters	10,000	70.00

World of Dance
1979 Prima Ballerina	15,000	70.00

Christmas
1981 And Heavens Rejoiced	6,500	90.00
1982 And There Came Wise Men	6,500	90.00
1983 Shepherd	6,500	90.00

Growing Up
1982 Ribbon for Her Hair	6,500	75.00
1983 Just Like Mother	6,500	75.00

See also: Judaic Heritage Society (U.S.A.)

B & J Art Designs

Old Fashioned Christmas
	Edition Limit	Issue Price (US)
1983 Carol	15,000	45.00
1984 Chris	15,000	45.00
1985 Noel	15,000	45.00

Country
1984 Cristina	20,000	39.00
1985 Laurel	20,000	42.50

Beacon Manufacturing

Pacesetters
1987 Frederick Douglass	2,500	50.00
1987 Marcus Garvey	5,000	50.00
1987 Mary McLeod Bethune	NA	50.00

Blue River Mill Publishing Co.

Once Upon a Barn
1986 Mail Pouch	5,000	45.00
1987 Rock City	5,000	45.00
1987 Meramec caverns	5,000	45.00
1988 Coca-Cola	5,000	45.00

Brantwood Collection

Marian Carlsen Mother's Day
1978 Jennifer and Jenny Fur	Year	45.00
1979 Football Brothers	5,000	45.00

Howe Christmas
1978 Visit from Santa	Year	45.00

(Single issue)
1978 Tribute to Rockwell	Year	35.00

John Falter Christmas
1979 Christmas Morning	5,000	24.50

Rockwell Mother's Day
1979 Homecoming	20,000	39.50

Little Clown
1979 Going to Circus	5,000	29.50

Braymer Hall

Childhood Sonatas
1981 Serenade	15,000	28.50
1982 Prelude	15,000	28.50
1982 Caprice	15,000	28.50

American Folk
1982 Spring Celebration	10,000	24.50
1982 Summer Bounty	10,000	24.50

Yesterday's Dreams
1983 Swing Quartet	5,000	50.00
1983 Sleigh Belles	5,000	50.00

Brentwood Fine Arts (Fairmont)

Nostalgic Memories
1982 Amy	12,500	39.50

Briarcrest

Good Ole Summertime
1982 Watermelon Eater	10 Days	42.00

This Ole Bear
1982 Chauncey James	5,000	45.00

(Single issue)
1982 Carousel	10,000	35.00

Brimark Ltd.

Yetta's Holidays
1986 Christmas Block	NA	29.50

John Brindle Fine Arts

Fantasy in Motion
1978 Little Blue Horse	3,000	75.00
1979 Horse of a Different Color	3,000	75.00
1980 Horse with Golden Horn	3,000	75.00

Moods of Orient
1978 Softly, Sun Sets	4,000	75.00
1980 Tranquil Morn	4,000	75.00

Expressions
1979 Quiet Eyes	3,000	60.00

(Single issue)
1980 Homage	2,500	125.00

Those Precious Years
1980 Little Curt and Friend	3,000	60.00

Cabochon

Nancy Doyle's Candy Girls

	Edition Limit	Issue Price (US)
1983 Rebecca	15,000	50.00
1984 Shantelle	15,000	50.00
1984 Kelly Ann	15,000	50.00

Calhoun's Collectors Society

Crystal Maidens

	Edition Limit	Issue Price (US)
1979 Spring–Strawberry Season	2,500	49.50
1979 Summer–Sunshine Season	2,500	49.50
1979 Autumn–Scenic Season	2,500	49.50
1979 Winter–Snowflake Season	2,500	49.50

Calhoun's Collectors Society (Schumann)

Imperial Christmas

	Edition Limit	Issue Price (US)
1979 Liebling	10,000	65.00
1980 Hallelujah	10,000	65.00
1981 Stille Nacht	10,000	65.00
1982 Winter Melodie	10,000	75.00

California Porcelain, Inc.

Best of Sascha

	Edition Limit	Issue Price (US)
1979 Flower Bouquet	7,500	65.00

Vanishing Animals

	Edition Limit	Issue Price (US)
1979 Asian Monarchs	7,500	40.00
1979 Snow Leopards	7,500	45.00
1980 Pandas	7,500	45.00
1981 Polar Bears	7,500	50.00

(Single issue)

	Edition Limit	Issue Price (US)
1983 Koala	5,000	29.95

Now Is Moment

	Edition Limit	Issue Price (US)
1984 Be Still	12,500	35.00

Seed of People

	Edition Limit	Issue Price (US)
1984 Keenah	10,000	29.95

Carmel Collection

Famous Parades

	Edition Limit	Issue Price (US)
1983 Thanksgiving Day Parade	Year	39.50

First Performances

	Edition Limit	Issue Price (US)
1983 Darling Diana	19,500	39.50

Joys of Childhood

	Edition Limit	Issue Price (US)
1983 Christmas Delight	19,500	39.50

Memories of Heart

	Edition Limit	Issue Price (US)
1984 Petals	15,000	28.50

Carson Mint (Viletta)

Yesterday's Children

	Edition Limit	Issue Price (US)
1978 Lisa and Jumeau Doll	5,000	60.00
1979 Adrianne and Bye-Lo Baby	5,000	60.00
1980 Lydia and Shirley Temple Doll	5,000	60.00
1981 Melanie and Scarlett O'Hara Doll	5,000	60.00

Hollywood Squares

	Edition Limit	Issue Price (US)
1979 Peter Marshall	100 Days	28.50
1980 George Gobel	100 Days	28.50

Moment in Time

	Edition Limit	Issue Price (US)
1979 Freedom Flight	5,000	55.00

Old Fashioned Mother's Day

	Edition Limit	Issue Price (US)
1979 Daisies from Mary-Beth	20 Days	37.50
1980 Daisies from Jimmy	20 Days	37.50
1981 Daisies from Meg	20 Days	37.50
1982 Daisies for Mommie	20 Days	37.50

America Has Heart

	Edition Limit	Issue Price (US)
1980 My Heart's Desire	Year	24.50
1981 Hearts and Flowers	Year	24.50
1982 Hearty Sailer	Year	28.50
1983 Shannon's Sweetheart	Year	28.50

Magic Afternoon

	Edition Limit	Issue Price (US)
1980 Enchanted Garden	5,000	39.50
1981 Delightful Tea Party	5,000	39.50

Big Top

	Edition Limit	Issue Price (US)
1981 White Face	60 Days	28.50
1982 Tramp	60 Days	28.50

Littlest Christmas

	Edition Limit	Issue Price (US)
1982 Littlest Stocking	12,500	29.50
1983 Littlest Santa	12,500	29.50

Nature's Children

	Edition Limit	Issue Price (US)
1982 Candice	12,500	29.50
1983 Cory	12,500	29.50
1984 Ryan's Retreat	12,500	29.50

Bear Feats

	Edition Limit	Issue Price (US)
1983 Teddy Bear Picnic	15,000	37.50
1984 On Beach	15,000	37.50

To Mom with Love

	Edition Limit	Issue Price (US)
1983 A Basket of Love	15,000	37.50

Castleton China

Natural History

	Edition Limit	Issue Price (US)
1973 Painted Lady	1,500	40.00
1973 Roseate Spoonbill	1,500	40.00

(Single issue)

	Edition Limit	Issue Price (US)
1976 Gen. Douglas MacArthur	1,000	30.00

Castleton China (Shenango)

Bicentennial

	Edition Limit	Issue Price (US)
1972 New Dawn	7,600	60.00
1972 Turning Point	7,600	60.00
1973 Valley Forge	7,600	60.00
1973 Declaration	7,600	60.00
1973 Star Spangled Banner	7,600	60.00
1973 U.S.S. Constitution	7,600	60.00
1974 One Nation	7,600	60.00
1974 Westward Ho	7,600	60.00

See also: American Historical Plates (U.S.A.)

Caverswall

See: Ghent Collection (U.S.A.)

Ceramic Art Studios

(Single issue)

	Edition Limit	Issue Price (US)
1986 Chessie	9,000	60.00

Certified Rarities

Indian Dancer

	Edition Limit	Issue Price (US)
1978 Eagle Dancer	2,500	300.00
1979 Hoop Dancer	2,500	300.00

Postal Artists

	Edition Limit	Issue Price (US)
1978 Colias Eurydice	15,000	60.00
1979 Euphydryas Phaeton	7,500	60.00

Renaissance Masters

	Edition Limit	Issue Price (US)
1978 Alba Madonna	15,000	55.00
1979 Pieta	5,000	55.00

Chilmark

Family Christmas

	Edition Limit	Issue Price (US)
1978 Trimming Tree	10,000	65.00

In Appreciation

	Edition Limit	Issue Price (US)
1979 Flowers of Field	10,000	65.00

Holy Night

	Edition Limit	Issue Price (US)
1979 Wisemen	10,000	65.00

Twelve Days of Christmas

	Edition Limit	Issue Price (US)
1979 Partridge in Pear Tree	10,000	89.50

Christian Fantasy Collectibles

Christian Fantasy

	Edition Limit	Issue Price (US)
1985 Legend/Prayer Bear I	5,100	50.00
1986 Legend/Prayer Bear II	5,100	50.00
1987 Legend/Prayer Bear III	5,100	50.00

Fantasy Cookbook

	Edition Limit	Issue Price (US)
1986 Picnic in Woods	7,100	50.00

Realms of Wonder

	Edition Limit	Issue Price (US)
1986 Wizard's Glade	9,100	50.00
1987 Mermaid's Grotto	9,100	50.00

Santa's Night Out

	Edition Limit	Issue Price (US)
1986 Santa Daydreams	9,100	50.00

Cleveland Mint

Da Vinci

	Edition Limit	Issue Price (US)
1972 Last Supper	5,000	125.00

Collector Creations (Reed & Barton)

Thomas Nast Christmas

	Edition Limit	Issue Price (US)
1973 Christmas	750	100.00

(Single issue)

	Edition Limit	Issue Price (US)
1973 Alice in Wonderland	750	100.00

Collector's Heirlooms (Fairmont)

Children at Play

	Edition Limit	Issue Price (US)
1979 Maple Leaf Noses	7,500	60.00

Passing of Plains Indians

	Edition Limit	Issue Price (US)
1979 Cheyenne Chieftain	5,000	65.00

Collector's Heirlooms (Viletta)

Childhood Memories

	Edition Limit	Issue Price (US)
1978 Jennifer by Candlelight	5,000	60.00
1979 Brian's Birthday	5,000	60.00

Joys of Motherhood

	Edition Limit	Issue Price (US)
1978 Crystal's Joy	7,500	60.00

Collectors Weekly

American

	Edition Limit	Issue Price (US)
1971 Miss Liberty	500	12.50
1972 Miss Liberty	900	12.50
1973 Eagle	900	9.75

Commemorative Imports

M. Seeley's French Fashion Dolls

	Edition Limit	Issue Price (US)
1986 Goldonna	5,000	39.00
1986 Schamare	5,000	39.00
1986 Jewelette	5,000	39.00

Concordia Publishing House

Life of Christ

	Edition Limit	Issue Price (US)
1987 Baptism of Jesus	7,500	34.95

Continental Mint

Tom Sawyer

	Edition Limit	Issue Price (US)
1976 Taking His Medicine	5,000	60.00
1977 Painting Fence	5,000	60.00
1978 Lost in Cave	5,000	60.00
1979 Smoking Pipe	5,000	60.00

(Single issue)

	Edition Limit	Issue Price (US)
1979 Butter Girl	7,000	60.00

Creative World

Pearl Buck (Single issue)

	Edition Limit	Issue Price (US)
1972 Good Earth	10,000	NA

Four Seasons

	Edition Limit	Issue Price (US)
1972 Fall (Silverplate)	2,000	75.00
1972 Fall (Sterling)	2,000	125.00
1973 Winter (Silverplate)	2,000	75.00
1973 Winter (Sterling)	250	125.00
1973 Spring (Silverplate)	300	75.00
1973 Spring (Sterling)	750	125.00
1974 Summer (Silverplate)	300	75.00
1974 Summer (Sterling)	750	125.00

Brown's Rockwells

	Edition Limit	Issue Price (US)
1977 Looking Out to Sea	15,000	50.00
1978 Yankee Doodle	15,000	50.00
1979 Girl at Mirror	15,000	55.00

Immortals of Early American Literature

	Edition Limit	Issue Price (US)
1978 Village Smithy	15,000	50.00
1979 Rip Van Winkle	15,000	55.00

Aesop's Fables

	Edition Limit	Issue Price (US)
1979 Fox & Grapes	9,750	85.00

Living Dolls

	Edition Limit	Issue Price (US)
1982 Eriko and Noriko	9,500	49.50
1983 Ingrid and Ingemar	9,500	49.50

Prize

	Edition Limit	Issue Price (US)
1982 Family Cares	12,500	45.00
1983 Wind in a Frolic	12,500	45.00

Wags to Riches

	Edition Limit	Issue Price (US)
1982 Benji Movie Star	100 Days	29.50
1982 Benji and Tiffany	100 Days	29.50
1983 Merry Christmas Benji	19,500	35.00
1984 Benji's Barbershop Blues	19,500	35.00

Help My Friends

	Edition Limit	Issue Price (US)
1983 Corky's Dream	100 Days	35.00

Crown Parian

Rosemary Calder

	Edition Limit	Issue Price (US)
1978 Affection	7,500	60.00

James Daly

	Edition Limit	Issue Price (US)
1978 Sweet Dreams	7,500	55.00

Beautiful Cats of World

	Edition Limit	Issue Price (US)
1979 Sheena	5,000	60.00
1979 Sheena and Sheena's Cubs	5,000	60.00
1980 Elisheba	5,000	60.00
1980 Elisheba's Cubs	5,000	60.00
1981 Atarah	5,000	60.00
1981 Atarah's Cubs	5,000	60.00
1982 Tamar	5,000	60.00
1982 Tamar's Cubs	5,000	60.00

Penni Anne Cross

	Edition Limit	Issue Price (US)
1979 Crow Baby	7,500	55.00
1981 Paiute Pals	7,500	55.00
1982 Big Sister's Buckskins	7,500	55.00
1984 Navajo Nanny	7,500	55.00

Julian Ritter

	Edition Limit	Issue Price (US)
1979 Reve de Ballet	7,500	55.00

Western

	Edition Limit	Issue Price (US)
1979 Under Surveillance	10,000	65.00
1979 Promised Land	10,000	65.00
1979 Winter Song	10,000	65.00
1979 Boomtown and Wildcatters	10,000	65.00

Sporting Dogs

	Edition Limit	Issue Price (US)
1980 Decoy	5,000	55.00
1981 Dusty	5,000	55.00
1982 Rummy	5,000	55.00
1983 Scarlet	5,000	55.00

Happy Art

	Edition Limit	Issue Price (US)
1981 Woody's Triple Self-Portrait	10,000	39.50
1982 Gothic Woody	10,000	39.50
1984 Blue Boy Woody	10,000	39.50

Portraits of Childhood

	Edition Limit	Issue Price (US)
1981 Miss Murray	7,500	65.00
1984 Master Lambton	10,000	65.00

Children to Love

	Edition Limit	Issue Price (US)
1982 Wendy	10,000	60.00
1983 Jake	10,000	60.00
1984 Katy	10,000	60.00
1985 Jed	10,000	60.00

Owl Family

	Edition Limit	Issue Price (US)
1982 Saw-Whet Owl Family	5,000	55.00
1982 Great Horned Owl Family	5,000	55.00
1983 Snowy Owl Family	5,000	55.00
1983 Barred Owl Family	5,000	55.00

Reflections of Seasons

	Edition Limit	Issue Price (US)
1982 Winter's Dream	7,500	39.50

(Single issue)

	Edition Limit	Issue Price (US)
1982 Buon Natale	1,000	300.00

Special Heart

	Edition Limit	Issue Price (US)
1983 Reaching Together	40,000	35.00
1983 Love in Your Heart	40,000	35.00

Holidays Around the World

	Edition Limit	Issue Price (US)
1984 Elysa's Christmas	12,500	39.50

Songs of Carolyn

	Edition Limit	Issue Price (US)
1985 Quiet Moment	5,000	35.00

See also: American Heritage Art (U.S.A.)

Curator Collection

Masterpieces of Impressionism

	Edition Limit	Issue Price (US)
1980 Woman with a Parasol	17,500	35.00
1981 Young Mother Sewing	17,500	35.00
1982 Sara in Green Bonnet	17,500	35.00
1983 Margot in Blue	17,500	35.00

Masterpieces of West

	Edition Limit	Issue Price (US)
1980 Texas Night Herder	17,500	35.00
1981 Indian Trapper	17,500	35.00
1982 Cowboy Style		
1982 Indian Style (Set of two)	17,500	70.00

Masterpieces of Rockwell

	Edition Limit	Issue Price (US)
1980 After Prom	17,500	35.00
1981 Challenger	17,500	42.50
1981 Girl at Mirror	17,500	50.00
1982 Missing Tooth	17,500	50.00

Jesse's World

	Edition Limit	Issue Price (US)
1981 This Simple Faith	17,500	39.95

Magical Moments

	Edition Limit	Issue Price (US)
1981 Happy Dreams	NA	29.95
1981 Harmony	NA	29.95
1982 His Majesty	NA	29.95
1982 Waiting for Daddy	NA	29.95
1983 Thank You, God	NA	29.95
1983 Lullaby	NA	29.95

Rockwell Americana

	Edition Limit	Issue Price (US)
1981 Shuffleton's Barbershop	17,500	75.00
1982 Breaking Home Ties	17,500	75.00
1983 Walking to Church	17,500	75.00

Special Occasions

	Edition Limit	Issue Price (US)
1981 Bubbles	NA	29.95
1982 Butterflies	NA	29.95

	Edition Limit	Issue Price (US)
Stockbridge Trilogy		
1981 Stockbridge in Winter, Part I	NA	45.00
1982 Stockbridge in Winter, Part II	NA	45.00
1983 Stockbridge in Winter, Part III	NA	45.00
Classic Circus		
1982 Favorite Clown	17,500	39.95
Playful Pets		
1982 Curiosity	10,000	45.00
1982 Master's Hat	10,000	45.00
Tribute		
1982 I Want You	NA	29.95
1982 Gee! I Wish I Were a Man	NA	29.95
1983 Soldier's Farewell	NA	29.95
Becker Babies		
1983 Snowpuff	NA	29.95
1984 Smiling Through	NA	29.95
1984 Pals	NA	29.95
Nursery		
1983 In Slumberland	NA	35.00
1983 Awakening	NA	35.00
Mother's Love		
1984 Contentment	7,500	35.00
On Road		
1984 Pride of Stockbridge	NA	35.00
1985 City Pride	NA	35.00
1985 Country Pride	NA	35.00
Simpler Times		
1984 Lazy Daze	7,500	35.00
Triple Play		
1984 Chums	NA	29.95
1984 Nitey-Nite	NA	29.95
1984 Oh, Oh! A Bunny	NA	29.95
Great Trains		
1985 Santa Fe	7,500	35.00
1985 Twentieth Century Ltd.	7,500	35.00
1986 Empire Builder	7,500	35.00
Portraits of American Brides		
1986 Caroline	10 Days	29.50
1986 Jacqueline	10 Days	29.50
1987 Elizabeth	10 Days	29.50
1987 Emily	10 Days	29.50
1987 Meredith	10 Days	29.50
1987 Laura	10 Days	29.50
1987 Sarah	10 Days	29.50
1987 Rebecca	10 Days	29.50
Portraits (cats)		
1986 Chantilly	NA	24.50
1986 Dynasty	NA	24.50
1986 Velvet	NA	24.50
Sailing Through History		
1986 Flying Cloud	14 Days	29.50
1986 Santa Maria	14 Days	29.50
1986 Mayflower	14 Days	29.50
(Single issue)		
1986 Motherhood	NA	37.50
(Single issue)		
1986 The Christening	NA	37.50
Danbury Mint		
Currier & Ives (Silver)		
1972 Road Winter	7,500	125.00
1973 Central Park Winter	7,500	125.00
1974 Winter in Country	7,500	125.00
1975 American Homestead	7,500	125.00
1976 American Winter-Evening	7,500	135.00
1977 Winter Morning	7,500	135.00
Christmas		
1975 Silent Night	NA	24.50
1976 Joy to World	NA	27.50
1977 Away in Manger	NA	27.50
1978 First Noel	NA	29.50
Bicentennial (Silver)		
1973 Boston Tea Party	7,500	125.00
1974 First Continental Congress	7,500	125.00
1975 Paul Revere's Ride	7,500	125.00
1976 Declaration of Independence	7,500	125.00
1977 Washington at Valley Forge	7,500	125.00

	Edition Limit	Issue Price (US)
1978 Molly Pitcher	7,500	125.00
1979 Bon Homme Richard	7,500	125.00
Michelangelo (Silver)		
1973 Creation of Adam	7,500	125.00
1973 Pieta	7,500	125.00
1973 Moses	7,500	125.00
1973 Holy Family	7,500	125.00
Great Art Masterpieces (Silver)		
1975 Mona Lisa	7,500	125.00
1975 Last Supper	7,500	125.00
1976 Sunflower	7,500	125.00
1976 Blue Boy	7,500	125.00
Derby Collection		
Mischief Makers		
1985 Puddles	10,000	39.95
1985 Buckles	10,000	39.95
Wild Innocence		
1985 My Buddy	5,000	29.95
Designers Collection		
Faerie Seasons		
1984 Meadow Nymph	10,000	29.00
1984 Flower Nymph	10,000	29.00
1984 Arbor Nymph	10,000	29.00
1984 Woodland Nymph	10,000	29.00
Stuart Devlin Silver		
Americana		
1972 Gaspee Incident	1,000	130.00
Walt Disney Productions		
Enchantment of Snow White		
1984 At Wishing Well	15,000	26.50
1984 Dance	15,000	26.50
1984 Witch and Apple	15,000	26.50
1984 Happily Ever After	15,000	26.50
1984 Enchantment of Snow White	15,000	26.50
Disney's Magic Memories		
1986 Snow White/Dwarfs	24,500	37.50
1986 Pinocchio	24,500	37.50
1986 Fantasia	24,500	37.50
1986 Dumbo	24,500	37.50
1986 Bambi	24,500	37.50
1986 Cinderella	24,500	37.50
1986 Alice in Wonderland	24,500	37.50
1986 Peter Pan	24,500	37.50
1986 Lady and Tramp	24,500	37.50
1986 Sleeping Beauty	24,500	37.50
1986 101 Dalmatians	24,500	37.50
1986 Sword in Stone	24,500	37.50
1986 Jungle Book	24,500	37.50
1986 Aristocats	24,500	37.50
1986 Robin Hood	24,500	37.50
1986 Rescuers	24,500	37.50
1986 Fox and Hound	24,500	37.50
Duncan Royale		
History of Santa Claus II		
1986 Lord of Misrule	10,000	80.00
1986 The Alsace Angel	10,000	80.00
Portraits of Santa		
1986 Dedt Moroz	10,000	40.00
1986 Medieval	10,000	40.00
1986 Pioneer	10,000	40.00
1986 Kris Kringle	10,000	40.00
1986 Soda Pop	10,000	40.00
1986 Nast	10,000	40.00
1986 Civil War	10,000	40.00
1986 Wassail	10,000	40.00
1986 St. Nick	10,000	40.00
1986 Russian	10,000	40.00
1986 Black Peter	10,000	40.00
1986 Victorian	10,000	40.00
Ebeling & Reuss		
Christmas		
1981 Waiting for Christmas	7,000	15.00
1982 Time of Song and Caroling	7,500	15.00
(Single issue)		
1983 Love One Another	12,500	17.50

	Edition Limit	Issue Price (US)
Enesco		
Christmas		
1981 Come Let Us Adore Him	15,000	40.00
1982 Heaven and Nature Sing	15,000	40.00
1983 Wee Three Kings	15,000	40.00
1984 Unto Us a Child Is Born	15,000	40.00
Inspired Thoughts		
1981 Love One Another	15,000	40.00
1981 Make a Joyful Noise	15,000	40.00
1982 I Believe in Miracles	15,000	40.00
1983 Love Is Kind	15,000	40.00
Mother's Love		
1981 Mother Sew Dear	15,000	40.00
1982 Purr-fect Grandma	15,000	40.00
1983 Hand That Rocks Future	15,000	40.00
1984 Loving Thy Neighbor	15,000	40.00
Little Bible Friends		
1981 Nativity	25,000	40.00
1982 Flight into Egypt	25,000	40.00
1982 Last Supper	25,000	40.00
Joy of Christmas		
1982 Play My Drum for Him	Year	40.00
1983 Christmas Time	Year	40.00
1984 Wonder of Christmas	Year	40.00
1985 Tell Me Story of Jesus	Year	40.00
Four Seasons		
1985 Voice of Spring	Year	40.00
1985 Summer's Joy	Year	40.00
1986 Autumn's Praise	Year	40.00
1986 Winter's Song	Year	40.00
Christmas Love		
1986 Sending You a White Christmas	NA	45.00
1987 My Peace I Give Unto Thee	Year	45.00
Birds of North America		
1987 Owl	2,500	40.00
Water Birds		
1987 Swan	2,500	40.00
Hummingbird		
1987 Hummingbird with Blue Flower	2,500	40.00
Ernst, Inc.		
Performance		
1979 Act I	5,000	65.00
Women of West		
1979 Expectation	10,000	39.50
1979 Silver Dollar Sal	10,000	39.50
1980 School Marm	10,000	39.50
1980 Dolly	10,000	39.50
Love Is		
1980 Rufus and Roxanne	19,000	14.95
A Beautiful World		
1981 Tahitian Dreamer	27,500	27.50
1982 Flirtation	27,500	27.50
1983 Elke of Oslo	27,500	27.50
Hollywood Greats		
1980 John Wayne	27,500	29.95
1981 Gary Cooper	27,500	29.95
1982 Clark Gable	27,500	29.95
1983 Alan Ladd	27,500	29.95
Classy Cars		
1981 '26 T	20 Days	24.50
1982 Model A	20 Days	24.50
1982 Model A Pickup	20 Days	24.50
1983 Panel Van	20 Days	24.50
Commemoratives		
1981 John Lennon	30 Days	39.50
1981 Elvis Presley	30 Days	39.50
1982 Marilyn Monroe	30 Days	39.50
1983 Judy Garland	30 Days	39.50
A Love Story		
1981 Chapter One	20 Days	24.50
Pinups		
1981 Stars and Stripes Forever	20 Days	24.50
So Young, So Sweet		
1981 Girl with Straw Hat	10 Days	39.50
1982 My Favorite Necklace	10 Days	39.50
1983 Breakfast Time	10 Days	39.50

	Edition Limit	Issue Price (US)
Turn of Century		
1981 Riverboat Honeymoon	10 Days	35.00
1982 Children's Carousel	10 Days	35.00
1982 Flower Market	10 Days	35.00
1983 Ballroom Race	10 Days	35.00
Little Misses Young and Fair		
1982 Heart of a Child	29,000	60.00
1983 Where Wild Flowers Grow	29,000	60.00
1984 Whispered Memories	29,000	60.00
1985 Final Touch	29,000	60.00
Mommie and Me		
1982 First Tea	10 Days	35.00
1983 Baby's Sleeping	10 Days	35.00
My Fair Ladies		
1982 Lady Sabrina	29,000	50.00
1983 Lady Victoria	29,000	50.00
(Single issue)		
1982 Henry Fonda	100 Days	45.00
Fondest Memories		
1983 A Touching Moment	NA	60.00
1984 Mother's Pearls	NA	60.00
Liebchen		
1983 Winter Liebchen	30 Days	19.50
1983 Spring Liebchen	30 Days	19.50
1984 Summer Liebchen	30 Days	19.50
1984 Autumn Liebchen	30 Days	19.50
Narrow Gauge		
1983 Halfway to Alamosa	10 Days	29.50
1984 Down from Rico	10 Days	29.50
Star Trek		
1983 Mr. Spock	90 Days	29.50
1983 Dr. McCoy	90 Days	29.50
1984 Sulu	90 Days	29.50
1984 Scotty	90 Days	29.50
1984 Uhura	90 Days	29.50
1984 Chekov	90 Days	29.50
1985 Captain Kirk	90 Days	29.50
1985 Beam Us Down Scotty	90 Days	29.50
1985 Enterprise	90 Days	29.50
Yesterdays		
1983 Amber	10 Days	24.50
1983 Elmer	10 Days	24.50
1986 Katie	10 Days	24.50
Americana		
1984 Somewhere in Autumn	20 Days	29.50
1985 Crystal Winds	20 Days	29.50
Childhood Memories		
1984 Sometimes an Angel	20 Days	24.50
1985 First Performance	20 Days	24.50
Children of Past		
1984 Buttercup Test	NA	29.50
1984 Minuet	NA	29.50
1986 Boy with Hoop	NA	29.50
Days Ago		
1984 Blue Belle	20 Days	24.50
Fishing Boats		
1984 Sunset at Monterey	10 Days	24.50
1984 Blue Sea	10 Days	24.50
Friends		
1984 I Love You Orville	20 Days	24.50
1985 Cookies for Corky	20 Days	24.50
Romantic Memories		
1984 Sunday Afternoon	14,400	60.00
1985 Freedom	5,000	29.50
1985 Lily	5,000	29.50
Bare Innocence		
1985 Singing in Rain	10 Days	24.50
1985 Free at Last	10 Days	24.50
Go for Gold		
1985 Valerie	5,000	29.50
Me and Mom		
1985 Beach Baby	5,000	29.50
Shades of Time		
1985 Morning Glo	5,000	45.00
1986 Scent and Satin	5,000	45.00
1987 Golden Flame	5,000	45.00
This Land Is Our Land		
1985 Oak Creek Canyon	5,000	29.50
1986 Dunes	5,000	29.50
1986 Emerald Bay	5,000	29.50
1986 Mohave	5,000	29.50

OVER-THE-COUNTER ISSUES

Fogg and Steam

	Edition Limit	Issue Price (US)
1986 Pride of Northwest	7,500	39.50
1986 Autumn in New England	7,500	39.50

Our Country Cousins

	Edition Limit	Issue Price (US)
1986 She's All Yours	NA	24.50
1987 Yep, That's It	NA	24.50

Americana

	Edition Limit	Issue Price (US)
1984 Somewhere in Autumn	5,000	29.50
1986 Spring Magic	5,000	29.50

Vintage Classics

	Edition Limit	Issue Price (US)
1986 Duesenberg	NA	29.50

Elvira

	Edition Limit	Issue Price (US)
1986 Night Rose	NA	29.50

Daddy's Little Girl

	Edition Limit	Issue Price (US)
1986 Look at Me Daddy	90 Days	29.95

Little Farmers

	Edition Limit	Issue Price (US)
1986 You Been Farming Long?	NA	24.50
1987 Are You Pushing, or Pulling?	NA	24.50

The Commemorative Collection

	Edition Limit	Issue Price (US)
1987 Trouble with Tribbles	NA	29.50

Evergreen Press

Catalina Island Series

	Edition Limit	Issue Price (US)
1986 Pleasure Pier	5,000	39.95

Fairmont

Carousel Horses

	Edition Limit	Issue Price (US)
1977 (Set of two)	3,000	80.00

Spencer Annual

	Edition Limit	Issue Price (US)
1977 Patient Ones	10,000	42.50
1978 Yesterday, Today and Tomorrow	10,000	47.50

Irene Spencer's Special Requests

	Edition Limit	Issue Price (US)
1978 Hug Me	10,000	55.00
1978 Sleep Little Baby	10,000	65.00

Olaf Wieghorst

	Edition Limit	Issue Price (US)
1978 Sioux Warrior	5,000	65.00
1979 Indian Scout	5,000	65.00

Rural America

	Edition Limit	Issue Price (US)
1978 Fence	5,000	45.00

Timeless Moments

	Edition Limit	Issue Price (US)
1978 Tenderness	5,000	45.00
1979 Renaissance	5,000	50.00
1980 Coming in Glory	5,000	39.95

Children of America

	Edition Limit	Issue Price (US)
1979 Eskimo Girl	3,000	48.00

Lords of Plains

	Edition Limit	Issue Price (US)
1979 Sitting Bull	5,000	60.00

Rockwell Early Works

	Edition Limit	Issue Price (US)
1979 Old Man Winter	15,000	19.95
1980 Inventor	15,000	19.95
1980 Ready for School	15,000	19.95
1980 Music Master	15,000	19.95
1981 Tinkerer	15,000	19.95

Gnome Holiday

	Edition Limit	Issue Price (US)
1980 Gnome Bliss	5,000	24.50
1981 Gift of Love	5,000	29.95

Gnomes Four Seasons

	Edition Limit	Issue Price (US)
1980 Little Swinger (Spring)	15,000	29.50
1980 Gnome de Bloom (Summer)	15,000	29.50
1980 Lookouts (Fall)	15,000	29.50
1980 First Skater (Winter)	15,000	29.50
1981 Spring Sharing (Spring)	15,000	29.95
1981 Fun and Games (Summer)	15,000	29.95
1981 Up Up and Away (Fall)	15,000	29.95
1981 First Skier (Winter)	15,000	29.95
1982 Gnome Knowledge (Spring)	15,000	29.95
1982 Summer Harvest (Summer)	15,000	29.95
1982 Gnome Family Tailors (Fall)	15,000	29.95
1982 Keep Gnome Fires Burning (Winter)	15,000	29.95

American's Most Beloved (Single issue)

	Edition Limit	Issue Price (US)
1980 John Wayne	5,000	13.95

Long Road West

	Edition Limit	Issue Price (US)
1981 Trailblazers	20,000	40.00
1981 Prairie Schooner	20,000	40.00

	Edition Limit	Issue Price (US)
1981 Pony Express	20,000	40.00
1981 Peacemakers	20,000	40.00
1981 Cowboys of West	20,000	40.00
1981 Lawmen of West	20,000	40.00

When I Grow Up

	Edition Limit	Issue Price (US)
1981 I'll Be Loved	7,500	29.95
1981 I'll Be Like Mommy	7,500	29.95
1982 I'll Be First Lady	7,500	29.95
1982 I'll Be a Star	7,500	29.95

Jansen's International Beauties

	Edition Limit	Issue Price (US)
1982 Lisa	7,500	55.00
1983 Ingrid	7,500	55.00

Vanishing Americana

	Edition Limit	Issue Price (US)
1983 American Eagle	15,000	13.50
1984 Country Doctor	15,000	13.50

(Single issue)

	Edition Limit	Issue Price (US)
1983 I Love Teddy Bears	NA	39.50

(Single issue)

	Edition Limit	Issue Price (US)
1983 My Little Sheltie	5,000	39.95

(Single issue)

	Edition Limit	Issue Price (US)
1983 Organ Grinder	5,000	19.95

Legends of Gnomes

	Edition Limit	Issue Price (US)
1984 Gnome Home	15,000	29.95

Dreams Do Come True

	Edition Limit	Issue Price (US)
1985 Little Ballerina	5,000	29.95

Secrets of the Gnomes

	Edition Limit	Issue Price (US)
1986 Search for the Stradivarius	15,000	29.95
1986 Rommelpots and Air Compressors	15,000	29.95
1986 Noah's Ark and the Gnomes	15,000	29.95
1986 Which Way the Wind Blows	15,000	29.95

Gnomes

	Edition Limit	Issue Price (US)
1987 Gnomatic Fitness	10,000	29.95
1987 Origin of The Newborn	10,000	29.95
1987 Origin of Santa Claus	10,000	29.95
1987 Supreme Justice	10,000	29.95

See also:
Brentwood Fine Arts (U.S.A.)
Collector's Heirlooms (U.S.A.)
Ghent Collection (U.S.A.)
Mistwood Designs (U.S.A.)

Fenton Glass

American Craftsman

	Edition Limit	Issue Price (US)
1970 Glassmaker	Year	10.00
1971 Printer	Year	10.00
1972 Blacksmith	Year	10.00
1973 Shoemaker	Year	10.00
1974 Cooper	Year	11.00
1975 Silversmith	Year	13.50
1976 Gunsmith	Year	13.50
1977 Potter	Year	15.00
1978 Wheelwright	Year	15.00
1979 Cabinetmaker	Year	15.00
1980 Tanner	Year	16.50
1981 Housewright	Year	17.50

Christmas in America

	Edition Limit	Issue Price (US)
1970 Little Brown Church (Blue Satin)	Year	12.50
1970 Little Brown Church (Carnival)	Year	12.50
1970 Little Brown Church (Brown)	Year	17.50
1971 Old Brick Church (Blue Satin)	Year	12.50
1971 Old Brick Church (Brown)	Year	17.50
1971 Old Brick Church (Carnival)	Year	12.50
1971 Old Brick Church (White Satin)	Year	12.50
1972 Two Horned Church (Blue Satin)	Year	12.50
1972 Two Horned Church (Brown)	Year	17.50
1972 Two Horned Church (Carnival)	Year	12.50
1972 Two Horned Church (White Satin)	Year	12.50
1973 St. Mary's (Blue Satin)	Year	12.50
1973 St. Mary's (Carnival)	Year	12.50
1973 St. Mary's (White Satin)	Year	12.50

	Edition Limit	Issue Price (US)
1973 St. Mary's (Brown)	Year	17.50
1974 Nation's Church (Blue Satin)	Year	13.50
1974 Nation's Church (Carnival)	Year	13.50
1974 Nation's Church (White Satin)	Year	13.50
1974 Nation's Church (Brown)	Year	18.50
1975 Birthplace of Liberty (Blue Satin)	Year	13.50
1975 Birthplace of Liberty (Carnival)	Year	13.50
1975 Birthplace of Liberty (White Satin)	Year	13.50
1975 Birthplace of Liberty (Brown)	Year	20.00
1976 Old North Church (Blue Satin)	Year	15.00
1976 Old North Church (Carnival)	Year	15.00
1976 Old North Church (White Satin)	Year	15.00
1976 Old North Church (Brown)	Year	25.00
1977 San Carlos (Blue Satin)	Year	15.00
1977 San Carlos (Carnival)	Year	15.00
1977 San Carlos (White Satin)	Year	15.00
1978 Church of Holy Trinity (Blue Satin)	Year	15.00
1978 Church of Holy Trinity (Carnival)	Year	15.00
1978 Church of Holy Trinity (White Satin)	Year	15.00
1979 San Jose y Miguel de Aguayo (Blue Satin)	Year	15.00
1979 San Jose y Miguel de Aguayo (Carnival)	Year	15.00
1979 San Jose y Miguel de Aguayo (White Satin)	Year	15.00
1980 Christ Church (Blue Satin)	Year	16.50
1980 Christ Church (Carnival)	Year	16.50
1980 Christ Church (White Satin)	Year	16.50
1981 Mission of San Xavier del Bac (Blue Satin)	Year	18.50
1981 Mission of San Xavier del Bac (Carnival)	Year	18.50
1981 Mission of San Xavier del Bac (White Satin)	Year	18.50

Mother's Day

	Edition Limit	Issue Price (US)
1971 Madonna, Sleeping Child (Blue Satin)	Year	12.50
1971 Madonna, Sleeping Child (Carnival)	Year	12.50
1972 Madonna of Goldfinch (Blue Satin)	Year	12.50
1972 Madonna of Goldfinch (Carnival)	Year	12.50
1972 Madonna of Goldfinch (White Satin)	Year	12.50
1973 Cowper Madonna (Blue Satin)	Year	12.50
1973 Cowper Madonna (Carnival)	Year	12.50
1973 Cowper Madonna (White Satin)	Year	12.50
1974 Madonna of Grotto (Blue Satin)	Year	12.50
1974 Madonna of Grotto (Carnival)	Year	12.50
1974 Madonna of Grotto (White Satin)	Year	12.50
1975 Taddei Madonna (Blue Satin)	Year	13.50
1975 Taddei Madonna (Carnival)	Year	13.50
1975 Taddei Madonna (White Satin)	Year	13.50
1976 Holy Night (Blue Satin)	Year	13.50
1976 Holy Night (Carnival)	Year	13.50
1976 Holy Night (White Satin)	Year	13.50
1977 Madonna & Child (Blue Satin)	Year	15.00

	Edition Limit	Issue Price (US)
1977 Madonna & Child (Carnival)	Year	15.00
1977 Madonna & Child (White Satin)	Year	15.00
1978 Madonnina (Blue Satin)	Year	15.00
1978 Madonnina (Carnival)	Year	15.00
1978 Madonnina (White Satin)	Year	15.00
1979 Madonna of Rose Hedge (Blue Satin)	Year	15.00
1979 Madonna of Rose Hedge (Carnival)	Year	15.00
1979 Madonna of Rose Hedge (White Satin)	Year	15.00

Valentine's Day

	Edition Limit	Issue Price (US)
1972 Romeo and Juliet (Blue Satin)	Year	15.00
1972 Romeo and Juliet (Carnival)	Year	15.00

Bicentennial

	Edition Limit	Issue Price (US)
1974 Eagle (Blue Satin)	Year	15.00
1975 Eagle (Red Satin)	Year	15.00
1976 Eagle (Chocolate)	Year	17.50
1976 Eagle (White Satin)	Year	15.00

Alliance

	Edition Limit	Issue Price (US)
1975 Lafayette and Washington (Blue Satin)	Year	15.00
1975 Lafayette and Washington (Red Satin)	Year	17.50
1975 Lafayette and Washington (White Satin)	Year	15.00
1976 Lafayette and Washington (Blue Satin)	Year	15.00
1976 Lafayette and Washington (Chocolate)	Year	17.50
1976 Lafayette and Washington (White Satin)	Year	15.00

Christmas Classics

	Edition Limit	Issue Price (US)
1979 Nature's Christmas	Year	30.00
1980 Going Home	Year	38.50
1981 All Is Calm	Year	42.50
1982 Country Christmas	Year	42.50

Currier & Ives

	Edition Limit	Issue Price (US)
1980 Old Grist Mill	Year	25.00
1981 Harvest	Year	25.00
1982 Old Homestead in Winter	Year	25.00
1983 Winter Pastime	Year	25.00

Mother's Day Classics

	Edition Limit	Issue Price (US)
1980 New Born	Year	28.50
1981 Gentle Fawn	Year	32.50
1982 Nature's Awakening	Year	35.00
1983 Where's Mom?	Year	35.00
1984 Precious Panda	Year	35.00

Artists

	Edition Limit	Issue Price (US)
1982 After Snow	15,000	14.50
1983 Winter Chapel	15,000	15.00

Childhood Treasures

	Edition Limit	Issue Price (US)
1983 Teddy Bear	15,000	15.00
1984 Hobby Horse	15,000	15.00

Christmas Fantasy

	Edition Limit	Issue Price (US)
1983 Anticipation	7,500	45.00
1984 Expectation	7,500	50.00

Designer

	Edition Limit	Issue Price (US)
1983 Down Home	1,000	65.00
1983 Lighthouse Point	1,000	65.00

(Single issue)

	Edition Limit	Issue Price (US)
1986 Statue of Liberty	1,250	75.00

American Classic

	Edition Limit	Issue Price (US)
1987 The Central Pacific Jupiter	5,000	75.00

Fine Arts Marketing Enterprise

Turn . . . Turn . . . Turn . . .

	Edition Limit	Issue Price (US)
1986 Autumn Back Home	5,000	50.00
1986 Winter Memories	5,000	50.00

Autumn Flights

	Edition Limit	Issue Price (US)
1987 Canadians	5,000	55.00
1987 Mallards	5,000	55.00

Firehouse

This Ole Bear
	Edition Limit	Issue Price (US)
1982 Emma Louise	5,000	39.50
1983 Buster and Sam	5,000	39.50
1984 Matilda Jane	5,000	39.50

Fleetwood Collection (Gorham)

Birds and Flowers of Meadow and Garden
	Edition Limit	Issue Price (US)
1980 Robin and Crab Apple Blossom	•	39.00
1980 Goldfinch and Bull Thistle	•	39.00
1980 Cardinal and Wild Lupine	•	39.00
1980 Chickadee and New England Aster	•	39.00
1980 Baltimore Oriole and Morning Glory	•	39.00
1980 Blue Bird and Black-Eyed Susan	•	39.00
1980 Painted Bunting and Blackberry	•	39.00
1980 Golden-Crowned Kinglet and Downey Phlox	•	39.00
1980 Red-Breasted Nuthatch and Japanese Honeysuckle	•	39.00
1980 Magnolia Warbler and Day Lily	•	39.00
1980 Ruby-Throated Hummingbird and Fire Pink	•	39.00
1980 Scarlet Tanager and Blue Columbine	•	39.00

*Subscription period

Christmas
	Edition Limit	Issue Price (US)
1980 Magi	7,500	49.50
1981 Holy Child	7,500	49.50
1982 Shepherds	7,500	49.50

Mother's Day
	Edition Limit	Issue Price (US)
1980 Cottontails	5,000	45.00
1981 Raccoons	5,000	45.00
1982 Whitetail Deer	5,000	50.00
1983 Canada Geese	5,000	50.00

Blossoms of China
	Edition Limit	Issue Price (US)
1981 Azalea	7,500	49.50
1981 Camelia	7,500	49.50
1981 Herbaceous Peony	7,500	49.50
1981 Chrysanthemum	7,500	49.50
1981 Lotus	7,500	49.50
1981 Magnolia	7,500	49.50
1981 Narcissus	7,500	49.50
1981 Orchid	7,500	49.50
1981 Peony	7,500	49.50
1981 Plum Blossom	7,500	49.50
1981 Rose	7,500	49.50
1981 Winter Jasmine	7,500	49.50

Tsarevich's Bride
	Edition Limit	Issue Price (US)
1981 Arrow in Air	7,500	50.00
1982 Boyar's Courtyard	7,500	50.00
1982 Rich Merchant's Yard	7,500	50.00
1983 Mouth of Frog	7,500	50.00

Golden Age of Sail
	Edition Limit	Issue Price (US)
1982 Flying Cloud	5,000	39.00
1982 New World	5,000	39.00
1982 Young America	5,000	39.00
1982 Courier	5,000	39.00
1982 Sea Witch	5,000	39.00
1982 Great Republic	5,000	39.00

(Single issue)
	Edition Limit	Issue Price (US)
1983 Mom's Apple Pie	NA	29.00

(Single issue)
	Edition Limit	Issue Price (US)
1985 Presidential Inaugural	9,500	50.00

Fostoria

American Milestones
	Edition Limit	Issue Price (US)
1971 Betsy Ross Flag	5,000	12.50
1972 National Anthem	8,000	12.50
1973 Washington Crossing Delaware	Year	12.50
1974 Spirit of '76	Year	13.00
1975 Mount Rushmore	Year	16.00

State Plates
	Edition Limit	Issue Price (US)
1971 California	6,000	12.50
1971 New York	12,000	12.50
1971 Ohio	3,000	12.50
1972 Florida	Year	12.50
1972 Hawaii	Year	12.50
1972 Pennsylvania	Year	12.50
1972 Massachusetts	Year	13.00
1972 Texas	Year	13.00
1973 Michigan	Year	13.50

Fountainhead

Wings of Freedom
	Edition Limit	Issue Price (US)
1985 Courtship Flight	2,500	250.00
1986 Wings of Freedom	2,500	250.00

The Seasons
	Edition Limit	Issue Price (US)
1987 Spring Robins	5,000	85.00
1987 Summer Goldfinches	5,000	85.00
1987 Fall Cardinals	5,000	85.00
1987 Winter Chickadees	5,000	85.00

Americana Cats
	Edition Limit	Issue Price (US)
1987 The Mantle	7,500	39.50
1987 The Pantry	7,500	39.50

Franklin Crystal

Historical
	Edition Limit	Issue Price (US)
1976 Liberty Tree	10,927	120.00

Seven Seas
	Edition Limit	Issue Price (US)
1976 Atlantic Ocean	2,799	120.00
1976 Caribbean	2,799	120.00
1976 Indian Ocean	2,799	120.00
1976 Mediterranean	2,799	120.00
1976 Pacific	2,799	120.00
1976 South China Sea	2,799	120.00
1976 Arctic	2,799	120.00

Annual
	Edition Limit	Issue Price (US)
1977 Snowflake	3,428	185.00
1978 Snowbird	798	185.00

Rockwell's American Sweethearts
	Edition Limit	Issue Price (US)
1977 Youngsters at Play	1,004	120.00
1977 Teenagers Together	1,004	120.00
1978 Bride and Groom	1,004	120.00
1978 Proud Parents	1,004	120.00
1978 Graduation Day	1,004	120.00
1978 Retirement Kiss	1,004	120.00

Franklin Mint

American West
	Edition Limit	Issue Price (US)
1972 Horizon's West (Silver)	5,860	150.00
1972 Horizon's West (Gold)	67	2200.00
1973 Mountain Man (Silver)	5,860	150.00
1973 Mountain Man (Gold)	67	2200.00
1973 Prospector (Silver)	5,860	150.00
1973 Prospector (Gold)	67	2200.00
1973 Plains Hunter (Silver)	5,860	150.00
1973 Plains Hunter (Gold)	67	2200.00

Audubon Society
	Edition Limit	Issue Price (US)
1972 Goldfinch	10,193	125.00
1972 Wood Duck	10,193	125.00
1973 Cardinal	10,193	125.00
1973 Ruffed Grouse	10,193	125.00

Mother's Day
	Edition Limit	Issue Price (US)
1972 Mother and Child	21,987	125.00
1973 Mother and Child	6,154	125.00
1974 Mother and Child	5,116	150.00
1975 Mother and Child	2,704	175.00
1976 Mother and Child	1,858	180.00

Presidential
	Edition Limit	Issue Price (US)
1972 George Washington	10,304	150.00
1972 John Adams	4,859	150.00
1972 Thomas Jefferson	4,933	150.00
1972 James Madison	3,058	150.00
1972 James Monroe	2,722	150.00
1972 John Quincy Adams	2,501	150.00
1972 Andrew Jackson	2,408	150.00
1973 Martin Van Buren	2,291	150.00
1973 William H. Harrison	2,182	150.00
1973 John Tyler	2,144	150.00
1973 James Polk	2,083	150.00
1973 Zachary Taylor	2,023	150.00
1973 Millard Fillmore	1,967	150.00
1974 Franklin Pierce	1,907	150.00
1974 James Buchanan	1,841	150.00
1974 Abraham Lincoln	2,955	150.00
1974 Andrew Johnson	1,777	150.00
1974 Ulysses S. Grant	1,754	150.00
1975 Rutherford B. Hayes	1,705	150.00
1975 James A. Garfield	1,675	150.00
1975 Chester A. Arthur	1,604	150.00
1975 Grover Cleveland	1,644	150.00
1976 Benjamin Harrison	1,619	150.00
1976 William McKinley	1,571	150.00
1976 Theodore Roosevelt	1,555	150.00
1976 William H. Taft	1,592	150.00
1976 Woodrow Wilson	1,563	150.00
1977 Warren G. Harding	1,544	150.00
1977 Calvin Coolidge	1,527	150.00
1977 Herbert Hoover	1,520	150.00
1977 Franklin D. Roosevelt	1,770	150.00
1977 Harry S. Truman	1,493	150.00
1978 Dwight D. Eisenhower	1,494	150.00
1978 John F. Kennedy	1,494	150.00
1978 Lyndon B. Johnson	1,483	150.00
1978 Richard M. Nixon	1,475	150.00
1978 Gerald R. Ford	NA	150.00
1978 Jimmy Carter	NA	150.00

Thanksgiving—by Dohanos
	Edition Limit	Issue Price (US)
1972 First Thanksgiving	10,142	125.00
1973 American Wild Turkey	3,547	125.00
1974 Thanksgiving Prayer	5,150	150.00
1975 Family Thanksgiving	3,025	175.00
1976 Home from Hunt	3,474	175.00

James Wyeth
	Edition Limit	Issue Price (US)
1972 Along Brandywine	19,670	125.00
1973 Winter Fox	10,394	125.00
1974 Riding to Hunt	10,751	150.00
1975 Skating on Brandywine	8,058	175.00
1976 Brandywine Battlefield	6,968	180.00

Younger's Bird
	Edition Limit	Issue Price (US)
1972 Cardinal	13,939	125.00
1972 Bobwhite	13,939	125.00
1972 Mallards	13,939	125.00
1972 American Bald Eagle	13,939	125.00

John James Audubon
	Edition Limit	Issue Price (US)
1973 Wood Thrush	5,273	150.00
1973 Bald Eagle	3,040	150.00
1974 Night Heron	3,005	150.00
1974 Audubon's Warbler	3,034	150.00

Bernard Buffet
	Edition Limit	Issue Price (US)
1973 Gazelle	570	150.00
1974 Panda	408	150.00
1975 Giraffe	333	150.00
1976 Lion	263	150.00
1977 Rhinoceros	200	150.00

Bicentennial
	Edition Limit	Issue Price (US)
1973 Jefferson Drafting Declaration of Independence	8,556	175.00
1974 John Adams Champions Cause of Independence	8,442	175.00
1975 Caesar Rodney Decides Vote on Independence	8,319	175.00
1976 John Hancock Signs Declaration of Independence	10,166	175.00

Easter
	Edition Limit	Issue Price (US)
1973 Resurrection	7,116	175.00
1974 He Is Risen	3,719	185.00
1975 Last Supper	2,004	200.00
1976 Crucifixion	3,904	250.00
1977 Resurrection	1,206	250.00

Presidential Inaugural
	Edition Limit	Issue Price (US)
1973 Nixon/Agnew	10,483	150.00
1974 Ford (Silver)	1,141	200.00
1974 Ford (Gold)	11	3500.00
1977 Carter	928	225.00

Roberts' Zodiac
	Edition Limit	Issue Price (US)
1973 Aries	NA	150.00
1973 Taurus	NA	150.00
1973 Gemini	NA	150.00
1973 Cancer	NA	150.00
1973 Leo	NA	150.00
1973 Virgo	NA	150.00
1973 Libra	NA	150.00
1973 Scorpio	NA	150.00
1973 Sagittarius	NA	150.00
1973 Capricorn	NA	150.00
1973 Aquarius	NA	150.00
1973 Pisces	NA	150.00

Four Seasons
	Edition Limit	Issue Price (US)
1975 Spring Blossoms	2,648	240.00
1975 Summer Bouquet	2,648	240.00
1976 Autumn Garland	2,648	240.00
1976 Winter Spray	2,648	240.00

American Revolution Bicentennial
	Edition Limit	Issue Price (US)
1976 Boston Tea Party	3,596	75.00
1976 Patrick Henry Urges Armed Resistance	3,596	75.00
1976 Paul Revere's Ride	3,596	75.00
1976 Battle of Concord Bridge	3,596	75.00
1976 Capture of Fort Ticonderoga	3,596	75.00
1976 Battle of Bunker Hill	3,596	75.00
1977 Signing of Declaration	3,596	75.00
1977 Washington Crosses Delaware	3,596	75.00
1977 Burgoyne Defeated at Saratoga	3,596	75.00
1977 Winter at Valley Forge	3,596	75.00
1977 Alliance with France	3,596	75.00
1977 Bonhomme Richard Defeats Serapis	3,596	75.00
1977 Victory at Yorktown	3,596	75.00

Annual
	Edition Limit	Issue Price (US)
1977 Tribute to Arts	1,901	280.00
1978 Tribute to Nature	435	280.00

Belskie
	Edition Limit	Issue Price (US)
1977 Mother's Day	290	210.00

Currier & Ives
	Edition Limit	Issue Price (US)
1977 Winter Pastime	1,836	39.50
1977 Preparing for Market	1,836	39.50
1977 Winter in Country	1,836	39.50
1977 American Homestead—Winter	1,836	39.50
1977 American Forest Scene	1,836	39.50
1977 American Homestead—Summer	1,836	39.50
1977 American Homestead—Autumn	1,836	39.50
1977 Haying Time—Last Load	1,836	39.50
1977 American Express Train	1,836	39.50
1977 Haying Time—First Load	1,836	39.50
1977 Catching a Trout	1,836	39.50
1977 Yosemite Valley	1,836	39.50

Freedom
	Edition Limit	Issue Price (US)
1977 Lafayette Joins Washington	546	275.00

Rockwell Thanksgiving
	Edition Limit	Issue Price (US)
1977 Old Fashioned Thanksgiving	2,361	85.00

Christmas
	Edition Limit	Issue Price (US)
1977 Skating Party	908	55.00

Franklin Porcelain

Hans Christian Andersen
	Edition Limit	Issue Price (US)
1976 Princess and Pea	16,875	38.00
1976 Ugly Duckling	16,875	38.00
1976 Little Mermaid	16,875	38.00
1976 Emperor's New Clothes	16,875	38.00
1976 Steadfast Tin Soldier	16,875	38.00
1976 Little Match Girl	16,875	38.00
1977 Snow Queen	16,875	38.00
1977 Red Shoes	16,875	38.00
1977 Tinder Box	16,875	38.00
1977 Nightingale	16,875	38.00
1977 Thumbelina	16,875	38.00
1977 Shepherdess & Chimney Sweep	16,875	38.00

Christmas Annual
	Edition Limit	Issue Price (US)
1976 Silent Night	19,286	65.00
1977 Deck Halls	9,185	65.00
1978 We Three Kings	Year	75.00
1979 Hark, Herald Angels Sing	Year	75.00
1980 Joy to World	Year	125.00
1981 O, Holy Night	Year	125.00

Flowers of Year
	Edition Limit	Issue Price (US)
1976 January	27,394	50.00
1976 February	27,394	50.00
1977 March	27,394	50.00
1977 April	27,394	50.00
1977 May	27,394	50.00
1978 June	27,394	50.00
1978 July	27,394	50.00
1978 August	27,394	50.00
1978 September	27,394	50.00
1979 October	27,394	50.00
1979 November	27,394	50.00
1979 December	27,394	50.00

	Edition Limit	Issue Price (US)
Mother's Day		
1977 A Mother's Love	Year	65.00
1978 A Mother's Joy	Year	65.00
1979 A Mother's Gift	Year	75.00
Songbirds of World		
1977 Baltimore Oriole	20,225	55.00
1977 Bohemian Waxwing	20,225	55.00
1977 Magnolia Warbler	20,225	55.00
1977 Bobolink	20,225	55.00
1977 Western Bluebird	20,225	55.00
1977 Cardinal	20,225	55.00
1977 European Goldfinch	20,225	55.00
1977 Wood Thrush	20,225	55.00
1977 Scarlet Tanager	20,225	55.00
1977 Barn Swallow	20,225	55.00
1977 Bluethroat	20,225	55.00
1977 Turquoise Wren	20,225	55.00
Mark Twain		
1977 Whitewashing Fence	2,645	38.00
1977 Stealing a Kiss	2,645	38.00
1977 Traveling River	2,645	38.00
1977 Trading Lives	2,645	38.00
1977 Rafting Down River	2,645	38.00
1978 Riding Bronc	2,645	38.00
1978 Jumping Frog Race	2,645	38.00
1978 Facing Charging Knight	2,645	38.00
1978 Disguising Huck	2,645	38.00
1978 Living Along River	2,645	38.00
1978 Learning to Smoke	2,645	38.00
1978 Finger Printing Pays Off	2,645	38.00
Flowers of American Wilderness		
1978 New England	8,759	39.00
1978 Alaska	8,759	39.00
1978 Everglades of Florida	8,759	39.00
1978 Mississippi Delta	8,759	39.00
1978 California	8,759	39.00
1978 Rocky Mountains	8,759	39.00
1978 Cape Cod	8,759	39.00
1978 Northwest	8,759	39.00
1978 Southwest	8,759	39.00
1978 Appalachian Mountains	8,759	39.00
1978 Prairies	8,759	39.00
1978 Great Lakes	8,759	39.00
Game Birds of World		
1978 Chinese Pheasant	76,294	55.00
1978 Red-Legged Partridge	76,294	55.00
1978 Common Snipe	76,294	55.00
1978 Common Partridge	76,294	55.00
1978 Rock Ptarmigan	76,294	55.00
1978 Woodcock	76,294	55.00
1978 Common Pheasant	76,294	55.00
1978 Hazel Grouse	76,294	55.00
1978 Red Grouse	76,294	55.00
1978 Black Grouse	76,294	55.00
1978 Capercaillie	76,294	55.00
1978 Common Quail	76,294	55.00
Grimm's Fairy Tales		
1978 Sleeping Beauty	27,006	42.00
1978 Twelve Dancing Princesses	27,006	42.00
1978 Brementown Musicians	27,006	42.00
1979 Golden Goose	27,006	42.00
1979 Hansel and Gretel	27,006	42.00
1979 Rapunzel	27,006	42.00
1980 Snow White/Seven Dwarfs	27,006	42.00
1980 Frog Prince	27,006	42.00
1980 Red Riding Hood	27,006	42.00
1981 Rumpelstilskin	27,006	42.00
1981 Cinderella	27,006	42.00
1981 Shoemaker and Elves	27,006	42.00
Days of Week		
1979 Monday's Child	1,890	39.00
1979 Tuesday's Child	1,890	39.00
1979 Wednesday's Child	1,890	39.00
1979 Thursday's Child	1,890	39.00
1979 Friday's Child	1,890	39.00
1979 Saturday's Child	1,890	39.00
1979 Sunday's Child	1,890	39.00
Hometown Memories		
1979 Country Fair	Year	29.00
1980 Little Red School House	Year	29.00
1981 Sunday Picnic	Year	29.00
1982 Skating Party	Year	29.00

	Edition Limit	Issue Price (US)
Country Year		
1980 Woodlands in April	89,173	55.00
1980 Country Path in May	89,173	55.00
1980 June in Country Garden	89,173	55.00
1980 July Beside River	89,173	55.00
1980 Wheatfields in August	89,173	55.00
1980 September on Moors	89,173	55.00
1980 Colors of Autumn in October	89,173	55.00
1980 Country Lane in December	89,173	55.00
1980 January—Lambing Season	89,173	55.00
1980 Country Church in March	89,173	55.00
1980 Secluded Stream in November	89,173	55.00
International Gallery of Flowers		
1980 Wheat	4,294	55.00
1980 Orchid	4,294	55.00
1980 Irises	4,294	55.00
1980 Camelias	4,294	55.00
1980 Cherry Blossoms	4,294	55.00
1980 English Wild Flowers	4,294	55.00
Woodland Birds of World		
1980 Blue Jay	5,507	65.00
1980 White-Winged Crossbill	5,507	65.00
1980 Painted Redstart	5,507	65.00
1980 Rivoli's Hummingbird	5,507	65.00
1980 Chaffinch	5,507	65.00
1980 Collared Trogon	5,507	65.00
Calendar		
1981 Turn-of-Century Scenes	Year	55.00
1982 Turn-of-Century Children	Year	58.00
Clipper Ships		
1982 Red Jacket	NA	55.00
1982 Sea Witch	NA	55.00
1982 Cutty Sark	NA	55.00
1982 Thermoplyae	NA	55.00
1982 Ariel	NA	55.00
1982 Patriarch	NA	55.00
1982 Nightingale	NA	55.00
1982 Flying Cloud	NA	55.00
1982 Marco Polo	NA	55.00
Cobblestone Kids		
1982 Making Friends	NA	65.00
1982 Extra, Extra	NA	65.00
1982 Just Ducky	NA	65.00
1982 Feeding Raccoon	NA	65.00
1982 A Stitch in Time	NA	65.00
1982 Testing Wind	NA	65.00
Golden Age of Sail (Royal Society of Marine Artists)		
1987 Sovereign of Seas	NA	55.00
Frankoma		
Christmas		
1965 Goodwill Toward Man	Year	5.00
1966 Bethlehem Shepherds	Year	5.00
1967 Gifts for Christ Child	Year	5.00
1968 Flight into Egypt	Year	5.00
1969 Laid in a Manger	Year	5.00
1970 King of Kings	Year	5.00
1971 No Room in Inn	Year	5.00
1972 Seeking Christ Child	Year	5.00
1973 Annunciation	Year	5.00
1974 She Loved & Cared	Year	5.00
1975 Peace on Earth	Year	5.00
1976 Gift of Love	Year	6.00
1977 Birth of Eternal Life	Year	6.00
1978 All Nature Rejoiced	Year	6.00
1979 Stay of Hope	Year	6.00
1980 Unto Us a Child Is Born	Year	10.00
1981 O Come Let Us Adore Him	Year	12.00
1982 Wise Men Rejoice	Year	12.00
1983 Wise Men Bring Gifts	Year	12.00
Bicentennial		
1972 Provocations	Year	6.00
1973 Patriots & Leaders	Year	6.00
1974 Battles, Independence	Year	5.00

	Edition Limit	Issue Price (US)
1975 Victories for Independence	Year	6.00
1976 Symbols of Freedom	Year	6.00
Teenagers of Bible		
1973 Jesus, Carpenter	Year	5.00
1974 David, Musician	Year	5.00
1975 Jonathan, Archer	Year	5.00
1976 Dorcas, Seamstress	Year	5.00
1977 Peter, Fisherman	Year	5.00
1978 Martha, Homemaker	Year	7.50
1979 Daniel, Courageous	Year	7.50
1980 Ruth, Devoted	Year	8.00
1981 Joseph, Dreamer	Year	8.00
1982 Mary, Mother	Year	8.00
Madonnas		
1977 Grace Madonna	Year	12.50
1978 Madonna of Love	Year	12.50
Gallery Classics		
Wild Duck Collection		
1986 Green Winged Teal	15,000	49.50
1986 Mallards	15,000	49.50
1986 Wood Ducks	15,000	49.50
1986 Pintails	15,000	49.50
Gartlan Associates		
(Single issue)		
1986 George Brett	2,000	100.00
(Single issue)		
1987 Roger Staubach (signed)	1,979	100.00
Ghent Collection		
Christmas Wildlife		
1974 Cardinals in Snow	10,135	20.00
1975 We Three Kings	12,750	29.00
1976 Partridge and Pear Tree	12,750	32.00
1977 Foxes and Evergreen	12,750	32.00
1978 Snowy Owls	12,750	32.00
Mother's Day		
1975 Cotton Tail	12,750	22.00
1976 Mallard Family	12,750	29.00
1977 Chipmunks & Trillium	12,750	32.00
1978 Raccoon Family	12,750	32.00
1979 Maytime	12,750	32.00
American Bicentennial Wildlife		
1976 American Bald Eagle	2,500	95.00
1976 American White-Tailed Deer	2,500	95.00
1976 American Bison	2,500	95.00
1976 American Wild Turkey	2,500	95.00
Fausett Mural (Single issue)		
1976 From Sea to Shining Sea	1,976	76.00
(Single issue)		
1978 Pilgrim of Peace	15 Days	29.50
Lands of Fable		
1981 Xanadu	17,500	55.00
1982 Atlantis	17,500	55.00
Man's Dream of Flight		
1981 Flight of Icarus	19,500	37.50
1981 Vision of Leonardo	19,500	37.50
1981 First Lighter-than-Air Flight	19,500	37.50
1981 Wright Brothers	19,500	37.50
1981 Lindbergh Flies Atlantic	19,500	37.50
1981 Barnstormers	19,500	37.50
1981 Jet Age	19,500	37.50
1981 Giant Leap for Mankind	19,500	37.50
Hans Brinker Delft		
1982 Hero of Haarlem	17,500	29.50
1982 Race	17,500	29.50
1982 Thousand Guilders	17,500	29.50
1982 On Canal	17,500	29.50
1982 Shadows in Home	17,500	29.50
1982 Mysterious Watch	17,500	29.50
Ghent Collection (Bing & Grøndahl)		
Hans Christian Andersen		
1979 Thumbelina	7,500	42.50
1979 Princess and Pea	7,500	42.50
1979 Wild Swans	7,500	42.50
1979 Emperor's New Clothes	7,500	42.50
1980 Little Mermaid	7,500	42.50
1980 Nightingale	7,500	42.50

	Edition Limit	Issue Price (US)
Ghent Collection (Caverswall)		
Christmas Annual		
1979 Good King Wenceslaus	2,500	350.00
Country Diary of an Edwardian Lady		
1979 April	10,000	80.00
1979 June	10,000	80.00
1980 September	10,000	80.00
1980 December	10,000	80.00
1981 July	10,000	80.00
1981 October	10,000	80.00
1982 January	10,000	80.00
1982 May	10,000	80.00
1983 February	10,000	80.00
1983 March	10,000	80.00
1984 August	10,000	80.00
1984 November	10,000	80.00
Ghent Collection (Fairmont)		
Legends of Christmas		
1979 Bringing in Tree	5,000	65.00
Memory Annual		
1978 1977 Memory Plate	1,977	77.00
1979 1978 Memory Plate	1,978	78.00
1980 1979 Memory Plate	1,979	79.00
Israeli Commemorative (Single issue)		
1978 Promised Land	5,738	79.00
Spirit of America		
1978 Making of a Nation	1,978	78.00
1979 Growing Years	1,978	78.00
Ghent Collection (Gorham)		
April Fool Annual		
1978 April Fool's Day	10,000	35.00
1979 April Fool's Day	10,000	35.00
1980 April Fool's Day	10,000	37.50
Ghent Collection (Kaiser)		
Treasures of Tutankhamun		
1978 Golden Mask	3,247	90.00
1978 Golden Throne	3,247	90.00
1978 Horus Falcon	3,247	90.00
1978 Ivory Chest	3,247	90.00
Ghent Collection (Viletta)		
Olympics		
1980 1980 Winter Olympics	13 Days	24.50
1980 1980 Summer Olympics	13 Days	29.50
Gnomes United		
Gnomes		
1979 Gnome on Range	10,000	23.00
Gnome Patrol		
1979 Dr. Kwik	5,000	45.00
Golf Digest		
Second Hole (Single issue)		
1973 Dorado Beach Club	2,000	45.00
Twelfth Hole (Single issue)		
1973 Spyglass Hill	2,000	45.00
Gorham		
(Single issue)		
1970 American Family Tree	5,000	17.00
Lionel Barrymore		
1971 Quiet Waters	15,000	25.00
1972 San Pedro Harbor	15,000	25.00
1972 Little Boatyard (Silver)	1,000	100.00
1972 Nantucket (Silver)	1,000	100.00
Bicentennial		
1971 Burning of Gaspee (Pewter)	5,000	35.00
1972 Burning of Gaspee (Silver)	750	550.00
1972 1776 (China)	18,500	17.50
1972 1776 (Vermeil)	500	500.00
1972 1776 (Silver)	750	250.00
1972 Boston Tea Party (Pewter)	5,000	35.00
1973 Boston Tea Party (Silver)	750	550.00
Gallery of Masters		
1971 Man in Gilt Helmet	10,000	50.00
1972 Self-Portrait Rembrandt, with Saskia	10,000	50.00
1973 Honorable Mrs. Graham	7,500	50.00

	Edition Limit	Issue Price (US)
Moppets Mother's Day		
1973 Flowers for Mother	20,000	10.00
1974 Mother's Hat	20,000	12.00
1975 In Mother's Clothes	20,000	13.00
1976 Flowers	20,000	13.00
1977 Gift for Mother	18,500	13.00
1978 Moppet's Mother's Day	18,500	10.00
Moppets Christmas		
1973 Christmas March	20,000	10.00
1974 Trimming Tree	20,000	12.00
1975 Carrying Tree	20,000	13.00
1976 Asleep under Tree	18,500	13.00
1977 Star for Treetop	18,500	13.00
1978 Presents	18,500	10.00
1979 Moppet's Christmas	18,500	12.00
1980 Happy Merry Christmas Tree	Year	12.00
1981 Happy Merry Christmas Tree	Year	12.00
1982 Happy Merry Christmas Tree	Year	12.00
Remington Western		
1973 Aiding a Comrade	Year	25.00
1973 New Year on Cimarron	Year	25.00
1973 Fight for Waterhole	Year	25.00
1973 Flight	Year	25.00
1974 Old Ramond	Year	20.00
1974 Breed	Year	20.00
1975 Cavalry Officer	5,000	37.50
1975 Trapper	5,000	37.50
Irene Spencer Annual		
1974 Dear Child	10,000	37.50
1975 Promises to Keep	10,000	40.00
(Single issue)		
1974 Streakers	Year	19.50
(Single issue)		
1974 Golden Rule	Year	19.50
(Single issue)		
1974 Big Three	10,000	17.50
(Single issue)		
1974 Weigh-In	10,000	17.50
(Single issue)		
1975 Benjamin Franklin	18,500	19.50
Boy Scouts of America		
1975 Our Heritage	18,500	19.50
1976 Scout Is Loyal	18,500	19.50
1977 Scoutmaster	18,500	19.50
1977 Good Sign	18,500	19.50
1978 Pointing Way	18,500	19.50
1978 Campfire Story	18,500	19.50
American Artists		
1976 Apache Mother & Child	9,800	25.00
1976 Black Regiment	7,500	25.00
America's Cup Plates (Set of five)		
1976 America, 1861		
1976 Puritan		
1976 Reliance		
1976 Ranger		
1976 Courageous	1,000	200.00
Omnibus Muralis		
1976 200 Years with Old Glory	5,000	60.00
1977 Life of Christ	5,000	65.00
First Lady		
1977 Amy and Rosalynn	Year	24.95
Presidential		
1977 John F. Kennedy	9,800	30.00
1977 Eisenhower	9,800	30.00
Prince Tatters		
1977 Johnny and Duke	7,500	40.00
1978 Randy and Rex	7,500	42.50
1979 Furry Friends	7,500	47.50
1980 Benji's Burro	7,500	50.00
Julian Ritter Christmas		
1977 Christmas Visit	9,800	24.50
Ritter's Four Seasons Clowns		
1977 Falling in Love (Set of four)	5,000	100.00
1978 To Love a Clown (Set of four)	5,000	120.00
Santa Fe Railway		
1977 Navajo Silversmith	7,500	37.50
1978 Turquoise Bead Maker	7,500	37.50

	Edition Limit	Issue Price (US)
1979 Basketweaver	7,500	42.50
1980 Arrow Maker	7,500	45.00
Borsato Masterpiece		
1977 Serenity	5,000	75.00
1978 Titian Madonna	5,000	75.00
1979 Ballerina	5,000	75.00
Little Men		
1977 Come Ride with Me	9,500	50.00
1978 Julian Ritter Valentine	7,500	45.00
Moppets Anniversary		
1979 Moppet Couple	20,000	13.00
(Single issue)		
1978 Triple Self-Portrait	Year	37.50
Wild West		
1980 Bronc to Breakfast	9,800	38.00
1981 In Without Knocking	9,800	38.00
1982 Cowboy Life	9,800	45.00
1983 Ignorance Is Bliss	9,800	45.00
Four Seasons Landscape		
1980 Summer Respite	15,000	45.00
1980 Autumn Reflections	15,000	45.00
1981 Winter Delights	15,000	45.00
1981 Spring Recess	15,000	45.00
Rockwell Four Seasons		
1981 Old Timers (Set of four)	Year	100.00
1982 Life with Father (Set of four)	Year	100.00
1983 Old Buddies (Set of four)	Year	115.00
1984 Traveling Salesman (Set of four)	Year	115.00
(Single issue—Set of two)		
1981 Day in Life of Boy		
1981 Day in Life of Girl	Year	50.00
Four Ages of Love		
1981 Sweet Song So Young	10,000	100.00
1982 Flowers in Tender Bloom	10,000	100.00
Masterpieces of Rockwell		
1981 Girl at Mirror	17,500	50.00
Young Love		
1981 Beguiling Buttercup	17,500	62.50
1982 Flying High	17,500	62.50
Encounters, Survival and Celebrations		
1982 A Fine Welcome	7,500	50.00
1983 Winter Trails	7,500	50.00
1984 Alouette	7,500	62.50
1984 Trader	7,500	62.50
1985 Winter Camp	7,500	62.50
1985 Trapper Takes a Wife	7,500	62.50
Pastoral Symphony		
1982 When I Was a Child	7,500	42.50
1983 Gather Children	7,500	42.50
1984 Sugar and Spice	7,500	42.50
1985 He Loves Me	7,500	42.50
A Merry Mouse		
1983 A Merry Mouse Christmas	5,000	15.00
Museum Doll		
1983 Lydia	5,000	29.00
1984 Belton Bebe	5,000	29.00
1984 Lucille	5,000	29.00
1985 Bebe Jumeau	5,000	29.00
Heaven Mother's Day		
1984 Mother Is Love	5,000	24.95
Museum Doll Christmas		
1985 Christmas Lady	7,500	32.50
Beverly Port Plate Series		
1986 Miss Emily "Bearing Up"	5,000	32.50
1987 Big Bear, The Toy Collector	5,000	32.50
See also:		
American Commemorative (U.S.A.)		
American Express (U.S.A.)		
American Preservation Guild (U.S.A.)		
American Rose Society (U.S.A.)		
Fleetwood Collection (U.S.A.)		
Ghent Collection (U.S.A.)		
Lincoln Mint (U.S.A.)		
Volair (U.S.A.)		

	Edition Limit	Issue Price (US)
Greentree Potteries		
Grant Wood		
1971 Studio	2,000	10.00
1972 Antioch School	2,000	10.00
1973 At Stone City	2,000	10.00
1974 Adolescence	2,000	10.00
1975 Birthplace	2,000	10.00
1976 American Gothic	2,000	10.00
Kennedy		
1972 Center for Performing Arts	2,000	20.00
1973 Birthplace, Brookline, Mass.	2,000	12.00
Motorcar		
1972 1929 Packard Dietrich Convertible	2,000	20.00
1973 Model "A" Ford	2,000	20.00
Mississippi River		
1973 Delta Queen	2,000	10.00
1973 Tri-Centennial	2,000	10.00
Dave Grossman Designs		
Margaret Keane		
1976 Balloon Girl	5,000	25.00
1977 My Kitty	5,000	25.00
1978 Bedtime	5,000	25.00
Tom Sawyer		
1975 Whitewashing Fence	10,000	24.00
1976 First Smoke	10,000	24.00
1977 Take Your Medicine	10,000	24.00
1978 Lost in Cave	10,000	25.00
Looney Tunes Mother's Day		
1976 Bugs Bunny	10,000	13.00
Looney Tunes Christmas		
1977 Christmas	10,000	13.00
1978 Christmas	5,000	14.00
Children of Week		
1978 Monday's Child	5,000	30.00
1979 Tuesday's Child	5,000	30.00
1979 Wednesday's Child	5,000	30.00
1980 Thursday's Child	5,000	30.00
1980 Friday's Child	5,000	30.00
1981 Saturday's Child	5,000	30.00
1981 Sunday's Child	5,000	30.00
Annual Fall		
1978 Peace	5,000	55.00
1979 Santa	5,000	55.00
Annual		
1979 Leapfrog	Year	50.00
1980 Lovers	Year	60.00
1981 Dreams of Long Ago	Year	60.00
Rockwell		
1979 Butter Boy	5,000	40.00
Huckleberry Finn		
1979 Secret	10,000	40.00
1980 Listening	10,000	40.00
1981 No Kings Nor Dukes	10,000	40.00
1982 Snake Escapes	10,000	40.00
(Single issue)		
1980 Norman Rockwell Back to School	10,000	24.00
Rockwell Christmas		
1980 Christmas Trio	Year	75.00
1981 Santa's Good Boys	Year	75.00
1982 Faces of Christmas	Year	75.00
Rockwell Boy Scout Annual		
1981 Can't Wait	10,000	30.00
1982 A Guiding Hand	10,000	30.00
1983 Tomorrow's Leader	10,000	30.00
Magic People		
1982 Music for a Queen	9,500	65.00
1982 Fantasy Festival	10,000	65.00
1983 Bubble Chariot	10,000	65.00
1983 Kite Carriage	10,000	65.00
Milk Glass		
1983 Dreamboats	15,000	24.00
(Single issue)		
1984 Secret	10,000	39.50
Emmett Kelly Christmas		
1986 Christmas Carol	NA	20.00
Hackett American Collectors		
Corita Kent Annual		
1979 I Love You Very	30,000	21.95
1980 You Bring Spring	10,000	21.95

	Edition Limit	Issue Price (US)
1981 Love	10,000	30.00
1982 Cheers	10,000	32.50
Endangered Species		
1980 California Sea Otters	7,500	35.00
1981 Asian Pandas	7,500	37.50
1982 Australian Koala Bears	7,500	39.50
1982 River Otters	7,500	39.50
Ocean Moods		
1980 Sunset Tide	5,000	50.00
1981 Moonlight Flight	5,000	50.00
1982 Morning Surf	5,000	50.00
1983 Afternoon Surf	5,000	50.00
Save Whales		
1980 Trust and Love	10,000	30.00
Snow Babies		
1980 Canadian Harp Seals	7,500	39.50
1981 Polar Bear Cubs	7,500	39.50
1982 Snow Leopards	7,500	42.50
Friends of Forest		
1981 Forest Alert	7,500	50.00
1982 Brookside Protection	7,500	50.00
1982 Mountain Guardian	7,500	50.00
1983 Lookouts	7,500	50.00
Horses in Action		
1981 Challenge	10,000	39.50
1982 Country Days	10,000	50.00
1983 Family Portrait	10,000	50.00
1983 All Grown Up	10,000	50.00
Parkhurst Christmas		
1981 Christmas Tear	7,500	39.50
1982 Christmas Morning	7,500	39.50
1983 Night Before Christmas	7,500	39.50
Wonderful World of Clowns		
1981 Kiss for a Clown	7,500	39.50
1981 Rainbow's End	7,500	39.50
1982 Happy Days	7,500	42.50
1982 Filling Pop's Shoes	7,500	42.50
Wonderous Years		
1981 After Rains	5,000	39.50
1982 I Got One	5,000	42.50
1982 Fascination	5,000	42.50
(Single issue)		
1981 John Lennon	90 Days	25.00
Crazy Cats		
1982 Primping Time	10,000	42.50
Daisy Cats		
1982 Daisy Kitten	10,000	42.50
1982 Daisy Cat	10,000	42.50
Days Remembered		
1982 First Birthday	19,500	29.50
1983 First Haircut	19,5000	35.00
Early Discoveries		
1982 Let's Play	10,000	42.50
Escalera Christmas		
1982 Special Delivery	19,500	32.50
1983 Especially for You	19,500	35.00
Everyone's Friends		
1982 Springtime	10,000	42.50
1982 Autumn Bandit	10,000	42.50
1983 Snowtime Bunnies	10,000	42.50
1983 Summer Bandits	10,000	42.50
Family Portraits		
1982 Mother's Joy	7,500	85.00
Fashions by Irene		
1982 Elegant Lady	15,000	45.00
Escalera Father's Day		
1982 Daddy's Rose	10,000	42.50
1983 Daddy's Wish	10,000	42.50
Impressions by Joanne Mix		
1982 Windy Day	10,000	42.50
1982 Sunny Day	10,000	42.50
1983 Summer's Day	10,000	42.50
Joanne Mix Christmas		
1982 Christmas Love	10,000	39.50
Kelly's Stable		
1982 My Champion	15,000	42.50
1983 Glory Bound	15,000	42.50
1983 Arabian Spring	15,000	42.50
1984 Summer Days	15,000	42.50
Landfalls		
1982 San Francisco Bay	7,500	39.50
1983 Newport Harbor	7,500	39.50
1983 Miami Beach	7,500	39.50

	Edition Limit	Issue Price (US)
Little Orphans		
1982 Surprise Package	19,500	29.50
1983 Castaway	19,500	32.50
1984 Furry Surprise	19,500	35.00
Mother and Child		
1982 Mother's Love	10,000	42.50
1982 Tenderness	10,000	42.50
1983 Serenity	10,000	42.50
1984 Navajo Madonna	10,000	42.50
Parkhurst Mother's Day		
1982 Daisies for Mother	10,000	42.50
Ocean Stars		
1982 Sea Horses	10,000	42.50
1982 Dolphins	10,000	42.50
1983 Whales	10,000	42.50
Parkhurst Diamond		
1982 Chance Encounter	1,500	300.00
Peaceful Retreat		
1982 Refuge	19,500	29.50
1983 Solitude	19,500	32.50
1983 Tranquility	19,500	35.00
1984 Seclusion	19,500	35.00
Prairie Children		
1982 Young Pioneers	19,500	32.50
1983 Adam	19,500	35.00
Side by Side		
1982 My Hero	19,500	32.50
1983 Sippin' Soda	19,500	35.00
Special Moments		
1982 April	10,000	42.50
1982 Rachel	10,000	42.50
Sunday Best		
1982 Stacey	10,000	42.50
1982 Laurie	10,000	42.50
Waterbird Families		
1982 Marsh Venture	10,000	42.50
1982 Afternoon Swim	10,000	42.50
1983 Nesting Wood Ducks	10,000	42.50
1983 Returning Home	10,000	42.50
World of Ozz Franca		
1982 Images	10,000	42.50
1982 Lost and Found	10,000	42.50
1983 Best Friends	10,000	42.50
(Single issue)		
1982 Hog Heaven	15,000	42.50
(Single issue)		
1982 Henry Fonda	10,000	39.50
(Single issue)		
1982 Reggie Jackson	10,000	60.00
(Single issue)		
1982 John Wayne	10,000	39.50
Classic Cars		
1983 '57 Chevy	5,000	39.50
1984 '57 Thunderbird	5,000	39.50
Costume Party		
1983 Belinda	7,500	39.50
Famous Planes of Yesterday		
1983 Spirit of St. Louis	5,000	39.50
1984 Byrd Antarctic	5,000	39.50
Favorite Dreams		
1983 Daddy's Sailor	7,500	39.50
1984 Daddy's Engineer	7,500	39.50
Golfing Greats		
1983 Arnold Palmer	100 Days	45.00
1984 Gary Player	100 Days	45.00
Huggable Moments		
1983 Naptime	10,000	39.50
1983 Playtime	10,000	39.50
Joan Horton Christmas		
1983 Moonlight Sleighride	5,000	39.50
Joys of Christmas		
1983 Toy Shop	5,000	39.50
Jungle Babies		
1983 Baby Bengals	5,000	39.50
Memorable Impressions		
1983 Beachcomber	7,500	39.50
1983 Beach Girl	7,500	39.50
Puzzling Moments		
1983 Problem Solver	7,500	39.50
1983 Practice Makes Perfect	7,500	39.50

	Edition Limit	Issue Price (US)
Reflections of Sea		
1983 Golden Shores	5,000	42.50
1984 Summer Sands	5,000	39.50
Sadako's Helpers		
1983 Artist's Pal	7,500	39.50
1984 Artist's Helper	7,500	39.50
Sensitive Moments		
1983 Sharing Beauty	5,000	39.50
Snow Babies		
1982 Arctic Foxes	7,500	42.50
1982 Canadian Harp Seal	7,500	42.50
1982 Polar Bear Cubs	7,500	42.50
1982 Snow Leopards	7,500	42.50
Summer Fun		
1983 Fishing Together	7,500	39.50
1983 Swinging Together	7,500	39.50
Yesterday's Expressions		
1983 Gloria	5,000	39.50
(Single issue-Set of two)		
1983 Bjorn Borg		
1983 Martina Navratilova	15,000	39.50
(Single issue)		
1983 Frog Heaven	5,000	39.50
(Single issue)		
1983 Hopalong Cassidy	7,500	42.50
(Single issue)		
1983 Laurel and Hardy	15,000	42.50
(Single issue)		
1983 Otter Heaven	5,000	39.50
(Single issue)		
1983 Steve Garvey	10,000	60.00
Billowing Sails		
1984 Flying Cloud	7,500	60.00
Childhood Memories		
1984 Cookie Thief	7,500	29.50
Grandparents		
1984 Grandpa's Delight	10,000	27.50
Little Friends		
1984 Tiny Creatures	5,000	35.00
Moments to Cherish		
1984 Kerry	5,000	29.50
(Single issue)		
1984 Steve Carlton	4,400	45.00
(Single issue)		
1984 Bill Rogers	7,991	42.50
(Single issue)		
1984 Babe	10,000	29.50
(Single issue)		
1984 Owl Heaven	10,000	39.50
(Single issue)		
1984 Forever Yours	15,000	42.50
(Single issue)		
1984 King Remembered	10,000	50.00
(Single issue)		
1984 Nolan Ryan	8,402	42.50
(Single issue)		
1984 Tom Seaver	6,728	42.50
Big Chiefs		
1985 Chief Joseph	5,000	32.50
Joyful Memories		
1985 Chrissy	15,000	39.50
Reggie Jackson's Famous Collector Cars		
1985 Jackson '65 Corvette	10,000	45.00
(Single issue)		
1985 Hank Aaron	5,000	45.00
(Single issue)		
1985 Sadako's Scotties	5,000	35.00
(Single issue)		
1985 Whitey Ford	4,528	45.00
(Single issue)		
1986 Ty Cobb	4,191	39.50
Hadley House		
Glow Series		
1986 Evening Glow	5,000	55.00
1986 Morning Glow	5,000	55.00
Redlin's Retreat		
1986 Morning Retreat	9,500	65.00
1987 Evening Retreat	9,500	65.00
1987 Golden Retreat	9,500	65.00

	Edition Limit	Issue Price (US)
(Single issue)		
1986 Quiet Water	9,500	44.95
Hamilton Collection		
Japanese Floral Calendar		
1981 New Year's Day	10 Days	32.50
1982 Early Spring	10 Days	32.50
1982 Spring	10 Days	32.50
1982 Girl's Day	10 Days	32.50
1982 Buddah's Birthday	10 Days	32.50
1983 Heralds of Spring	10 Days	32.50
1983 Boy's Doll Day	10 Days	32.50
1983 Summer	10 Days	32.50
1983 Autumn	10 Days	32.50
1983 Festival of Full Moon	10 Days	32.50
1983 Late Autumn	10 Days	32.50
1983 Winter	10 Days	32.50
Legends of Camelot		
1981 Secret Romance	12,500	62.50
1982 Merlin Magician	12,500	62.50
1982 Sir Lancelot	12,500	62.50
1982 King Arthur	12,500	62.50
1982 Jousting Tournament	12,500	62.50
1982 Sword and Stone	12,500	62.50
1982 Rescued	12,500	62.50
1982 Knights of Round Table	12,500	62.50
Story of Heidi		
1981 Heidi	14,750	45.00
1981 Grandfather	14,750	45.00
1981 Heidi and Peter	14,750	45.00
1981 Grandmother	14,750	45.00
1982 Kittens	14,750	45.00
1982 Mountain Cure	14,750	45.00
Story of Noah's Ark		
1981 Two by Two . . .	12,500	45.00
1982 In Divine Harmony	12,500	45.00
1982 Rainbow	12,500	45.00
1982 Ark Beckons	12,500	45.00
1982 Be Fruitful	12,500	45.00
1982 Journey's End	12,500	45.00
Treasures of Chinese Mandarins		
1981 Bird of Paradise	2,500	75.00
1982 Guardians of Heaven	2,500	75.00
1982 Tree of Immortality	2,500	75.00
1982 Dragon of Eternity	2,500	75.00
Tribute to Ballet		
1981 Nutcracker	15,000	62.50
Fairies of Fields and Flowers		
1982 Willow Fairy	NA	45.00
Lewis & Clark Expedition		
1982 In Bitterroots	NA	55.00
1982 Sacajawea at Big Water	NA	55.00
1982 Lewis Crossing	NA	55.00
1982 Buffalo Gangue	NA	55.00
1982 Salt Makers	NA	55.00
1982 Up Jefferson	NA	55.00
1982 Arrival of Sgt. Pryor	NA	55.00
1982 Visitors at Fort Clatsop	NA	55.00
Eternal Wishes of Good Fortune		
1983 Friendship	10 Days	34.95
1983 Love	10 Days	34.95
1983 Fertility	10 Days	34.95
1983 Purity and Perfection	10 Days	34.95
1983 Illustrious Offspring	10 Days	34.95
1983 Peace	10 Days	34.95
1983 Longevity	10 Days	34.95
1983 Immortality	10 Days	34.95
1983 Marital Bliss	10 Days	34.95
1983 Beauty	10 Days	34.95
1983 Fortitude	10 Days	34.95
1983 Youth	10 Days	34.95
Gardens of Orient		
1983 Flowering of Spring	10 Days	19.50
1983 Festival of May	10 Days	19.50
1983 Cherry Blossom Brocade	10 Days	19.50
1983 A Winter's Repose	10 Days	19.50
1983 Garden Sanctuary	10 Days	19.50
1983 Summer's Glory	10 Days	19.50
1983 June's Creation	10 Days	19.50
Majestic Birds of Prey		
1983 Golden Eagle	12,500	55.00
1983 Cooper's Hawk	12,500	55.00
1983 Great Horned Owl	12,500	55.00
1983 Bald Eagle	12,500	55.00
1983 Barred Owl	12,500	55.00
1983 Sparrow Hawk	12,500	55.00

	Edition Limit	Issue Price (US)
1983 Peregrine Falcon	12,500	55.00
1983 Osprey	12,500	55.00
Utz Mother's Day		
1983 A Gift of Love	Year	27.50
1984 A Helping Hand	Year	27.50
1985 Mother's Angel	Year	27.50
(Single issue)		
1983 Princess Grace	NA	40.00
America at Work		
1984 School Teacher	10 Days	29.50
1984 Piano Workman	10 Days	29.50
1984 Zoo Keeper	10 Days	29.50
1984 Cleaning Women	10 Days	29.50
1984 Hatcheck Girl	10 Days	29.50
1984 Census Taker	10 Days	29.50
1984 Shop Owner	10 Days	29.50
1984 Artist	10 Days	29.50
A Child's Garden of Verses		
1984 Picture Books in Winter	10 Days	24.50
1984 Drops in Water	10 Days	24.50
1984 A Child's Question	10 Days	24.50
1984 Glass River	10 Days	24.50
1984 Busy Bee	10 Days	24.50
1984 At Seaside	10 Days	24.50
1984 Tea Party	10 Days	24.50
1984 Foreign Land	10 Days	24.50
1984 In Hayloft	10 Days	24.50
1984 Among Poppies	10 Days	24.50
1984 5:00 Tea	10 Days	24.50
1984 Love for Kittens	10 Days	24.50
Gamebirds of North America		
1985 Ring-necked Pheasant	15,000	62.50
1985 Bobwhite	15,000	62.50
1985 American Woodcock	15,000	62.50
1985 Wild Turkey	15,000	62.50
1985 California Quail	15,000	62.50
1985 Ruffed Grouse	15,000	62.50
1985 Willow Partridge	15,000	62.50
1985 Prairie Grouse	15,000	62.50
Tale of Genji		
1985 Serene Autumn Moon	NA	45.00
1985 Dragon and Phoenix Boats	NA	45.00
1985 Romantic Duet	NA	45.00
1985 Blue Ocean Dance	NA	45.00
1985 Evening Faces	NA	45.00
1985 Archery Meet	NA	45.00
1985 Moon Viewing	NA	45.00
1985 Table Game	NA	45.00
A Child's Best Friend		
1986 In Disgrace	14 Days	24.50
Poetic Gardens of Japan		
1986 Golden Tranquility	15,000	55.00
Butterfly Garden Collection		
1987 Spicebush Swallowtail	NA	29.50
Star Wars Collection		
1987 Han Solo	NA	29.50
Noble Owls of North America		
1987 Morning Mist	15,000	55.00
Treasure Days		
1987 Ashley	NA	24.50
Hamilton Collection (Boehm Studios)		
Rose		
1979 Peace Rose	15,000	45.00
1979 Queen Elizabeth Rose	15,000	45.00
1979 White Masterpiece Rose	15,000	45.00
1979 Angel Face Rose	15,000	45.00
1979 Tropicana Rose	15,000	45.00
1979 Elegance Rose	15,000	45.00
1979 Royal Highness Rose	15,000	45.00
1979 Mister Lincoln Rose	15,000	45.00
Boehm Owl		
1980 Snowy Owl	15,000	45.00
1980 Boreal Owl	15,000	45.00
1980 Barn Owl	15,000	45.00
1980 Saw Whet Owl	15,000	45.00
1980 Great Horned Owl	15,000	45.00
1980 Screech Owl	15,000	45.00
1980 Short Eared Owl	15,000	45.00
1980 Barred Owl	15,000	45.00

		Edition Limit	Issue Price (US)
Hummingbird			
1980	Calliope Hummingbird	15,000	62.50
1980	Broadtail Hummingbird	15,000	62.50
1980	Rufous Flame-Bearer Hummingbird	15,000	62.50
1980	Broad-Billed Hummingbird	15,000	62.50
1980	Streamer-Tail Hummingbird	15,000	62.50
1980	Blue-Throated Hummingbird	15,000	62.50
1980	Crimson-Topaz Hummingbirds	15,000	62.50
1980	Brazilian Ruby	15,000	62.50
Roses of Excellence			
1981	Love Rose	Year	62.50
1982	White Lightnin'	Year	62.50
1983	Brandy	Year	62.50
Water Bird Collection			
1981	Canadian Geese	15,000	55.00
1981	Wood Ducks	15,000	55.00
1981	Common Mallards	15,000	55.00
1981	Green-Winged Teals	15,000	55.00
1981	Ross' Geese	15,000	55.00
1981	Canvas-Backs	15,000	55.00
1981	Hooded Mergansers	15,000	55.00
1981	American Pintails	15,000	55.00
Blossoms and Berries			
1982	Winter Holiday Bouquet	15,000	62.50
1982	Thanksgiving	15,000	62.50
1982	School Days	15,000	62.50
1982	Indian Summer	15,000	62.50
1982	Mid-Summer	15,000	62.50
1982	Autumn	15,000	62.50
1982	Warm Days	15,000	62.50
1982	Summer Majesty	15,000	62.50
1982	Harvest Time	15,000	62.50
1982	Spring Images	15,000	62.50
1982	Mid-Winter	15,000	62.50
1982	Late-Summer	15,000	62.50
Life's Best Wishes			
1982	Longevity	15,000	75.00
1982	Happiness	15,000	75.00
1982	Fertility	15,000	75.00
1982	Prosperity	15,000	75.00
Miniature Roses			
1982	Toy Clown	28 Days	39.50
1982	Rise 'n Shine	28 Days	39.50
1982	Cuddles	28 Days	39.50
1982	Puppy Love	28 Days	39.50
1982	Magic Carousel	28 Days	39.50
1982	Pacesetter	28 Days	39.50
1982	Gloriglo	28 Days	39.50
1982	Beauty Secret	28 Days	39.50
Tribute to Award-Winning Roses			
1983	Irish Gold	15,000	62.50
1983	Handel	15,000	62.50
1983	Queen Elizabeth	15,000	62.50
1983	Elizabeth of Glamis	15,000	62.50
1983	Iceberg	15,000	62.50
1983	Mountbatten	15,000	62.50
1983	Silver Jubilee	15,000	62.50
1983	Peace	15,000	62.50
A Country Summer			
1986	Butterfly Beauty	10 Days	29.50
1986	Golden Puppy	10 Days	29.50
1987	The Rocking Chair	10 Days	29.50
1987	My Bunny	10 Days	29.50

Hamilton Collection (Caverswall)

		Edition Limit	Issue Price (US)
Woodland Serenade			
1986	American Redstart	15,000	45.00

Hamilton Collection (Hutschenreuther)

		Edition Limit	Issue Price (US)
Roses of Redouté			
1983	China Rose	17,500	32.50

Hamilton Collection (Kaiser)

		Edition Limit	Issue Price (US)
Summer Days of Childhood			
1983	Mountain Friends	10 Days	29.50
1983	Garden Magic	10 Days	29.50

Hamilton Collection (Porcelaine Ariel)

		Edition Limit	Issue Price (US)
A Tribute to Love			
1980	Shaft of Light	17,500	45.00
1980	Jug of Wine	17,500	45.00
1981	Sultan After Sultan	17,500	45.00

		Edition Limit	Issue Price (US)
1981	Bird Is on Wing	17,500	45.00
1982	If Today Be Sweet	17,500	45.00
1982	Flower Once Has Blown	17,500	45.00
Greatest Show on Earth			
1981	Clowns-Heart of Circus	10 Days	30.00
1981	Elephants	10 Days	30.00
1981	Aerialists	10 Days	30.00
1981	Great Parade	10 Days	30.00
1982	Midway	10 Days	30.00
1982	Equestrians	10 Days	30.00
1982	Lion Tamer	10 Days	30.00
1982	Grande Finale	10 Days	30.00

Hamilton Collection (River Shore)

		Edition Limit	Issue Price (US)
Favorite American Songbirds			
1985	Western Tanager	14 Days	24.50
Lovable Teddies			
1986	Bedtime Blues	10 Days	21.50
1986	Bearly Frightful	10 Days	21.50
1986	Caught in the Act	10 Days	21.50
1987	Fireside Friends	10 Days	21.50
Passage to China			
1986	Alliance	15,000	55.00
1986	Grand Turk	15,000	55.00
1987	Seawitch	15,000	55.00
1987	Flying Cloud	15,000	55.00

Hamilton Collection (Roman)

		Edition Limit	Issue Price (US)
Lord's Prayer			
1986	Our Father	10 Days	24.50

Hamilton Collection (Royal Devon)

		Edition Limit	Issue Price (US)
Rockwell Home of Brave			
1981	Reminiscing	18,000	35.00
1981	Hero's Welcome	18,000	35.00
1981	Back to His Old Job	18,000	35.00
1981	War Hero	18,000	35.00
1982	Willie Gillis in Church	18,000	35.00
1982	War Bond	18,000	35.00
1982	Uncle Sam Takes Wings	18,000	35.00
1982	Mother over Top	18,000	35.00
Woodland Serenade			
1986	American Redstart	15,000	45.00
Japanese Blossoms of Autumn			
1986	Bellflower	NA	45.00
Little Rascals			
1986	Three for the Show	NA	24.50
1987	Butch's Challenge	NA	24.50

Hamilton Collection (Viletta)

		Edition Limit	Issue Price (US)
Coppelia Ballet			
1980	Franz' Fantasy Love	28 Days	25.00
1980	Creation of a Doll	28 Days	25.00
1981	Secret Is Unlocked	28 Days	25.00
1981	Swanhilda's Deception	28 Days	25.00
1981	An Uneasy Sleep	28 Days	25.00
1981	Coppelia Awakens	28 Days	25.00
1982	A Shattered Dream	28 Days	25.00
1982	Wedding	28 Days	25.00
Portraits of Childhood			
1981	Butterfly Magic	28 Days	24.95
1982	Sweet Dreams	28 Days	24.95
1983	Turtle Talk	28 Days	24.95
Waltzes of Johann Strauss			
1981	Emperor's Waltz	28 Days	25.00
1981	Blue Danube	28 Days	25.00
1981	Voices of Spring	28 Days	25.00
1981	Vienna Life	28 Days	25.00
1982	Roses of South	28 Days	25.00
1982	Wine, Women and Song	28 Days	25.00
1982	Artist's Life	28 Days	25.00
1982	Tales of Vienna Woods	28 Days	25.00
Carefree Days			
1982	Autumn Wanderer	10 Days	24.50
1982	Best Friends	10 Days	24.50
1982	Feeding Time	10 Days	24.50
1983	Bathtime Visitor	10 Days	24.50
1983	First Catch	10 Days	24.50
1983	Monkey Business	10 Days	24.50
1984	Touchdown	10 Days	24.50
1984	Nature Hunt	10 Days	24.50

Hamilton Mint

		Edition Limit	Issue Price (US)
Picasso			
1972	Le Gourmet	5,000	125.00
1972	Tragedy	5,000	125.00
1973	Lovers	5,000	125.00
Kennedy			
1974	(Gold on Pewter)	Year	40.00
1974	(Pewter)	Year	25.00
Man's Best Friend			
1978	Hobo	9,500	40.00
1978	Doctor	9,500	40.00
1979	Making Friends	9,500	40.00
1979	Gone Fishing	9,500	40.00
1980	Thief	9,500	40.00
1980	Puppy Love	9,500	40.00

Hartman House

		Edition Limit	Issue Price (US)
Sounds of Innocence			
1987	Fleishhacker Carousel	5,000	45.00

Heirloom Tradition

		Edition Limit	Issue Price (US)
Christmas			
1985	It's a Wonderful Life	10,000	35.00
1986	Dickens' Christmas Carol	10,000	35.00
Cinema Classics			
1985	High Noon	10,000	35.00
1985	Indiscreet	10,000	35.00
(Single issue)			
1985	Barry Manilow	20,000	35.00
(Single issue)			
1986	Varga	10,000	45.00

Historic Providence Mint

		Edition Limit	Issue Price (US)
(Single issue)			
1979	Children's Year	3,000	95.00
Children of Seasons			
1980	Children of Spring	3,000	107.50
America Beautiful			
1981	Spacious Skies	17,500	37.50
1981	Amber Waves of Grain	17,500	27.50
1981	Purple Mountain Majesties	17,500	37.50
1981	God Shed His Grace	17,500	37.50
1981	Crown Good with Brotherhood	17,500	37.50
1981	From Sea to Shining Sea	17,500	37.50
Vanishing American Barn			
1983	Bucks County Barn	14,500	39.50
1983	Victorian Barn	14,500	39.50
1983	New England Barn	14,500	39.50
1983	Southern Tobacco Barn	14,500	39.50
1983	Forebay Barn	14,500	39.50
1983	Appalachian Barn	14,500	39.50
1983	Connected Barn	14,500	39.50
1983	Hudson River Barn	14,500	39.50
1983	Log Barn	14,500	39.50
1983	Thatched Barn	14,500	39.50
1983	Lancaster Barn	14,500	39.50
1983	Round Barn	14,500	39.50
Alice in Wonderland			
1986	Tea Party	45 Days	29.50
1986	Caterpillar	45 Days	29.50
1986	Duchess and Cook	45 Days	29.50
1986	White Knight	45 Days	29.50
1986	Off With Their Heads!	45 Days	29.50
1987	The Red & White Queens	45 Days	29.50
1987	The White Rabbit	45 Days	29.50
Lil' Peddlers			
1986	Forget Me Nots	NA	29.50
1986	Extra, Extra	NA	29.50
1987	Coolin' Off	NA	29.50
1987	Poppin' Corn	NA	29.50
1987	Oven Fresh	NA	29.50

Ralph Homan Studios (Viletta)

		Edition Limit	Issue Price (US)
Seasons of Oak			
1979	Lazy Days	5,000	55.00
1980	Come Fly with Me	5,000	55.00

Home Plates (Mingolla)

		Edition Limit	Issue Price (US)
Christmas (Enamel on Copper)			
1973	Christmas	1,000	95.00
1974	Christmas	1,000	110.00
1975	Christmas	1,000	125.00

		Edition Limit	Issue Price (US)
1976	Christmas	1,000	125.00
1977	Scene from Childhood	2,000	200.00
Christmas (Porcelain)			
1974	Christmas	5,000	35.00
1975	Christmas	5,000	35.00
1976	Christmas	5,000	35.00
1977	Winter Wonderland	7,000	45.00
Four Seasons (Enamel on Copper)			
1978	Dashing Thru Snow	2,000	150.00
1979	Spring Flowers	2,000	150.00
1980	Beach Fun	2,000	150.00
1981	Balloon Breeze	2,000	150.00
Christmas in Country (Enamel on Copper)			
1979	Dear Santa	1,000	70.00
1980	Country Cousin	1,000	90.00

Hoyle Products

		Edition Limit	Issue Price (US)
Clown			
1977	Runaway	7,500	45.00
1978	It's Your Move	7,500	45.00
1979	Understudy	7,500	45.00
1980	Idol	7,500	45.00
Traveling Salesman			
1977	Traveling Salesman	7,500	35.00
1978	Country Pedlar	7,500	40.00
1979	Horse Trader	7,500	40.00
1980	Expert Salesman	7,500	45.00
Wilderness Wings			
1978	Gliding In	5,000	35.00
1979	Taking Off	5,000	45.00
1980	Joining Up	5,000	45.00
1981	Canvasbacks	5,000	47.50
Four Seasons			
1978	Gay Blades	Year	55.00
1979	Boy Meets Dog	Year	55.00
1980	Chilly Reception	Year	65.00
Rockwell Four Seasons (Bronze)			
1979	Adventurers Between Adventures	9,500	55.00
Cowboy			
1977	Sharing an Apple	5,000	35.00
1978	Split Decision	5,000	35.00
1979	Hiding Out	5,000	35.00
1980	In Trouble	5,000	35.00
Family Circus Christmas			
1980	Christmas	5,000	25.00
1981	Christmas	5,000	30.00
Mother's Day			
1980	Mother's Day	5,000	25.00
Rare Rockwells			
1980	Mrs. O'Leary's Cow	7,500	30.00
1981	Come and Get It	7,500	30.00
Hilda			
1981	Toasting Marshmallows	5,000	25.00
Nostalgia			
1981	Pepsi Cola Girl	5,000	25.00
1982	Olympia Girl	5,000	30.00
1982	Savannah Beer Girl	5,000	30.00
1983	Dr. Pepper Girl	5,000	30.00
Remember When			
1982	A Surprise for Kitty	10,000	30.00
1982	Washday	10,000	30.00
1983	Playing Grandmother	10,000	30.00
1983	Physician	10,000	30.00
Wings of Wild			
1982	Cinnamon Teal	5,000	30.00
1982	Moment of Rest	5,000	30.00
1983	Mourning Doves	5,000	30.00
Gothic Romance			
1982	Moonlight Romance	5,000	30.00
By-Gone Days			
1983	Breakfast with Teddy	12,500	35.00
1984	Flower Basket	12,500	35.00
Nostalgia–Children			
1983	Pear's Soap Ad	12,500	35.00
1984	Morton Salt Ad	12,500	35.00
Nostalgia–Magazine Covers			
1983	Ladies Home Journal	12,500	35.00
1984	Saturday Evening Post	12,500	35.00

Hudson Pewter

		Edition Limit	Issue Price (US)
Bicentennial			
1975	Spirit of '76	10,000	45.00

OVER-THE-COUNTER ISSUES

	Edition Limit	Issue Price (US)
Mother's Day		
1979 Cherished	10,000	35.00
Songbirds of Four Seasons		
1979 Hummingbird	7,500	35.00
America's Sailing Ships		
1979 U.S.S. Constitution	5,000	35.00
A Child's Christmas		
1979 Littlest Angels	10,000	35.00
1980 Heaven's Christmas Tree	10,000	42.50
Twas Night Before Christmas		
1982 Not a Creature Was Stirring	10,000	47.50
1983 Visions of Sugar Plums	10,000	47.50

Imperial

	Edition Limit	Issue Price (US)
America Beautiful		
1969 U.S. Capitol	500	17.50
1970 Mount Rushmore	500	17.50
1971 Statue of Liberty	500	17.50
1972 Monument Valley, Arizona	500	17.50
1973 Liberty Bell	500	17.50
1974 Golden Gate	500	19.95
1975 Mt. Vernon	500	19.95
Christmas		
1970 Partridge (Carnival)	Year	12.00
1970 Partridge (Crystal)	Year	15.00
1971 Two Turtle Doves (Carnival)	Year	12.00
1971 Two Turtle Doves (Crystal)	Year	16.50
1972 Three French Hens (Carnival)	Year	12.00
1972 Three French Hens (Crystal)	Year	16.50
1973 Four Colly Birds (Carnival)	Year	12.00
1973 Four Colly Birds (Crystal)	Year	16.50
1974 Five Golden Rings (Carnival)	Year	12.00
1974 Five Golden Rings (Crystal)	Year	16.50
1975 Six Geese A-Laying (Carnival)	Year	14.00
1975 Six Geese A-Laying (Crystal)	Year	19.00
1976 Seven Swans (Carnival)	Year	16.00
1976 Seven Swans (Crystal)	Year	21.00
1977 Eight Maids A-Milking (Carnival)	Year	18.00
1977 Eight Maids A-Milking (Crystal)	Year	23.00
1978 Nine Ladies Dancing (Carnival)	Year	20.00
1978 Nine Ladies Dancing (Crystal)	Year	25.00
1979 Ten Lords A-Leaping (Carnival)	Year	22.00
1979 Ten Lords A-Leaping (Crystal)	Year	27.00
1980 Eleven Pipers Piping (Carnival)	Year	24.00
1980 Eleven Pipers Piping (Crystal)	Year	29.00
1981 Twelve Drummers Drumming (Carnival)	Year	28.00
1981 Twelve Drummers Drumming (Crystal)	Year	34.00
Coin Crystal		
1971 1964 Kennedy Half Dollar	Year	15.00
1972 Eisenhower Dollar	Year	15.00
(Single issue)		
1976 Bicentennial	Year	20.00

Incolay Studios

	Edition Limit	Issue Price (US)
Life's Interludes		
1979 Uncertain Beginning	Year	95.00
1980 Finally Friends	12,000	95.00
Four Elements		
1983 Air	9,170	25.00
Enchanted Moments		
1984 Tiffany's World	7,500	95.00
1985 Jennifer's World	7,500	95.00

International Museum

	Edition Limit	Issue Price (US)
Christmas Stamp Art		
1979 Gingerbread Santa	9,900	29.00
1980 Madonna and Child	9,900	37.50
1981 Botticelli's Madonna and Child	9,900	45.00
1982 Madonna of Goldfinch	9,900	45.00
Dance, Ballerina, Dance		
1982 First Slippers	14,500	47.50
1982 At Barre	14,500	47.50
1982 Recital	14,500	47.50
1982 Pirouette	14,500	47.50
1982 Swan Lake	14,500	47.50
1982 Opening Night	14,500	47.50
Letter Writers		
1982 Portrait of Michelangelo	15,000	45.00
1982 Mrs. John Douglas	15,000	45.00
1983 Don Antonio de Noriega	15,000	45.00
1983 Lovely Reader	15,000	45.00
1984 Lady Writing Letter	15,000	45.00
1984 Five Feminine Virtues	15,000	45.00
Super Heroes		
1983 Superman	NA	29.50
1983 Wonder Woman	NA	39.50
1983 Batman and Robin	NA	39.50
1984 Shazam	NA	39.50
1984 Aquaman	NA	39.50
1984 Justice League	NA	39.50

International Silver

	Edition Limit	Issue Price (US)
We Are One		
1972 Declaration of Independence	7,500	40.00
1973 Midnight Ride of Paul Revere	7,500	40.00
1973 Stand at Concord Bridge	7,500	40.00
1974 Crossing Delaware	7,500	50.00
1974 Battle of Valley Forge	7,500	50.00
1975 Surrender at Yorktown	7,500	50.00
Christmas		
1974 Tiny Tim	7,500	75.00
1975 Caught	7,500	75.00
1976 Bringing Home Tree	7,500	75.00
1977 Fezziwig's Christmas Ball	7,500	75.00
1978 Alleluia	7,500	75.00
1979 Rejoice	7,500	100.00
1980 Adoration	7,500	125.00
Presidential		
1975 Washington	7,500	75.00
1976 Jefferson	7,500	75.00
1976 Lincoln	7,500	75.00
1976 F. Roosevelt	7,500	75.00
1977 Eisenhower	7,500	75.00
1977 Kennedy	7,500	75.00
Seasons American Past		
1976 Autumn	7,500	60.00
1976 Spring	7,500	60.00
1976 Summer	7,500	60.00
1976 Winter	7,500	60.00

See also: American Archives (U.S.A.)

Interpace

	Edition Limit	Issue Price (US)
Modigliani (Single issue)		
1972 Caryatid	10,000	60.00
Architects of Democracy (Set of four)		
1974 George Washington		
1974 John Adams		
1974 Thomas Jefferson		
1974 Alexander Hamilton	1,776	225.00

JM Company

	Edition Limit	Issue Price (US)
Competitive Sports		
1979 Downhill Racing Slalom	10,000	25.00
Oriental Birds		
1979 Window at Tiger Spring Temple	10,000	39.00
Love		
1980 Love's Serenade	5,000	50.00

Joys (Viletta)

	Edition Limit	Issue Price (US)
Precious Moments		
1979 Friend in Sky	28 Days	21.50
1980 Sand in Her Shoe	28 Days	21.50
1980 Snow Bunny	28 Days	21.50
1980 Seashells	28 Days	21.50
1981 Dawn	28 Days	21.50
1981 My Kitty	28 Days	21.50

Judaic Heritage Society

	Edition Limit	Issue Price (US)
Jewish Holidays		
1972 Chanukah (Silver)	2,000	150.00
1972 Chanukah (Gold)	25	1900.00
1972 Pesach (Silver)	2,000	150.00
1972 Pesach (Gold)	25	1900.00
1972 Purim (Silver)	2,000	150.00
(Single issue)		
1974 Purim (Silver)	1,000	150.00
Great Jewish Women		
1976 Golda Meir	4,000	35.00
1976 Henrietta Szold	4,000	35.00
1976 Emma Lazarus	4,000	35.00
Heritage Plates		
1976 Rabbi	4,000	35.00
1976 Hasidim	4,000	35.00
1976 Shtetl	4,000	35.00
(Single issue)		
1977 Jacob and Angel	5,000	45.00
(Single issue)		
1977 Hatikvah (Copper)	5,000	55.00
(Single issue)		
1977 Hatikvah (Gold Plated)	1,000	75.00
(Single issue)		
1977 Hatikvah (Sterling Silver)	500	180.00
Jewish Holidays		
1979 Chanukah	2,500	50.00
1979 Purim	2,500	50.00
1979 Shavouth	2,500	50.00
1979 Rosh Hashanah	2,500	50.00
1979 Simchat Torah	2,500	50.00
1979 Pesach	2,500	50.00
Jerusalem Wedding		
1979 Bride of Jerusalem	6,000	65.00
1979 Hasidic Dancers	6,000	65.00

Judaic Heritage Society (Avondale)

	Edition Limit	Issue Price (US)
(Single issue)		
1980 Shalom–Peace	6,000	95.00

Judaic Heritage Society (Viletta)

	Edition Limit	Issue Price (US)
Israel's 30th Anniversary (Single issue)		
1979 L'Chayim to Israel	10,000	59.50
Israel's 30th Anniversary (Single issue)		
1979 Prophecy of Isaiah	4,000	59.50

David Kaplan Studio

	Edition Limit	Issue Price (US)
Fiddler's People		
1978 Fiddler on Roof	7,500	60.00
1979 Tevya	7,500	60.00
1980 Miracle of Love	7,500	60.00
1981 Wedding	7,500	60.00
Loveables		
1982 Little Angel	12,500	40.00

Keller & George (Reed & Barton)

	Edition Limit	Issue Price (US)
Bicentennial		
1972 Monticello (Damascene)	1,000	75.00
1972 Monticello (Silver Plate)	200	200.00
1973 Mt. Vernon (Damascene)	Year	75.00

Kensington

	Edition Limit	Issue Price (US)
Children of Week		
1980 Wednesday's Child	27,500	28.50

Kern Collectibles

	Edition Limit	Issue Price (US)
Linda's Little Loveables		
1977 Blessing	7,500	30.00
1978 Appreciation	7,500	37.50
1979 Adopted Burro	7,500	42.50
Runci Mother's Day		
1977 Darcy	5,000	50.00
1978 A Moment to Reflect	5,000	55.00
1979 Fulfillment	5,000	45.00
1980 A Renewal of Faith	5,000	45.00
Christmas of Yesterday		
1978 Christmas Call	5,000	45.00
1979 Woodcutter's Christmas	5,000	50.00
1980 Making Christmas Goodies	5,000	55.00
1981 Singing Christmas Carols	5,000	55.00
Adventures of Old West		
1981 Grizzly Ambush	7,500	65.00
1982 Train Robbers	7,500	65.00
1983 Bank Holdup	7,500	65.00
1984 Nature Strikes	7,500	65.00
My Favorite Pets		
1981 Schnauzers	7,500	39.95
1982 Cocker Spaniels	7,500	39.95
1983 Pointers	7,500	42.50
Horses of Harland Young		
1982 Quarterhorses	10,000	55.00
1983 Arabians	10,000	55.00
1984 Mustangs	10,000	55.00
1985 Thoroughbreds	10,000	55.00
School Days		
1982 Apple for My Teacher	7,500	65.00
1983 Arithmetic Lesson	7,500	65.00
This Little Pig		
1982 Pig Went to Market	9,800	39.95
1983 Pig Stayed Home	9,800	42.50
1984 Pig Had Roast Beef	9,800	45.00
1985 Pig Had None	9,800	45.00
Childhood Innocence		
1983 Sarah	7,500	55.00
1984 Kelly	7,500	55.00
A Child's World		
1983 Kathie	9,800	45.00
1983 Meredith	9,800	45.00
1984 Freddie	9,800	45.00
1984 Jamie	9,800	45.00
1985 Robbie	9,800	45.00
Kitty Cats		
1983 Morrie	7,500	39.00
1984 Tattoo	7,500	39.00
1985 Topsie	7,500	39.00
1987 Zorba	7,500	39.00
North American Game Birds		
1983 Canadian Geese	7,500	60.00
1984 Mallards	7,500	60.00
1984 Pheasants	7,500	60.00
1987 Ruffed Grouse	7,500	60.00
Zoological Garden		
1983 Elephants	5,000	55.00
1984 Tigers	5,000	55.00
Children of Southwest		
1984 Navaho Pixie	7,500	36.00
1984 Morning Sun	7,500	36.00
1987 Dark Eyes	7,500	36.00
Country Friends		
1984 Elizabeth	7,500	35.00
Memories of Yesterday		
1984 Patricia	7,500	35.00
Tribal Companions		
1984 My Best Friend	6,000	35.00
(Single issue)		
1984 Champ	7,500	39.50
Birds of Distinction		
1985 New Light, New Life	NA	29.50
Women of Timeless Beauty		
1985 Melinda	5,000	35.00

Kern Collectibles (Haviland & Parlon)

	Edition Limit	Issue Price (US)
Patti Canaris Songbird		
1980 Cardinals	5,000	65.00
1981 Blue Birds	5,000	70.00
1982 Orioles	5,000	70.00
1983 Goldfinches	5,000	70.00
Patti Canaris Butterfly		
1984 Monarchs	7,500	75.00
1985 Sonora Blue	7,500	80.00

Kern Collectibles (Pickard)

	Edition Limit	Issue Price (US)
Cowboy Artists (Sets of two)		
1976 Out There		
1976 Cutting Out a Stray	3,000	130.00

	Edition Limit	Issue Price (US)
1977 Broken Cinch		
1977 No Place to Cross	1,000	130.00
Companions		
1977 Cubs	5,000	40.00
1978 Mighty Sioux	5,000	40.00
1979 Nature Girl	5,000	50.00
1980 Buffalo Boy	5,000	50.00
1981 Shepherds	5,000	55.00

Kern Collectibles (Rosenthal)

	Edition Limit	Issue Price (US)
John Falter Harvest Time		
1976 Gathering Pumpkins	5,000	70.00
1977 Honest Day's Work	4,000	70.00
Runci Classic		
1977 Summertime	5,000	95.00
1978 Springtime	5,000	95.00

Kern Collectibles (Royal Bayreuth)

	Edition Limit	Issue Price (US)
Christmas		
1972 Carriage in Village	4,000	15.00
1973 Snow Scene	5,000	16.50
1974 Old Mill	4,000	24.00
1975 Forest Chalet "Serenity"	4,000	27.50
1976 Christmas in Country	5,000	40.00
1977 Peace on Earth	5,000	40.00
1978 Peaceful Interlude	5,000	45.00
1979 Homeward Bound	5,000	50.00
Sun Bonnet Babies (Set of seven)		
1974 Monday (Washing Day)		
1974 Tuesday (Ironing Day)		
1974 Wednesday (Mending Day)		
1974 Thursday (Scrubbing Day)		
1974 Friday (Sweeping Day)		
1974 Saturday (Baking Day)		
1974 Sunday (Fishing Day)	15,000	120.00
Antique American Art		
1976 Farmyard Tranquility	3,000	50.00
1977 Half Dome	3,000	55.00
1978 Down Memory Lane	3,000	65.00
(Single issue)		
1976 Sun Bonnet Babies Composite	15,000	75.00
L. Henry		
1976 Just Friends	5,000	50.00
1977 Interruption	4,000	55.00
Anniversary		
1980 Young Americans	5,000	125.00
Sun Bonnet Babies Playtime		
1981 Swinging	5,000	60.00
1981 Round Dance	5,000	60.00
1982 Marbles	5,000	60.00
1982 Playing Catch	5,000	60.00

Kern Collectibles (Sango)

	Edition Limit	Issue Price (US)
Living American Artist		
1976 Sweethearts (Rockwell)	10,000	30.00
1977 Apache Girl (Perillo)	5,000	35.00
1978 Natural Habitat	5,000	40.00
Great Achievements in Art		
1980 Arabian	3,000	65.00
1981 Texas Longhorns	3,000	70.00

Kilkelly

	Edition Limit	Issue Price (US)
St. Patrick's Day		
1975 Pipe and Shamrock	Year	16.50
1976 Third Look in Logan	Year	20.00

Killman Art Gallery

	Edition Limit	Issue Price (US)
Native Wildcat Kittens of North America		
1985 The Adorable Oselot	7,500	39.00
1986 Bashful Babies	7,500	39.00
1987 Bouncy Bobcat	7,500	45.00

Kirk

	Edition Limit	Issue Price (US)
DeGrazia		
1972 Heavenly Blessing	200	75.00
Mother's Day		
1972 Mother and Child	3,500	75.00
1973 Mother and Child	2,500	80.00
Bicentennial		
1972 U.S.S. Constellation	825	75.00
1972 Washington	5,000	75.00

	Edition Limit	Issue Price (US)
Thanksgiving		
1972 Thanksgiving Ways and Means	3,500	150.00
Christmas		
1972 Flight into Egypt	3,500	150.00

Lake Shore Prints

	Edition Limit	Issue Price (US)
Rockwell		
1973 Butter Girl	9,433	14.95
1974 Truth about Santa	15,141	19.50
1975 Home from Fields	8,500	24.50
1976 A President's Wife	2,500	70.00

Lapsys

	Edition Limit	Issue Price (US)
Crystal Christmas		
1977 Snowflake	5,000	47.50
1978 Peace on Earth	5,000	47.50

Legacy, Ltd.

	Edition Limit	Issue Price (US)
Christmas		
1986 Whitetail Buck	5,000	39.50

Lenox

	Edition Limit	Issue Price (US)
Boehm Birds, Young America		
1972 Bird of Peace (Mute Swan)	5,000	150.00
1973 1776	6,000	175.00
Boehm Woodland Wildlife		
1973 Raccoons	Year	50.00
1974 Red Foxes	Year	52.50
1975 Cottontail Rabbits	Year	58.50
1976 Eastern Chipmunks	Year	62.50
1977 Beaver	Year	67.50
1978 Whitetail Deer	Year	70.00
1979 Squirrels	Year	76.00
1980 Bobcats	Year	92.50
1981 Martens	Year	100.00
1982 Otters	Year	100.00
Christmas Tree		
1976 Douglas Fir	Year	50.00
1977 Scotch Pine	Year	55.00
1978 Blue Spruce	Year	65.00
1979 Balsam Fir	Year	65.00
1980 Brewer's Spruce	Year	75.00
1981 China Fir	Year	75.00
1982 Aleppo Pine	Year	80.00
Colonial Christmas Wreath		
1981 Virginia	Year	65.00
1982 Massachusetts	Year	65.00
1983 Maryland	Year	70.00
1984 Rhode Island	Year	70.00
1985 Connecticut	Year	70.00
1986 New Hampshire	Year	39.50
Butterflies and Flowers		
1982 Question Mark and New England Aster	25,000	65.00
1983 Sonoran Blue and Mariposa Lily	25,000	65.00
1983 Malachite and Orchid	25,000	65.00
1984 Ruddy Daggerwing and Lantana	25,000	70.00
1984 American Lady and Virginia Rose	25,000	70.00
1985 Buckeye and Bluebells	25,000	75.00
American Wildlife		
1983 Red Foxes	9,500	65.00
1983 Ocelots	9,500	65.00
1983 Sea Lions	9,500	65.00
1983 Raccoons	9,500	65.00
1983 Dall Sheep	9,500	65.00
Nature's Nursery		
1983 Snow Leopards	15,000	65.00
1983 Koalas	15,000	65.00
1984 Llamas	15,000	70.00
1984 Bengal Tigers	15,000	70.00
1985 Emperor Penguins	15,000	75.00
1985 Polar Bears	15,000	75.00
1986 Harp Seals	15,000	80.00
1986 Zebras	15,000	80.00

See also: American Express (U.S.A.)

Lincoln Mint

	Edition Limit	Issue Price (US)
Great Artists (Dali)		
1971 Unicorn Dyonisiaque (Gold)	100	1500.00
1971 Unicorn Dyonisiaque (Silver)	5,000	100.00

	Edition Limit	Issue Price (US)
1972 Dyonisiaque et Pallas Athens (Gold)	300	2000.00
1972 Dyonisiaque et Pallas Athens (Gold Plate)	2,500	150.00
1972 Dyonisiaque et Pallas Athens (Silver)	7,500	125.00
Easter		
1972 Christ (Silver)	20,000	150.00
1972 Christ (Gold Plate)	10,000	200.00
1974 Christ (Pewter)	Year	45.00
Mother's Day		
1972 Collies (Silver)	3,000	125.00
Christmas		
1972 Madonna Della Seggiola (Gold Plate)	125	150.00
1972 Madonna Della Seggiola (Silver)	3,000	125.00
Dali Cross Plate		
1977 Gold Cross	5,000	225.00
1977 Silver Cross	10,000	175.00

Lincoln Mint (Gorham)

	Edition Limit	Issue Price (US)
Christmas		
1978 Santa Belongs to All Children	7,500	29.50

Litt

	Edition Limit	Issue Price (US)
Christmas		
1978 Madonna & Child	1,000	200.00
1979 O Holy Night	1,000	200.00
Annual		
1979 Apache Sunset	1,250	275.00

Lynell Studios

	Edition Limit	Issue Price (US)
Little Traveler		
1978 On His Way	4,000	45.90
1979 On Her Way	4,000	45.00
American Adventure		
1979 Whaler	7,500	50.00
1979 Trapper	7,500	50.00
1980 Forty-Niner	7,500	50.00
1981 Pioneer Woman	7,500	50.00
1981 Wagon Master	7,500	50.00
1982 Wagon Ho!	7,500	50.00
All-American Soap Box Derby		
1979 Last Minute Changes	Year	24.50
1980 At Gate	Year	24.50
1981 In Stretch	Year	29.50
Rockwell Legendary Art Christmas		
1979 Snow Queen	60 Days	29.50
1980 Surprises for All	60 Days	29.50
1981 Grandpop and Me	60 Days	29.50
1982 Santa's Secret	10,000	35.00
1983 Looking for Santa	10,000	35.00
John Wayne		
1979 Man of Golden West	Year	45.00
RCA Victor Nipper Plate		
1980 His Master's Voice	NA	24.50
Rockwell Legendary Art Annual		
1980 Artist's Daughter	Year	65.00
Rockwell Legendary Art Mother's Day		
1980 Cradle of Love	60 Days	29.50
1981 A Mother's Blessing	60 Days	29.50
1982 Memories	60 Days	29.50
1983 Dear Mother	60 Days	29.50
1984 First Mother's Day	60 Days	29.50
Rockwell Legendary Art Rare Rockwell Paintings		
1980 Poor Richard	17,500	45.00
Popeye's 50th Anniversary (Single issue)		
1980 Happy Birthday Popeye	Year	22.50
Great Chiefs of Canada		
1980 Chief Joseph Brant	7,500	65.00
1981 Crowfoot	7,500	65.00
1982 Tecumseh	7,500	65.00
Betsey Bates Christmas		
1979 Olde Country Inn	7,500	38.50
1980 Village School House	7,500	38.50
1981 Village Blacksmith	7,500	38.50
1982 Christmas Village	7,500	38.50
Children's World		
1981 Official Babysitter	15,000	24.50
1981 Cowboy Capers	15,000	29.50
1982 Nurse Nancy	15,000	29.50
1982 Pet Shop	15,000	29.50

	Edition Limit	Issue Price (US)
Eyes of Seasons		
1981 Winter	19,500	38.50
1981 Spring	19,500	38.50
1981 Summer	19,500	38.50
1981 Autumn	19,500	38.50
Hagel Christmas		
1981 Shhh!	17,500	29.50
1982 Kiss for Santa	10,000	35.00
How West Was Won		
1981 Pony Express	19,500	38.50
1982 Oregon Trail	19,500	38.50
1982 California Gold Rush	19,500	38.50
1982 Cattle Drive	19,500	38.50
1983 Peace Pipe	19,500	38.50
1983 Driving Golden Spike	19,500	38.50
North American Wildlife		
1981 Snuggling Cougars	7,500	65.00
Oriental Dreams		
1981 Tranquility	15,000	55.00
Rockwell's Scotty		
1981 Scotty Stowaway	17,500	45.00
1982 Scotty Strikes Bargain	17,500	35.00
(Single issue)		
1981 Reagan-Bush Inaugural	17,500	45.00
Best of Times		
1982 Candy Shop	15,000	38.50
Circus Dreams		
1982 Two for Show	19,500	24.50
Greatest Clowns of Circus		
1982 Emmett Kelly	NA	38.50
1982 Lou Jacobs	NA	38.50
1982 Felix Adler	NA	38.50
1982 Otto Griebling	NA	38.50
Hagel Mother's Day		
1982 Once Upon a Time	60 Days	29.50
Hobo Joe		
1982 Hold Onions	10,000	50.00
1982 Do Not Disturb	10,000	50.00
1983 No Camping or Fishing	10,000	50.00
1983 Traveling in Style	10,000	50.00
Little House on Prairie		
1982 Welcome to Walnut Creek	19,500	45.00
1982 Country Girls	19,500	45.00
1982 Women at Harvestime	19,500	45.00
1982 Sweethearts Tree	19,500	45.00
1983 School Marm	19,500	45.00
1983 Bell for Grove	19,500	45.00
1983 Mary's Gift	19,500	45.00
1983 Caroline's Eggs	19,500	45.00
1983 Medicine Show	19,500	45.00
1983 Brotherhood on the Prairie	19,500	45.00
1983 The Founders' Day Picnic	19,500	45.00
1983 The Ingalls Family	19,500	45.00
(Single issue)		
1982 Betty Boop	15,000	24.50
(Single issue)		
1982 I Love Lucy	100 Days	45.00
(Single issue)		
1982 Norman Rockwell Tribute	5,000	55.00
(Single issue)		
1982 Thanks for Memories	100 Days	45.00
(Single issue)		
1982 Young at Heart	100 Days	45.00
Lionel Barrymore		
1983 Nantucket	7,500	45.00
(Single issue)		
1984 Wayne Gretzky	Year	39.95

Mallek Studios

	Edition Limit	Issue Price (US)
Navajo Christmas		
1971 Indian Wise Men	1,000	15.00
1972 On Reservation	2,000	17.00
1973 Hoke Denetsosie	2,000	17.00
1974 Monument Valley	2,000	18.00
1975 Coming Home for Christmas	2,000	18.00
1976 Deer with Rainbow	2,000	20.00
1977 Goat Herders	2,000	20.00
1978 Hogan Christmas	2,000	20.00
1979 Navajo Madonna	3,000	25.00
1980 Children's Playmates	3,500	25.00

Chinese Lunar Calendar

	Edition Limit	Issue Price (US)
1972 Year of Rat	1,000	15.00
1973 Year of Ox	1,000	15.00
1974 Year of Rabbit	1,000	15.00

Christmas Game Birds
	Edition Limit	Issue Price (US)
1972 Gambel Quail	1,000	15.00
1973 Partridge	1,000	15.00
1974 Owl and Cactus	1,000	15.00
1975 Chinese Wood Duck	1,000	15.00
1976 Wild Turkey	1,000	15.00
1977 Mallard	1,000	15.00
1978 Canadian Geese	1,000	15.00
1979 American Woodcock	1,000	15.00

Mexican Christmas
	Edition Limit	Issue Price (US)
1972 Manger	1,000	15.00
1973 Madonna	1,000	15.00
1974 Corona	1,000	18.00
1975 Pinata	1,000	18.00
1976 Procession	1,000	20.00
1977 Wisemen	1,000	20.00

Navidad (Single issue)
	Edition Limit	Issue Price (US)
1972 Navidad en Mexico	500	15.00

(Single issue)
	Edition Limit	Issue Price (US)
1972 Amish Harvest	1,000	17.00

A.B.C.'s
	Edition Limit	Issue Price (US)
1974 A.B.C. Rabbit	1,000	15.00
1975 A.B.C. Mice	1,000	15.00
1976 A.B.C. Ducklings	1,000	15.00
1977 A.B.C. Elephant	1,000	15.00
1978 A.B.C. Owls	1,000	15.00

(Single issue)
	Edition Limit	Issue Price (US)
1976 Kewpie Doll	1,000	15.00

(Single issue)
	Edition Limit	Issue Price (US)
1982 Barnyard Serenade	5,000	25.00

(Single issue)
	Edition Limit	Issue Price (US)
1982 Beep, Beep	2,000	25.00

Marigold

Super Stars
	Edition Limit	Issue Price (US)
1983 Mickey Mantle	10,000	60.00
1984 Joe DiMaggio	10,000	60.00
1984 Willie Mays	10,000	60.00

Mary Engelbreit Society

Believe
	Edition Limit	Issue Price (US)
1986 Santa's Treasure	10,000	29.95

Master Engravers of America

Indian Dancers
	Edition Limit	Issue Price (US)
1979 Eagle Dancer	2,500	300.00
1980 Hoop Dancer	2,500	300.00

McCalla Enterprises (Viletta)

Making Friends
	Edition Limit	Issue Price (US)
1978 Feeding Neighbor's Pony	5,000	45.00
1979 Cowboys 'n' Indians	5,000	47.50
1980 Surprise for Christy	5,000	47.50

Love Letters
	Edition Limit	Issue Price (US)
1980 Mail Order Bride	5,000	60.00

Metal Arts

America's First Family (Single issue)
	Edition Limit	Issue Price (US)
1977 Carters	9,500	40.00

Freedom (Single issue)
	Edition Limit	Issue Price (US)
1977 Washington at Valley Forge (Sterling)	500	225.00

Freedom (Single issue)
	Edition Limit	Issue Price (US)
1977 Washington at Valley Forge (Pewter)	1,000	95.00

Winslow Homer's Sea
	Edition Limit	Issue Price (US)
1977 Breezing Up	9,500	29.95

Rockwell Copper Christmas
	Edition Limit	Issue Price (US)
1978 Christmas Gift	Year	48.00
1979 Big Moment	Year	48.00

Metlox Potteries
See: Vernonware (U.S.A.)

Metropolitan Museum of Art

Treasures of Tutankhamun
	Edition Limit	Issue Price (US)
1977 King Tut	2,500	150.00

Mingolla
See: Home Plates (U.S.A.)

Mistwood Designs (Fairmont)

American Wildlife
	Edition Limit	Issue Price (US)
1981 Desperado at Waterhole	5,000	45.00
1981 Bayou Bunnies	5,000	50.00

Woodland Game Birds
	Edition Limit	Issue Price (US)
1981 After Flight	5,000	60.00

Modern Concepts

Special Moments
	Edition Limit	Issue Price (US)
1982 David's Dilemma	12,500	35.00
1983 Secrets	12,500	35.00
1983 Enough for Two	12,500	38.50
1984 Chatterbox	12,500	38.50

Magic of Sea
	Edition Limit	Issue Price (US)
1983 Future Miss	NA	25.00
1984 One, Two, Three!	NA	26.50

Signs of Love
	Edition Limit	Issue Price (US)
1983 When Hearts Touch	17,500	39.00
1984 My Very Own	17,500	39.00

Nursery Rhyme Favorites
	Edition Limit	Issue Price (US)
1984 Sugar & Spice	7,500	35.00
1985 Snips & Snails	7,500	35.00

Modern Masters

Through Eyes of Love
	Edition Limit	Issue Price (US)
1981 Enchanted Eyes	9,500	55.00
1982 Summer Secrets	9,500	55.00
1983 Garden Gathering	9,500	55.00

Babes in Woods
	Edition Limit	Issue Price (US)
1982 Newborn Fawn	9,500	45.00
1983 First Outing	9,500	45.00
1983 Baby Bandit	9,500	50.00
1984 Moment's Rest	9,500	50.00

Floral Felines
	Edition Limit	Issue Price (US)
1982 Baron	9,500	55.00
1983 Her Majesty	9,500	55.00
1984 Duchess	9,500	55.00
1984 His Lordship	9,500	55.00

Will Moses America
	Edition Limit	Issue Price (US)
1982 September Fair	7,500	45.00
1983 Spring Recess	7,500	45.00

Litter Basket
	Edition Limit	Issue Price (US)
1983 Last of Litter	15 Days	35.00
1984 Double Delight	15 Days	35.00
1984 Tender Trio	15 Days	35.00
1985 Litter Bug	15 Days	35.00
1985 Hide and Seek	15 Days	35.00
1985 Poodle Picnic	15 Days	35.00

Little Ladies
	Edition Limit	Issue Price (US)
1983 When Mommy's Away	15 Days	29.50
1984 Before Show Begins	15 Days	29.50

(Single issue)
	Edition Limit	Issue Price (US)
1983 Twelve Days of Christmas	12 Days	45.00

Childhood Revisited
	Edition Limit	Issue Price (US)
1984 Young Virtuoso	9,500	39.50
1985 Fantasy and Fairy Tales	9,500	39.50
1985 Petit Fleur	9,500	39.50

Wings of Nobility
	Edition Limit	Issue Price (US)
1984 American Bald Eagle	7,500	49.50
1984 Peregrine Falcon	7,500	49.50
1984 Red-Shouldered Hawk	7,500	49.50

Sally Miller Christmas
	Edition Limit	Issue Price (US)
1985 They Came to Adore Him	5,000	39.50

(Single issue)
	Edition Limit	Issue Price (US)
1985 They Came to Adore Him	5,000	39.50

Modern Masters/GBS

Family Treasures
	Edition Limit	Issue Price (US)
1981 Cora's Recital	18,500	39.50
1982 Cora's Tea Party	18,500	39.50
1983 Cora's Garden Party	18,500	39.50

Horses of Fred Stone
	Edition Limit	Issue Price (US)
1981 Patience	9,500	55.00
1982 Arabian Mare and Foal	9,500	55.00
1982 Safe and Sound	9,500	55.00
1983 Contentment	9,500	55.00

A Child's Best Friend
	Edition Limit	Issue Price (US)
1982 Christi's Kitty	15 Days	29.50
1982 Patrick's Puppy	15 Days	29.50

Moussalli

Birds of Four Seasons
	Edition Limit	Issue Price (US)
1978 Cardinal (Winter)	1,000	375.00
1979 Indigo Bunting (Fall)	1,000	375.00
1979 Hummingbird (Summer)	1,000	375.00
1980 Wren (Spring)	1,000	375.00

Mother's Day
	Edition Limit	Issue Price (US)
1979 Chickadee	500	450.00

Museum Collections

Coca Cola Collection
	Edition Limit	Issue Price (US)
1987 Barefoot Boy	10,000	35.00

Museum Editions (Ridgewood)

Colonial Heritage
	Edition Limit	Issue Price (US)
1974 Tidewater, Virginia	9,900	40.00
1975 Pennsbury Manor	9,900	40.00
1975 Old New York	9,900	40.00
1976 Hammond-Harwood House	9,900	40.00
1976 Joseph Webb House	9,900	40.00
1977 Old Court House	9,900	40.00
1977 Mulberry Plantation	9,900	40.00

Museum Editions (Viletta)

Christmas Annual
	Edition Limit	Issue Price (US)
1978 Expression of Faith	7,400	49.95
1979 Skating Lesson	7,400	49.95

Colonial Heritage
	Edition Limit	Issue Price (US)
1978 Moffatt-Ladd House	9,900	40.00
1978 Trent House	9,900	40.00
1979 Cupola House	9,900	40.00
1979 Nicholas House	9,900	40.00
1980 Derby House	9,900	40.00
1980 Davenport House	9,900	40.00

Northwest Highland Supply Ltd

The Argyll & Sutherland Highlander
	Edition Limit	Issue Price (US)
1987 The Scottish Soldier	5,000	34.50

Nostalgia Collectibles

Shirley Temple
	Edition Limit	Issue Price (US)
1982 Baby Take a Bow	25,000	75.00
1983 Curly Top	25,000	75.00
1983 Stand Up and Cheer	25,000	75.00

Shirley Temple Classics
	Edition Limit	Issue Price (US)
1983 Captain January	25,000	35.00
1984 Heidi	25,000	35.00
1984 Little Miss Marker	25,000	35.00
1984 Bright Eyes	25,000	35.00
1985 Little Colonel	25,000	35.00
1985 Rebecca of Sunnybrook Farm	25,000	35.00
1986 Poor Little Rich Girl	25,000	35.00
1986 Wee Willie Winkie	25,000	35.00

(Single issue)
	Edition Limit	Issue Price (US)
1985 Elvis—Once and Forever King	25,000	40.00

(Single issue)
	Edition Limit	Issue Price (US)
1985 James Dean—America's Rebel	25,000	45.00

(Single issue)
	Edition Limit	Issue Price (US)
1986 Mircle on 34th Street	15,000	35.00

Ohio Arts

Norman Rockwell
	Edition Limit	Issue Price (US)
1979 Looking Out to Sea	20,000	19.50

OK Collectibles

Fantasy Farm
	Edition Limit	Issue Price (US)
1984 Lowena	3,000	39.95

Meadow
	Edition Limit	Issue Price (US)
1984 Chester	5,000	55.00

Pacific Art

Just Like Daddy's Hats
	Edition Limit	Issue Price (US)
1983 Jessica	10,000	29.00

(Single issue)
	Edition Limit	Issue Price (US)
1983 Guardian Angel	7,500	29.50

Paramount Classics (Pickard)

(Single issue)
	Edition Limit	Issue Price (US)
1977 Coronation Plate	5,000	95.00

(Single issue)
	Edition Limit	Issue Price (US)
1977 Queen Victoria	5,000	95.00

(Single issue)
	Edition Limit	Issue Price (US)
1977 King George III	5,000	95.00

Pemberton & Oakes (Viletta)

Moments Alone
	Edition Limit	Issue Price (US)
1980 Dreamer	15 Days	28.80
1981 Reverie	15 Days	28.80
1982 Gentle Thoughts	15 Days	28.80
1983 Wheat Field	4,800	28.80

Nutcracker II
	Edition Limit	Issue Price (US)
1981 Nutcracker Grand Finale	28 Days	24.40
1982 Arabian Dancers	28 Days	24.40
1983 Dewdrop Fairy	28 Days	24.40
1984 Clara's Delight	28 Days	24.40

Swan Lake
	Edition Limit	Issue Price (US)
1983 Swan Queen	15,000	35.00

Robert Anderson's Little Girls
	Edition Limit	Issue Price (US)
1985 Curious Kitten	15,000	29.00
1986 Making Magic	15,000	29.00
1987 Sunny Umbrellas	15,000	29.00

Zolan Father's Day
	Edition Limit	Issue Price (US)
1986 Daddy's Home	19 Days	19.00

Childhood Friendship
	Edition Limit	Issue Price (US)
1987 Beach Break	NA	19.00

Pickard

Presidential
	Edition Limit	Issue Price (US)
1971 Truman	3,000	35.00
1973 Lincoln	5,000	35.00

Children of Mexico
	Edition Limit	Issue Price (US)
1981 Maria	5,000	85.00
1981 Miguel	5,000	85.00
1982 Regina	5,000	90.00
1983 Raphael	5,000	90.00

(Single issue)
	Edition Limit	Issue Price (US)
1982 Great Seal of United States	10,000	95.00

Children of Christmas Past
	Edition Limit	Issue Price (US)
1983 Sledding on Christmas Day	7,500	60.00

Children of Mary Cassatt
	Edition Limit	Issue Price (US)
1983 Simone in a White Bonnet	7,500	60.00
1983 Children Playing on Beach	7,500	60.00
1984 Child in a Straw Hat	7,500	60.00

Let's Pretend
	Edition Limit	Issue Price (US)
1984 Cleopatra	5,000	80.00
1984 Mark Antony	5,000	80.00
1985 Robin Hood	5,000	80.00
1985 Maid Marian	5,000	80.00

(Single Issue)
	Edition Limit	Issue Price (US)
1984 Statue of Liberty	10,000	150.00

Wings of Freedom
	Edition Limit	Issue Price (US)
1985 Courtship Flight	2,500	250.00
1986 Wings of Freedom	2,500	250.00

Gardens of Monet
	Edition Limit	Issue Price (US)
1986 Summer Splendor	3,500	85.00
1987 Time Gone By	3,500	85.00

The Nativity Triptych
	Edition Limit	Issue Price (US)
1986 Unto Us a Child is Born	3,500	95.00

See also:
Kern Collectibles (U.S.A.)
Paramount Classics (U.S.A.)

Porcelain Limited

Children of Seasons
	Edition Limit	Issue Price (US)
1982 Spring Joy	9,800	49.95
1982 Summer Love	9,800	49.95
1982 Fall's Adventure	9,800	49.95
1982 Winter's Dreamer	9,800	49.95

Ram

Boston 500
	Edition Limit	Issue Price (US)
1973 Easter	500	30.00
1973 Mother's Day	500	30.00
1973 Father's Day	500	30.00
1973 Christmas	500	30.00

Great Bird Heroes
	Edition Limit	Issue Price (US)
1973 Cher Ami	1,000	7.95
1973 Mocker	1,000	7.95

Reco International

Americana (Single issue)
	Edition Limit	Issue Price (US)
1972 Gaspee	1,000	130.00

	Edition Limit	Issue Price (US)
Four Seasons (Set of four)		
1973 Fall		
1973 Spring		
1973 Summer		
1973 Winter	2,500	200.00
Western (Single issue)		
1974 Mountain Man	1,000	165.00
Christmas (Single issue)		
1977 Old Mill in Valley	5,000	28.00
Games Children Play		
1979 Me First	10,000	45.00
1980 Forever Bubbles	10,000	45.00
1981 Skating Pals	10,000	45.00
1982 Join Me	10,000	45.00
Grandparents		
1981 Grandma's Cookie Jar	Year	37.50
1981 Grandpa and Doll House	Year	37.50
Arabelle and Friends		
1982 Ice Delight	15,000	35.00
1983 First Love	15,000	35.00
Little Professionals		
1982 All Is Well	10,000	39.50
1983 T.L.C.	10,000	39.50
1984 Lost and Found	10,000	39.50
1985 Reading, Writing and ...	10,000	39.50
A Childhood Almanac		
1984 School Days	14 Days	29.50
1984 Fireside Dreams	14 Days	29.50
1984 Be Mine	14 Days	29.50
1985 Easter Morning	14 Days	29.50
1985 For Mom	14 Days	29.50
1985 Summer Secrets	14 Days	29.50
1985 Just Dreaming	14 Days	29.50
1985 Star-Spangled Sky	14 Days	29.50
1985 Christmas Magic	14 Days	29.50
1986 Indian Summer	14 Days	29.50
1986 Giving Thanks	14 Days	29.50
1986 Winds of March	14 Days	29.50
Mother's Day		
1985 Once Upon a Time	Year	29.50
1986 Times Remembered	Year	29.50
1987 A Cherished Time	Year	29.50
Sophisticated Ladies		
1985 Felicia	21 Days	29.50
1985 Samantha	21 Days	29.50
1985 Phoebe	21 Days	29.50
1985 Cleo	21 Days	29.50
1986 Cerissa	21 Days	29.50
1986 Natasha	21 Days	29.50
1986 Bianka	21 Days	29.50
1986 Chelsea	21 Days	29.50
Springtime of Life		
1985 Teddy's Bathtime	14 Days	29.50
Children's Christmas Pageant		
1986 Silent Night	Year	32.50
Vanishing Animal Kingdom		
1986 Rami the Tiger	21,000	35.00
1987 Olepi the Buffalo	21,500	35.00
Great Stories From the Bible		
1987 Moses in the Bulrushes	14 Days	29.50
Barefoot Children		
1987 Night Time Story	NA	29.50
Reed & Barton		
Audubon		
1970 Pine Siskin	5,000	60.00
1971 Red-Shouldered Hawk	5,000	60.00
1972 Stilt Sandpiper	5,000	60.00
1973 Red Cardinal	5,000	60.00
1974 Boreal Chickadee	5,000	60.00
1975 Yellow-Breasted Chat	5,000	65.00
1976 Bay-Breasted Warbler	5,000	65.00
1977 Purple Finch	5,000	65.00
(Single issue)		
1970 Zodiac	1,500	75.00
California Missions		
1971 San Diego	1,500	75.00
1972 Carmel	1,500	75.00
1973 Santa Barbara	1,500	60.00
1974 Santa Clara	1,500	60.00
1976 San Gabriel	1,500	65.00
Annual		
1972 Free Trapper	2,500	65.00
1973 Outpost	2,500	65.00
1974 Toll Collector	2,500	65.00
1975 Indians Discovering Lewis & Clark	2,500	65.00
Currier & Ives		
1972 Village Blacksmith	1,500	85.00
1972 Western Migration	1,500	85.00
1973 Oaken Bucket	1,500	85.00
1973 Winter in Country	1,500	85.00
1974 Preparing for Market	1,500	85.00
Kentucky Derby		
1972 Nearing Finish	1,000	75.00
1973 Riva Ridge	1,500	75.00
1974 100th Running	1,500	75.00
(Single issue)		
1972 Delta Queen	2,500	75.00
(Single issue)		
1972 Road Runner	1,500	65.00
Founding Father		
1973 Ben Franklin	2,500	65.00
1974 George Washington	2,500	65.00
1975 Thomas Jefferson	2,500	65.00
1976 Patrick Henry	2,500	65.00
1976 John Hancock	2,500	65.00
1976 John Adams	2,500	65.00
(Single issue)		
1975 Chicago Fire	Year	60.00
(Single issue)		
1975 Mississippi Queen	2,500	75.00
See also:		
Collector Creations (U.S.A.)		
Keller & George (U.S.A.)		
Ridgewood		
Bicentennial		
1974 First in War	12,500	40.00
Tom Sawyer (Set of four)		
1974 Trying a Pipe		
1974 Lost in Cave		
1974 Painting Fence		
1974 Taking Medicine	3,000	39.95
Wild West (Set of four)		
1975 Discovery of Last Chance Gulch		
1975 Doubtful Visitor		
1975 Bad One		
1975 Cattleman	15,000	65.00
Leyendecker Christmas		
1975 Christmas Morning	10,000	24.50
1976 Christmas Surprise	10,000	24.50
Leyendecker Mother's Day		
1976 Grandma's Apple Pie	5,000	24.50
1977 Tenderness	10,000	35.00
Little Women		
1976 Sweet Long Ago	5,000	45.00
1976 Song of Spring	5,000	45.00
1977 Joy in Morning	5,000	45.00
See also: Museum Editions (U.S.A.)		
River Shore		
Baby Animals		
1979 Akiku	20,000	65.00
1980 Roosevelt	20,000	65.00
1981 Clover	20,000	65.00
1982 Zuela	20,000	65.00
Della Robbia Annual		
1979 Adoration	5,000	550.00
1980 Virgin and Child	5,000	450.00
Remington Bronze		
1977 Bronco Buster	15,000	55.00
1978 Coming Thru Rye	15,000	60.00
1979 Cheyenne	15,000	60.00
1980 Mountain Man	15,000	60.00
(Single issue)		
1979 Spring Flowers	17,000	75.00
(Single issue)		
1980 Looking Out to Sea	17,000	75.00
Grant Wood		
1981 American Gothic	17,000	80.00
Rockwell's Four Freedoms		
1981 Freedom of Speech	17,000	65.00
Vignette		
1981 Broken Window	22,500	19.50
1982 Sunday Best	22,500	19.50
(Single issue)		
1981 Grandpa's Guardian	17,000	80.00
Christmas After Christmas		
1982 Kay's Doll	9,500	75.00
River Shore—Woodmere		
Children of American Frontier		
1986 In Trouble Again	NA	24.50
1986 Desperados	NA	24.50
1986 Riders Wanted	NA	24.50
Rockford Editions		
Little Mothers		
1985 Love is Blind	NA	29.95
1986 Little Bit Independent	NA	29.95
1987 First Step	NA	29.95
1987 May We Come In?	NA	29.95
A Child's Best Friend		
1986 On The Up and Up	NA	24.50
1987 Mine	NA	24.50
1987 Going to Town	NA	24.50
Precious Portraits		
1987 Sunbeam	NA	24.50
Rockwell Collectors Club		
Christmas		
1978 Christmas Story	15,000	24.50
Rockwell Museum		
American Family		
1978 Baby's First Step	9,900	28.50
1978 Happy Birthday Dear Mother	9,900	28.50
1978 Sweet Sixteen	9,900	28.50
1978 First Haircut	9,900	28.50
1979 First Prom	9,900	28.50
1979 Student	9,900	28.50
1979 Wrapping Christmas Presents	9,900	28.50
1979 Birthday Party	9,900	28.50
1979 Little Mother	9,900	28.50
1980 Washing Our Dog	9,900	28.50
1980 Mother's Little Helper	9,900	28.50
1980 Bride & Groom	9,900	28.50
Christmas		
1979 Day After Christmas	25,000	75.00
1980 Checking His List	Year	75.00
1981 Ringing in Good Cheer	Year	75.00
1982 Waiting for Santa	Year	75.00
1983 High Hopes	Year	75.00
1984 Space Age Santa	Year	55.00
1985 Christmas Prayers	Year	35.00
(Single issue)		
1979 Norman Rockwell Remembered	Year	45.00
American Family II		
1980 New Arrival	22,500	35.00
1980 Sweet Dreams	22,500	35.00
1980 Little Shaver	22,500	35.00
1980 We Missed You Daddy	22,500	35.00
1980 Home Run Slugger	22,500	35.00
1980 Giving Thanks	22,500	35.00
1980 Space Pioneers	22,500	35.00
1980 Little Salesman	22,500	35.00
1980 Almost Grown Up	22,500	35.00
1980 Courageous Hero	22,500	35.00
1980 At Circus	22,500	35.00
1980 Good Food, Good Friends	22,500	35.00
Classic		
1981 Puppy Love	60 Days	24.50
1981 While Audience Waits	60 Days	24.50
1981 Off to School	60 Days	24.50
1982 Country Doctor	60 Days	24.50
1982 Spring Fever	60 Days	24.50
1982 Dollhouse for Sis	60 Days	24.50
Mother's Day		
1982 A Tender Moment	5,000	70.00
World of Children		
1982 Downhill Racer	15,000	45.00
1982 Vacation's Over	15,000	45.00
1982 Little Patient	15,000	45.00
1982 Bicycle Boys	15,000	45.00
(Single issue)		
1983 A Tribute to J.F.K.	NA	39.50
(Single issue)		
1983 With This Ring	NA	45.00
A Touch of Rockwell		
1984 Songs of Praise	NA	14.95
1984 Bedtime Prayers	NA	14.95
1984 First Day of School	NA	14.95
1984 Surprise Treat	NA	14.95
1984 Runaway	NA	14.95
Roman		
Child's World		
1982 Baby Blossoms	15,000	24.95
1982 I Wish, I Wish	15,000	24.95
1982 Trees So Tall	15,000	24.95
1982 Daisy Dreamer	15,000	24.95
1983 Caught it Myself	15,000	24.95
1983 Winter Wrappings	15,000	24.95
1983 So Cuddley	15,000	24.95
1983 Can I Keep Him?	15,000	24.95
Ice Capades Clown		
1983 Presenting Freddie Trenkler	30 Days	24.50
Petty Girls of Ice Capades		
1983 Ice Princess	30 Days	24.50
Cats		
1984 Grizabella	30 Days	29.50
1984 Mr. Mistoffelees	30 Days	29.50
1984 Rum Tum Tugger	30 Days	29.50
1985 Growltiger	30 Days	29.50
1985 Skimbleshanks	30 Days	29.50
1985 Mungojerrie and Rumpelteazer	30 Days	29.50
Magic of Childhood		
1984 Special Friends	10 Days	24.50
1985 Feeding Time	10 Days	24.50
(Single issue)		
1984 Carpenter	NA	100.00
Lord's Prayer		
1986 Our Father	NA	24.50
1986 Thy Kingdom Come	NA	24.50
1987 Forgive Our Trespasses	NA	24.50
1987 As We Forgive	NA	24.50
1987 Give Us This Day	NA	24.50
Sweetest Songs		
1986 A Baby's Prayer	NA	39.50
1987 This Little Piggy	NA	39.50
Fontanini Christmas Story		
1986 A King is Born	NA	60.00
1987 O Come, Let Us Adore Him	NA	50.00
(Single issue)		
1987 The Christening	NA	24.50
Royal Cornwall		
Bethlehem Christmas		
1977 First Christmas Eve	10,000	29.95
1978 Glad Tidings	10,000	34.50
1979 Gift Bearers	10,000	34.50
1980 Great Joy	10,000	39.95
Creation		
1977 In Beginning	19,500	45.00
1977 In His Image	19,500	45.00
1977 Adam's Rib	19,500	45.00
1977 Banished from Eden	19,500	45.00
1977 Noah and Ark	19,500	45.00
1977 Tower of Babel	19,500	45.00
1978 Sodom & Gomorrah	19,500	45.00
1978 Jacob's Wedding	19,500	45.00
1978 Rebekah at Well	19,500	45.00
1978 Jacob's Ladder	19,500	45.00
1978 Joseph's Coat of Many Colors	19,500	45.00
1978 Joseph Interprets Pharaoh's Dream	19,500	45.00
Classic Christmas		
1978 Child of Peace	17,500	55.00
1978 Silent Night	17,500	55.00
1978 Most Precious Gift	17,500	55.00
1978 We Three Kings	17,500	55.00
Four Seasons		
1978 Warmth	17,500	60.00
1978 Voices of Spring	17,500	60.00
1978 Fledgling	17,500	60.00
1978 We Survive	17,500	60.00
Golden Age of Cinema		
1978 King & His Ladies	22,500	45.00
1978 Fred & Ginger	22,500	45.00
1978 Judy & Mickey	22,500	45.00
1979 Philadelphia Story	22,500	45.00

		Edition Limit	Issue Price (US)
1979	Thin Man	22,500	45.00
1979	Gigi	22,500	45.00
Mother's Day			
1978	God Bless Mommy	10,000	35.00
Alice in Wonderland			
1979	Alice and White Rabbit	27,500	45.00
1979	Advice from a Caterpillar	27,500	45.00
1979	Cheshire Cat's Grin	27,500	45.00
1979	Mad Hatter's Tea Party		
1979	Queen's Croquet Match	27,500	45.00
1979	Who Stole Tarts?	27,500	45.00
Kitten's World			
1979	Just Curious	27,500	45.00
1979	Hello, World	27,500	45.00
1979	Are You a Flower?	27,500	45.00
1979	Talk to Me	27,500	45.00
1979	My Favorite Toy	27,500	45.00
1979	Purr-Fect Pleasure	27,500	45.00
Promised Land			
1979	Pharaoh's Daughter Finds Moses	24,500	45.00
1979	Burning Bush	24,500	45.00
1979	Let My People Go	24,500	45.00
1979	Parting of Red Sea	24,500	45.00
1979	Miriam's Song of Thanksgiving	24,500	45.00
1979	Manna from Heaven	24,500	45.00
1979	Water from Rock	24,500	45.00
1979	Battle of Amalek	24,500	45.00
1979	Ten Commandments	24,500	45.00
1979	Golden Calf	24,500	45.00
1979	Moses Smashes Tablets	24,500	45.00
1979	Glorious Tabernacle	24,500	45.00
Treasures of Childhood			
1979	My Cuddlies Collection	19,500	45.00
1979	My Coin Collection	19,500	45.00
1979	My Shell Collection	19,500	45.00
1979	My Stamp Collection	19,500	45.00
1979	My Doll Collection	19,500	45.00
1979	My Rock Collection	19,500	45.00
Beauty of Bouguereau			
1980	Lucie	19,500	35.00
1980	Madelaine	19,500	35.00
1980	Frere et Soeur	19,500	35.00
1980	Solange et Enfant	19,500	35.00
1980	Colette	19,500	35.00
1980	Jean et Jeanette	19,500	35.00
Four Faces of Love			
1980	Romeo & Juliet	17,500	55.00
1980	Young Galahad	17,500	55.00
1980	At Locksley Hall	17,500	55.00
1980	St. Agnes Eve	17,500	55.00
Dorothy's Day			
1980	Brand New Day	15,000	55.00
1980	All by Myself	15,000	55.00
1981	Off to School	15,000	55.00
1981	Best Friends	15,000	55.00
1981	Helping Mommy	15,000	55.00
1981	Bless Me Too	15,000	55.00
Legendary Ships of Seas			
1980	Flying Dutchman	19,500	49.50
1981	Refanu	19,500	49.50
1981	Gaspé Bay	19,500	49.50
1981	Rescue	19,500	49.50
1980	Copenhagen	19,500	49.50
1982	Palatine	19,500	49.50
1982	Pride	19,500	49.50
1982	Foochow Sea Junk	19,500	49.50
1982	Roth Ramhach	19,500	49.50
1982	Frigorifique	19,500	49.50
Little People			
1980	Off to Picnic	19,500	34.50
1981	Decorating Tree	19,500	34.50
1981	Cruising Down River	19,500	34.50
1981	Sweetest Harvest	19,500	34.50
1981	Happy Chorus	19,500	34.50
1981	Painting Leaves	19,500	34.50
Memories of America			
1980	Bringing in Maple Sugar	5,000	120.00
1980	Old Automobile	5,000	120.00
1981	Halloween	5,000	120.00
1981	Rainbow	5,000	120.00

		Edition Limit	Issue Price (US)
Windows on World			
1980	Golden Gate of San Francisco	19,500	45.00
1981	Snow Village/Madulain	19,500	45.00
1981	Rainy Day in London	19,500	45.00
1981	Water Festival/Venice	19,500	45.00
1981	Harvesting in Ukraine	19,500	45.00
1981	Serengeti Plain	19,500	45.00
1982	Springtime in Paris	19,500	45.00
1982	Lunch in Michelstadt	19,500	45.00
1982	Flamenca of Madrid	19,500	45.00
1982	Tokyo at Cherry Time	19,500	45.00
1982	Palace of Winds, Jaipur	19,500	45.00
1982	Carnival Time in Rio	19,500	45.00
Exotic Birds of Tropique			
1981	Scarlet Macaws	19,500	49.50
1981	Toco Toucan	19,500	49.50
1981	Rosy Flamingos	19,500	49.50
1982	Greater Cockatoo	19,500	49.50
1982	Ultramarine King	19,500	49.50
1982	Red Fan Parrot	19,500	49.50
1982	Bird of Paradise	19,500	49.50
1982	Mariqua Sunbird	19,500	49.50
1982	Andean Cock-of-Rock	19,500	49.50
1983	Rufous Hornbill	19,500	49.50
1983	Seven-colored Tanager	19,500	49.50
1983	Ivory-billed Aracari	19,500	49.50
Love's Precious Moments			
1981	Love's Sweet Vow	17,500	55.00
1981	Love's Sweet Verse	17,500	55.00
1981	Love's Sweet Offering	17,500	55.00
1981	Love's Sweet Embrace	17,500	55.00
1981	Love's Sweet Melody	17,500	55.00
1981	Love's Sweet Kiss	17,500	55.00
Most Precious Gifts of Shen-Lung			
1981	Fire	19,500	49.50
1981	Water	19,500	49.50
1981	Sun	19,500	49.50
1982	Moon	19,500	49.50
1982	Earth	19,500	49.50
1982	Sky	19,500	49.50
Puppy's World			
1981	1st Birthday	19,500	49.50
1981	Beware of Dog	19,500	49.50
1981	Top Dog	19,500	49.50
1981	Need a Friend?	19,500	49.50
1981	Double Trouble	19,500	49.50
1981	Just Clowning	19,500	49.50
1981	Guest for Dinner	19,500	49.50
1981	Gift Wrapped	19,500	49.50
Courageous Few			
1982	Fall of Jericho	24,500	59.50
1982	Gideon's Three Hundred	24,500	59.50
1982	Strength of Samson	24,500	59.50
1982	Ruth	24,500	59.50
1982	David and Goliath	24,500	59.50
1982	Solomon's Wisdom	24,500	59.50
1983	Building of Temple	24,500	59.50
1983	Elijah	24,500	59.50
1983	Job	24,500	59.50
1983	A Psalm of David	24,500	59.50
1983	Daniel and Lions	24,500	59.50
1983	Jonah and Whale	24,500	59.50
Impressions of Yesteryear			
1982	Moon Mist	19,500	59.50
1982	Fall Flowers	19,500	59.50
1982	Wishing Well	19,500	59.50
1982	Letter	19,500	59.50
1982	Sledding	19,500	59.50
1982	Swans	19,500	59.50
1983	Winter Park	19,500	59.50
1983	Seashore	19,500	59.50
1983	Red Tree	19,500	59.50
1983	Sailboat	19,500	59.50
1983	Red Balloon	19,500	59.50
1983	Snowman	19,500	59.50
Legend of Peacock Maidens			
1982	Dance of Peacock Maiden	19,500	69.50
1982	Promise of Love	19,500	69.50
1982	Betrayal	19,500	69.50
1982	Prince and Python	19,500	69.50
Noble Flower Maidens			
1982	Iris Maiden	19,500	65.00
1982	Plum Blossom Maiden	19,500	65.00
1982	Quince Maiden	19,500	65.00

		Edition Limit	Issue Price (US)
1982	Cherry Blossom Maiden	19,500	65.00
1982	Crysanthemum Maiden	19,500	65.00
1982	August Lily Maiden	19,500	65.00
2000 Years of Sailing Ships			
1982	USS Constitution	NA	39.50
1982	Santa Maria	NA	39.50
1983	Mayflower	NA	39.50
1983	Drakar	NA	39.50
1983	Cutty Sark Thermopylae	NA	39.50
1983	HMS Royal Sovereign	NA	39.50
1983	Vasa	NA	39.50
1983	Bounty	NA	39.50
1983	HMS Victory	NA	39.50
1983	Royal Barge	NA	39.50
1984	America	NA	39.50
1984	Golden Hind	NA	39.50
America's Golden Years			
1983	County Fair	19,000	49.50
1983	Sunday Picnic	19,500	49.50
1983	Barnstorming	19,500	49.50
1983	Amusement Park	19,500	49.50
1983	Fourth of July	19,500	49.50
1983	County Fair	19,500	49.50
1983	Big Top	19,500	49.50
1983	Old Boardwalk	19,500	49.50
1983	On Bay	19,500	49.50
1983	Harvest Dance	19,500	49.50
1983	Whistle Stop	19,500	49.50
1983	Halloween	19,500	49.50
1983	Christmas Eve	19,500	49.50
Memories of Western Prairies			
1983	Picking Daisies	Year	49.50
1984	Feeding Colt	Year	49.50
Joyful World of Children			
1984	China Doll	NA	29.50
Royal Devon			
See: Hamilton Collection (U.S.A.)			
Royal Oaks Limited			
Love's Labor			
1982	Intruder	15,000	50.00
1982	It's My Turn!	15,000	50.00
1983	Look! I Can Fly!	15,000	50.00
1983	Just Like Your Own!	15,000	50.00
Royal Orleans			
Pink Panther Christmas			
1982	Sleigh Ride	13,000	25.00
1983	Happy Landings	13,000	18.50
1984	Down Chimney	13,000	18.50
(Single issue)			
1982	M*A*S*H	Year	25.00
In Trompe L'Oeil			
1984	Up to Mischief	10,000	25.00
Yorkshire Brontes			
1984	Wuthering Heights	30 Days	35.00
1985	Jane Eyre	30 Days	35.00
Coca-Cola Classic Santa			
1983	Good Boys and Girls	15,000	55.00
1983	Gift to Santa	15,000	65.00
1985	Santa, Pause Here	15,000	65.00
1986	Santa's Favorite Gift	15,000	65.00
Marilyn—An American Classic			
1983	Seven Year Itch	20,000	35.00
1984	Gentlemen Prefer Blondes	20,000	35.00
1985	Niagara	20,000	35.00
1987	Monkey Business	15,000	35.00
Elvis in Concert			
1984	Aloha in Hawaii	20,000	35.00
1985	Las Vegas	20,000	35.00
1986	Detroit New Year's Eve	15,000	35.00
(Single issue)			
1984	Buddy Holly	Year	25.00
Famous Movies			
1985	Cat on Hot Tin Roof	20,000	35.00
Dynasty			
1985	Dynasty	20,000	35.00
1986	Krystal and Baby	NA	35.00
N.F.L. Hall of Fame			
1986	Class of 1986	10,000	35.00

		Edition Limit	Issue Price (US)
Royal Worcester			
Birth of a Nation			
1972	Boston Tea Party	10,000	45.00
1973	Ride of Paul Revere	10,000	45.00
1974	Incident at Concord Bridge	10,000	50.00
1975	Declaration of Independence	10,000	65.00
1976	Washington Crossing Delaware	10,000	65.00
Currier & Ives			
1974	Road-Winter	10,000	59.50
1975	Old Grist Mill	10,000	59.50
1976	Winter Pastime	10,000	59.50
American History			
1977	Washington's Inauguration	1,250	65.00
Annual			
1977	Home to Thanksgiving	500	59.50
Royalwood			
(Single issue)			
1977	Doctor and Doll	Year	21.50
Leyendecker			
1978	Cornflake Boy	10,000	25.00
1978	Cornflake Girl	10,000	25.00
John A. Ruthven			
Moments of Nature			
1977	Screech Owls	5,000	37.50
1979	Chickadees	5,000	39.50
1980	California Quail	5,000	39.50
Schofield Gallery			
Clowns, Klowns, Klownz			
1986	Painting on a Smile	7,500	47.50
1987	Keystone Kop	7,500	47.50
Sebastian			
America's Favorite Scenes			
1978	Motif #1	10,000	75.00
1979	Grand Canyon	10,000	75.00
Seeley's Doll Plates			
Antique French Dolls			
1979	Bru	5,000	39.00
1979	E.J.	5,000	39.00
1979	A.T.	5,000	39.00
1980	Alexandre	5,000	39.00
1980	Schmitt	5,000	39.00
1980	Marque	5,000	39.00
Old German Dolls			
1981	Lucy	7,500	39.00
1981	Whistler	7,500	39.00
1982	April	7,500	39.00
1982	Elise	7,500	39.00
(Single issue)			
1981	Dear Googly	7,500	39.00
Old Baby Dolls			
1982	Hilda	9,500	43.00
1982	Goldie	9,500	43.00
1982	Lori	9,500	43.00
1982	Bye-Lo	9,500	43.00
1982	Laughing Baby	9,500	43.00
French Dolls II			
1983	Snow Angel	5,000	39.00
1983	"H's" Bébé Halo	5,000	39.00
1983	Bru's Faith	5,000	39.00
1984	Steiner's Easter	5,000	39.00
1984	Marque's Alyce	5,000	39.00
1984	Jumeau's Gaynell	5,000	39.00
Seven Seas			
Historical Event			
1969	Moon Landing, No Flag	2,000	13.50
1969	Moon Landing, with Flag	25,000	13.50
1970	Year of Crisis	4,000	15.00
1971	First Vehicular Travel	3,000	15.00
1972	Last Moon Journey	2,000	15.00
1973	Peace	3,000	15.00
Mother's Day			
1970	Girl of All Nations	5,000	15.00
1971	Sharing Confidence	1,400	15.00
1972	Scandinavian Girl	1,600	15.00
1973	All-American Girl	1,500	15.00

	Edition Limit	Issue Price (US)
Christmas Carols		
1970 I Heard Bells	4,000	15.00
1971 Oh Tannenbaum	4,000	15.00
1972 Deck Halls	1,500	18.00
1973 O Holy Night	2,000	18.00
1974 Jingle Bells	1,200	25.00
1975 Winter Wonderland	1,500	25.00
1976 Twelve Days of Christmas	1,200	25.00
1977 Up on Housetop	1,500	25.00
1978 Little Town of Bethlehem	1,500	25.00
1979 Santa Claus Is Coming to Town	1,500	25.00
1980 Frosty Snowman	1,500	25.00
New World		
1970 Holy Family	3,500	15.00
1971 Three Wise Men	1,500	15.00
1972 Shepherds Watched	1,500	18.00
Passion Play (Single issue)		
1970 Oberammergau	2,500	18.00

Shenango

See: Castleton China (U.S.A.)

Sierra Productions

My Favorite Puppy		
1984 Caught	7,500	30.00
War Parties		
1984 Sioux	5,000	30.00

Signature Collection

Carnival		
1982 Knock 'em Down	19,500	39.95
1982 Carousel	19,500	39.95
1983 Fortune Teller	19,500	39.95
1983 Ring Bell	19,500	39.95
How Do I Love Thee . . .		
1982 Alaina	24,000	39.95
1982 Taylor	24,000	39.95
1983 Rendezvous	24,000	39.95
1983 Embrace	24,000	39.95
Legends		
1982 Paul Bunyan	10,000	45.00
1983 Rip Van Winkle	10,000	45.00
Melodies of Childhood		
1982 Twinkle, Twinkle	25,000	35.00
1983 Row Your Boat	25,000	39.95
1984 Mary Had a Lamb	19,500	35.00
Angler's Dream		
1983 Brook Trout	9,800	55.00
1983 Striped Bass	9,800	55.00
1984 Largemouth Bass	9,800	55.00
1984 Chinook Salmon	9,800	55.00
Baker Street Duo		
1983 Sherlock Holmes	9,800	55.00
1983 Watson	9,800	55.00
Childhood Delights		
1983 Amanda	10,000	45.00
Grandma's Scrapbook		
1983 Courting	12,500	45.00
1983 Sunday Drive	12,500	45.00
Unicorn Magic		
1983 Morning Encounter	10,000	50.00
1983 Afternoon Outing	10,000	50.00
Songs of Stephen Foster		
1984 Oh! Susannah	3,500	60.00
1984 Jeanie/Light Brown Hair	3,500	60.00

Silver Creations

Churchillian Heritage		
1972 Hour of Decision	NA	150.00
1973 Yalta Conference	NA	150.00
1973 Clydesdales	NA	150.00

Smith Glass

Americana		
1971 Morgan Silver Dollar	5,000	10.00
Christmas		
1971 Family at Christmas	NA	10.00
1972 Flying Angel	NA	10.00
1973 St. Mary's in Mountains	NA	10.00
Famous Americans		
1971 Kennedy	2,500	10.00
1971 Lincoln	2,500	10.00

	Edition Limit	Issue Price (US)
1972 Jefferson Davis	5,000	11.00
1972 Robert E. Lee	5,000	11.00

Southern Living Gallery

Wildflowers of South		
1981 Wild Honeysuckle	19,500	49.50
1981 Flowering Dogwood	19,500	49.50
1981 Buttercup	19,500	49.50
1981 Regal Lily	19,500	49.50
1981 Queen Anne's Lace	19,500	49.50
1981 Bluebonnet	19,500	49.50
1981 Southern Magnolia	19,500	49.50
1981 Bee Balm	19,500	49.50
1981 Lady Slipper Orchid	19,500	49.50
1981 Birdsfoot Violet	19,500	49.50
1981 Frost Aster	19,500	49.50
1981 Black-Eyed Susan	19,500	49.50
Game Birds of South		
1982 Bobwhite Quail	19,500	39.95
1982 Wild Turkey	19,500	39.95
1982 Mourning Dove	19,500	39.95
1982 Mallard Duck	19,500	39.95
1982 Wood Duck	19,500	39.95
1982 Ruffed Grouse	19,500	39.95
1982 Pintail Duck	19,500	39.95
1982 Ring-necked Pheasant	19,500	39.95
1982 American Woodcock	19,500	39.95
1982 American Coot	19,500	39.95
1982 Canada Goose	19,500	39.95
1982 Green-winged Teal	19,500	39.95
Southern Forest Families		
1984 Eastern Cottontail	19,500	39.50
1984 Raccoon	19,500	39.50
1984 Whitetail Deer	19,500	39.50
1984 Oppossum	19,500	39.50
1984 Striped Skunk	19,500	39.50
1984 Bobcat	19,500	39.50
1984 Fox Squirrel	19,500	39.50
1984 Chipmunk	19,500	39.50
1984 Flying Squirrel	19,500	39.50
1984 Beaver	19,500	39.50
1984 Muskrat	19,500	39.50
Songbirds of South		
1985 American Goldfinch	19,500	39.90
1985 Cardinal	19,500	39.95
1985 Tufted Titmouse	19,500	39.95
1985 Blue Jay	19,500	39.95

Sports Impression

(Single issue)		
1986 Mickey Mantle (signed)	1,000	95.00
1986 Mickey Mantle (unsigned)	2,000	60.00
(Single issue)		
1986 Darryl Strawberry (signed)	1,000	95.00
1986 Darryl Strawberry (unsigned)	2,000	60.00
(Single issue)		
1986 Al Kaline (signed)	1,000	95.00
1986 Al Kaline (unsigned)	2,000	60.00
(Single issue)		
1987 Mickey, Willie, & The Duke (signed)	1,500	150.00
1987 Mickey, Willie, & The Duke (unsigned)	3,500	75.00
(Single issue)		
1987 Mickey at Night (signed)	1,500	100.00
1987 Mickey at Night (unsigned)	3,500	60.00
(Single issue)		
1987 Larry Bird (signed)	2,000	100.00
1987 Larry Bird (unsigned)	5,000	60.00
(Single issue)		
1987 Don Mattingly (signed)	2,500	125.00
1987 Don Mattingly (unsigned)	5,000	60.00

Sterling America

Christmas Customs		
1970 England	2,500	18.00
1971 Holland	2,500	18.00
1972 Norway	2,500	18.00
1973 Germany	2,500	20.00
1974 Mexico	2,500	24.00

	Edition Limit	Issue Price (US)
Twelve Days of Christmas		
1970 Partridge	2,500	18.00
1971 Turtle Doves	2,500	18.00
1972 French Hens	2,500	18.00
1973 Colly Birds	2,500	18.00
1974 Five Rings	2,500	24.00
1975 Six Geese	2,500	24.00
1976 Seven Swans	2,500	24.00
1977 Eight Maids	2,500	28.00
Mother's Day		
1971 Mare & Foal	2,500	18.00
1972 Horned Owl	2,500	18.00
1973 Raccoons	2,500	20.00
1974 Deer	2,500	24.00
1975 Quail	2,500	24.00

Stieff

Bicentennial		
1972 Declaration of Independence	10,000	50.00
1974 Betsy Ross	10,000	50.00
1975 Crossing Delaware	10,000	50.00
1976 Serapio & Bon Homme	10,000	50.00

Stratford Collection

Famous Clowns		
1982 Emmett Looking Out	10,000	35.00
1982 Jack Thum and Child	10,000	35.00
Real Children		
1982 Michael's Miracle	24,500	45.00
1983 Susan's World	24,500	45.00
Young Wildlife		
1982 Siberian Cub at Play	15,000	35.00
1982 Curious Raccoon	15,000	35.00

Stuart International

Childhood Secrets		
1983 Billy's Treasure	19,500	39.50
American Road		
1984 Farmer Takes a Ride	9,800	22.50
1984 Henry's First Ride	9,800	22.50
Spring Flowers		
1984 Megan	5,500	55.00
1985 Danielle	5,500	55.00

Syracuse China

Grandma Moses (Sets of four)		
1972 Old Checkered House in Winter		
1972 Mary and Little Lamb		
1972 In Harvest Time		
1972 Sugaring Off	NA	80.00
1972 Hoosick Valley from Window		
1972 Taking in Laundry		
1972 It Snows, Oh it Snows		
1972 Joy Ride	NA	80.00

Towle Silversmiths

Valentines		
1972 Single Heart	Year	10.00
1973 Entwined Hearts	Year	10.00
Christmas		
1972 Three Wise Men	2,500	250.00

Transparent Images

(Single issue)		
1986 Our Great Lady	500	75.00

U.S. Historical Society

Annual Historical		
1974 Thomas Jefferson	2,500	75.00
1974 Abigail Adams	2,500	75.00
1975 Patrick Henry	2,500	75.00
1975 John Paul Jones	2,500	75.00
1976 Benjamin Franklin	2,500	75.00
1976 Alexander Hamilton	2,500	75.00
1977 Great Events	5,000	60.00
1978 Great Events	10,000	75.00
Stained Glass Cathedral Christmas		
1978 Nativity	10,000	87.00
1979 Flight into Egypt	10,000	97.00
1980 Madonna and Child	10,000	125.00
1981 Magi	10,000	150.00
1982 Flight into Egypt	10,000	150.00
1983 Shepherds at Bethlehem	10,000	150.00

	Edition Limit	Issue Price (US)
1984 O Come Let Us Adore Him	10,000	150.00
1985 Tidings of Great Joy	10,000	160.00
American Christmas Carols		
1982 Deck Halls	10,000	55.00
1983 O Christmas Tree	10,000	55.00
1984 Winter Wonderland	10,000	55.00
1985 Here We Come A' Caroling	10,000	65.00
1986 Chestnuts Roasting on an Open Fire	10,000	55.00
Great American Sailing Ships		
1983 Old Ironsides–U.S.S. Constitution	10,000	135.00
1984 Charles W. Morgan	10,000	135.00
1985 Flying Cloud	10,000	150.00
Stained Glass Flowers		
1983 Spring Flowers	10,000	135.00
200 Years of Flight		
1983 Man's First Flight	5,000	85.00
1983 Miracle at Kitty Hawk	5,000	85.00
1984 China Clipper	5,000	85.00
1984 Man in Space	5,000	85.00
Buffalo Bill's Wild West		
1984 Pony Express	5,000	55.00
1984 Annie Oakley	5,000	55.00
1984 Sitting Bull	5,000	55.00
1984 Buffalo Hunter	5,000	55.00
1984 Farewell Appearance	5,000	55.00
1984 Deadwood Stage	5,000	55.00
1984 Rough Riders	5,000	55.00
1984 Royal Visit	5,000	55.00
Stained Glass with Pewter—Easter		
1987 The Good Shepard	5,000	160.00
Stained Glass Mother's Day		
1987 A Mother's Love	5,000	160.00
(Single issue)		
1984 Robert E. Lee	10,000	150.00

Vague Shadows

Plainsmen		
1979 Buffalo Hunt	2,500	300.00
1979 Proud One	2,500	300.00
Professionals		
1979 Big Leaguer	15,000	29.95
1980 Ballerina's Dilemma	15,000	32.50
1981 Quarterback	15,000	32.50
1982 Rodeo Joe	15,000	35.00
1983 Major Leaguer	15,000	35.00
1983 Hockey Player	15,000	35.00
Santa		
1980 Santa's Joy	Year	29.95
1981 Santa's Bundle	Year	29.95
Storybook Collection		
1980 Little Red Riding Hood	18 Days	29.95
1981 Cinderella	18 Days	29.95
1981 Hansel and Gretel	18 Days	29.95
1982 Goldilocks and Three Bears	18 Days	29.95
Arctic Friends (Set of two)		
1981 Siberian Love		
1981 Snow Pals	7,500	100.00
Four Princesses		
1981 Lily of Mohawks	7,500	50.00
1981 Pocahontas	7,500	50.00
1982 Minnehaha	7,500	50.00
1982 Sacajawea	7,500	50.00
(Single issue)		
1981 Apache Boy	5,000	95.00
Child Life		
1982 Siesta	12,500	45.00
1983 Sweet Dreams	3,500	45.00
Legends of West		
1982 Daniel Boone	10,000	65.00
1982 Davy Crockett	10,000	65.00
1983 Kit Carson	10,000	65.00
1983 Buffalo Bill	10,000	65.00
Nature's Harmony		
1982 Peaceable Kingdom	12,500	100.00
1982 Zebra	12,500	50.00
1982 Tiger	12,500	50.00
1983 Black Panther	12,500	50.00
1983 Elephant	12,500	50.00

	Edition Limit	Issue Price (US)
War Ponies		
1982 Sioux War Pony	7,500	60.00
1983 Nez Perce War Pony	7,500	60.00
1983 Apache War Pony	7,500	60.00
Chieftains II		
1983 Chief Pontiac	7,500	70.00
1984 Chief Victorio	7,500	70.00
1984 Chief Tecumseh	7,500	70.00
1984 Chief Cochise	7,500	70.00
1985 Chief Black Kettle	7,500	70.00
Indian Nations		
1983 Blackfoot	7,500	35.00
1983 Cheyenne	7,500	35.00
1983 Apache	7,500	35.00
1983 Sioux	7,500	35.00
Motherhood		
1983 Madre	12,500	50.00
1984 Madonna of Plains	3,500	50.00
1985 Abuela	3,500	50.00
1986 Naptime	3,500	50.00
Perillo Masterpiece		
1983 Papoose	3,000	100.00
Thoroughbreds		
1984 Whirlaway	9,500	50.00
1984 Secretariat	9,500	50.00
1984 Seabiscuit	9,500	50.00
1984 Man O'War	9,500	50.00
Tribal Ponies		
1984 Arapaho	3,500	65.00
1984 Comanche	3,500	65.00
1984 Crow	3,500	65.00
(Single issue)		
1984 Lovers	NA	50.00
(Single issue)		
1984 Navajo Girl	3,000	95.00
Indian Horses		
1985 Pinto	5,000	40.00
Pride of America's Indians		
1986 Brave and Free	10 Days	24.50
1986 Dark-Eyed Friends	10 Days	24.50
1986 Noble Companions	10 Days	24.50
1987 Kindred Spirits	10 Days	24.50
1987 Loyal Alliance	10 Days	24.50
1987 Small and Wise	10 Days	24.50
1987 Winter Scouts	10 Days	24.50
1987 Peaceful Comrades	10 Days	24.50
(Single issue)		
1986 Navajo Boy	3,500	95.00
The Arabians		
1986 Silver Streak	3,500	95.00
Young Emotions (Set of Two)		
1986 Tears		
1986 Smiles	5,000	75.00

Vette Vues Magazine

Corvette Collection		
1986 '86 Pace Care Convertible	2,000	29.95
1987 '63 Split Window Coupe	2,000	29.95
1987 1953–1954–1955 Corvettes	2,000	29.95

Vernonware (Metlox Potteries)

Songs of Christmas		
1971 Twelve Days	9,000	15.00
1972 Jingle Bells	9,000	17.50
1973 First Noel	9,000	20.00
1974 Upon a Midnight Clear	9,000	20.00
1975 O Holy Night	10,000	20.00
1976 Hark! Herald Angels	10,000	20.00
1977 Away in Manger	10,000	30.00
1978 White Christmas	10,000	30.00
1979 Little Drummer Boy	10,000	30.00

Viletta

Disneyland	Edition Limit	Issue Price (US)
1976 Betsy Ross	3,000	15.00
1976 Crossing Delaware	3,000	15.00
1976 Signing Declaration	3,000	15.00
1976 Spirit of '76	3,000	15.00
Bicentennial		
1977 Patriots	15,000	37.00
In Tribute to America's Great Artists		
1978 DeGrazia by Don Marco	5,000	65.00
Days of West		
1978 Cowboy Christmas	5,000	55.00
Alice in Wonderland		
1980 Alice and White Rabbit	28 Days	25.00
1981 Mad Hatter's Tea Party	28 Days	25.00
1981 Alice and Cheshire Cat	28 Days	25.00
1981 Alice and Croquet Match	28 Days	25.00
1982 Advice to Caterpillar	28 Days	25.00
1982 End of a Dream	28 Days	25.00
Down Home Memories		
1984 Watermelon Party	19,500	39.95
1984 Cleaning off Cemetery	19,500	39.95
1984 Waiting for Bedtime	19,500	39.95
1984 Hunting Blackberries	19,500	39.95
1984 Opossum Hunt	19,500	39.95
1984 Weighing up Cotton	19,500	39.95
1984 Hilly Town	19,500	39.95
1984 April Plowing	19,500	39.95
1984 Churning on Front Porch	19,500	39.95
1984 Summer Rain	19,500	39.95
1984 Sunning Quilts	19,500	39.95
1984 Summer Baptism	19,500	39.95

See also:
Abbey Press (U.S.A.)
American Arts Services (U.S.A.)
Carson Mint (U.S.A.)
Collector's Heirlooms (U.S.A.)
R. J. Ernst Enterprises (U.S.A.)
Ghent Collection (U.S.A.)
Hamilton Collection (U.S.A.)
Ralph Homan Studios (U.S.A.)
Joys (U.S.A.)
Judaic Heritage Society (U.S.A.)
McCalla Enterprises (U.S.A.)
Museum Editions (U.S.A.)
Pemberton & Oakes (U.S.A.)
Warwick (U.S.A.)
Westbury (U.S.A.)
Edward Weston Editions (U.S.A.)

Volair (Gorham)

Audubon American Wildlife Heritage		
1977 House Mouse	2,500	90.00
1977 Royal Louisiana Heron	2,500	90.00
1977 Virginia Deer	2,500	90.00
1977 Snowy Owl	2,500	90.00

Warwick (Viletta)

Great Comedians		
1978 Little Tramp	7,500	35.00
1978 Outrageous Groucho	7,500	35.00

George Washington Mint

American Indian		
1972 Curley (Gold)	100	2000.00
1972 Curley (Proof)	100	1000.00
1972 Curley (Sterling)	7,300	150.00
1973 Two Moons (Gold)	100	2000.00
1973 Two Moons (Proof)	100	1000.00
1973 Two Moons (Sterling)	7,300	150.00
Mother's Day		
1972 Whistler's Mother (Gold)	100	2000.00
1972 Whistler's Mother (Proof)	100	1000.00
1972 Whistler's Mother (Sterling)	9,800	150.00

	Edition Limit	Issue Price (US)
1974 Motherhood (Gold)	100	2000.00
1974 Motherhood (Proof)	100	1000.00
1974 Motherhood (Sterling)	2,300	175.00
Picasso		
1972 Don Quixote (Gold)	100	2000.00
1972 Don Quixote (Proof)	100	1000.00
1972 Don Quixote (Sterling)	9,800	125.00
Remington		
1972 Rattlesnake (Gold)	100	2000.00
1972 Rattlesnake (Proof)	100	1000.00
1972 Rattlesnake (Sterling)	800	250.00
Da Vinci		
1972 Last Supper	NA	125.00
N. C. Wyeth		
1972 Uncle Sam's America (Gold)	100	2000.00
1972 Uncle Sam's America (Proof)	100	1000.00
1972 Uncle Sam's America (Sterling)	9,800	150.00
1973 Massed Flags (Gold)	100	2000.00
1973 Massed Flags (Proof)	100	1000.00
1973 Massed Flags (Sterling)	2,300	150.00
Israel Anniversary (Single issue)		
1973 Struggle	10,000	300.00
Picasso (Single issue)		
1974 Rites of Spring (Sterling)	9,800	125.00
Remington (Single issue)		
1974 Coming Through Rye (Sterling)	2,500	300.00

Wendell August Forge

Great Americans		
1971 J.F.K. (Pewter)	5,000	40.00
1971 J.F.K. (Silver)	500	200.00
1972 Lincoln (Pewter)	5,000	40.00
1972 Lincoln (Silver)	500	200.00
Great Moments		
1971 Columbus (Pewter)	5,000	40.00
1971 Columbus (Silver)	500	200.00
1972 Landing of Pilgrims (Pewter)	5,000	40.00
1972 Landing of Pilgrims (Silver)	500	200.00
1973 First Thanksgiving (Pewter)	5,000	40.00
1973 First Thanksgiving (Silver)	500	200.00
1974 Patrick Henry (Pewter)	5,000	40.00
1974 Patrick Henry (Silver)	500	200.00
1975 Paul Revere (Pewter)	5,000	45.00
1975 Paul Revere (Silver)	500	200.00
1976 Signing of Declaration (Pewter)	5,000	50.00
1976 Signing of Declaration (Silver)	500	200.00
Wings of Man		
1971 Columbus' Ships (Pewter)	5,000	40.00
1971 Columbus' Ships (Silver)	500	200.00
1972 Conestoga Wagon (Pewter)	5,000	40.00
1972 Conestoga Wagon (Silver)	500	200.00
Peace (Single issue)		
1973 Facing Doves (Silver)	2,500	250.00
Christmas		
1974 Caroler (Bronze)	2,500	25.00
1974 Caroler (Pewter)	2,500	30.00
1975 Christmas in Country (Bronze)	2,500	30.00
1975 Christmas in Country (Pewter)	2,500	35.00
1976 Lamplighter (Bronze)	2,500	35.00
1976 Lamplighter (Pewter)	2,500	40.00

	Edition Limit	Issue Price (US)
1977 Covered Bridge (Bronze)	2,500	40.00
1977 Covered Bridge (Pewter)	2,500	45.00
Wildlife		
1977 On Guard (Aluminum)	1,900	35.00
1977 On Guard (Bronze)	1,500	45.00
1977 On Guard (Pewter)	1,500	55.00
1977 On Guard (Silver)	100	250.00
1978 Thunderbird (Aluminum)	1,900	40.00
1978 Thunderbird (Bronze)	1,500	50.00
1978 Thunderbird (Pewter)	1,500	60.00
1978 Thunderbird (Silver)	100	250.00

Westbury (Viletta)

Tender Moments		
1978 Old Fashioned Persuasion	7,500	40.00
1979 Dandelions	7,500	45.00

Westminster Collectibles

Holidays		
1976 All Hallows Eve	5,000	38.50
1977 Christmas	5,000	38.50

Westmoreland

Christmas		
1972 Holy Birth	2,500	35.00
1973 Manger Scene	3,500	35.00
1974 Gethsemane	1,500	35.00
1975 Christ Is Risen	1,500	45.00

Edward Weston Editions (Viletta)

Unicorn Fantasies		
1979 Follower of Dreams	5,000	55.00
1980 Twice Upon a Time	5,000	55.00
1981 Familiar Spirit	5,000	60.00
1982 Noble Gathering	5,000	65.00
Weddings Around World		
1979 Hawaiian Wedding	5,000	75.00
1980 Dutch Wedding	5,000	75.00

Wheaton

Presidential		
1971 Adams	9,648	5.00
1971 Eisenhower	8,856	5.00
1971 Hoover	10,152	5.00
1971 Kennedy	11,160	5.00
1971 Lincoln	9,648	5.00
1971 Madison	9,504	5.00
1971 Monroe	9,792	5.00
1971 F. D. Roosevelt	9,432	5.00
1971 Taft	9,648	5.00
1971 Van Buren	9,576	5.00
1971 Washington	10,800	5.00
1971 Wilson	8,712	5.00

Whitehall China

Raphael Sower		
1979 Model on Bed	10,000	39.95

Wildlife Internationale

Water Fowl		
1983 Wood Ducks	5,000	65.00

Windemere Collection

Classical Images		
1984 Piano Moods	7,500	60.00
1985 Young Flutist	7,500	60.00

Yankee Collection

Birds of Prey		
1986 The Bald Eagle	1,000	250.00

Zanobia

African Violet Miniatures		
1985 Half Pint	5,000	29.50
1986 Luvkins	5,000	29.50
Violet Portraits		
1986 Canadian Sunset	5,000	34.50
1987 Kiss't	5,000	34.50